IB Physics HL   For exams 2016 onwards

Note from the author

The new physics syllabus is much more open to interpretation than the pre   .o far as the OSC guide goes, this has meant more detail is necessary to fully explain co.   ⊸ts. This guide has therefore been designed as a thorough set of revision notes which also serves well as a set of course notes. Each chapter covers one topic and the topics are the same order as that presented in the IB Physics syllabus.

The first page of each chapter summarizes the checklist of "key understandings" as identified in the syllabus. A list of relevant formulae is also offered (again, in accordance with what is provided by the IB in the data booklet) and explained, for the benefit of those who struggle with their use.

To ensure thorough coverage of the syllabus, the content in each chapter is worked in the same order as the key understandings – bold type is used to accentuate **these subtitles**.

Where it has been necessary to provide additional concepts or subtopics, underlined subtitling has been used.

Solutions to the problems are all provided at the back of the book. Selected solutions have been fully worked or hints provided.

Apologies in advance if you do come across any errors in the text. If so, please contact me via Oxford Study Courses.

I hope you find this guide very helpful.

Best of luck with your studies in physics!

Pat Roby

Table of Contents

Topic 1: Measurement and Uncertainties

Summary Checklist

1.1	Measurement in Physics
	Fundamental and derived S.I. units Scientific notation and metric multipliers Significant figures Orders of magnitude Estimation
1.2	**Uncertainties and Errors**
	Random and systematic errors Absolute, fractional and percentage uncertainties Error bars Uncertainty of gradient and intercepts
1.3	**Vectors and Scalars**
	Vector and scalar quantities Combination and resolution of vectors

Equations Provided (in IB databook) & Explanations

$$If\ y = a \pm b\ \ then\ \Delta y = \Delta a + \Delta b$$	If a quantity is found by **adding or subtracting** two or more uncertain quantities, their **absolute uncertainties add** to give the **absolute** uncertainty of the new quantity.
$$If\ y = \frac{ab}{c}\ \ then\ \ \frac{\Delta y}{y} = \frac{\Delta a}{a} + \frac{\Delta b}{b} + \frac{\Delta c}{c}$$	If a quantity is found by **multiplying or dividing** two or more uncertain quantities, their **percentage (or fractional) uncertainties add** to give the **percentage (or fractional)** uncertainty of the new quantity.
$$If\ y = a^n\ \ then\ \ \frac{\Delta y}{y} = \left| n \frac{\Delta a}{a} \right|$$	If a quantity is found by raising an uncertain quantity to a **power** its **percentage (or fractional) uncertainty is multiplied by the power** to give the **percentage (or fractional)** uncertainty of the new quantity.
$$A_H = A cos\theta$$ $$A_v = A sin\theta$$	A vector quantity can be **resolved** (split) into two perpendicular **components**. If the vector quantity has **magnitude** A and is at an angle θ to the horizontal, then the component of the vector in the horizontal direction (the horizontal component) is given by $A cos\theta$ and the vertical component by $A sin\theta$

1.1   Measurement in Physics

❖ Fundamental and derived S.I. units

A physical quantity has a unit and a magnitude. The unit describes the nature of the quantity and the magnitude, the size.

An S.I. unit (Système International d'Unités) is the accepted unit to be used in academic systems worldwide. For example, length can be measured in the following units: inches, miles, yards, centimetres, metres, etc. The S.I. unit for length is the metre (m).

Certain units are defined by quantities that exist in reality and remain constant. Such units are called fundamental units.

For example, the unit of mass: the kilogram, is a fundamental unit – 1 kilogram is defined as the mass of a block of platinum-iridium kept in Sevres, France (to avoid problems of metals slightly changing mass, the definition of the kilogram will soon be changed to a more complicated but fixed standard!)

The 6 fundamental quantities you must know are: mass (kg), length (m), time (s), temperature (K), current (A) and amount of substance (mol).

All units can be derived from fundamental units. Hence the set of all units comprise fundamental (or base) units and derived units. Fundamental units on their own are sufficient to define all quantities.

Example T 1.1 – complete the table

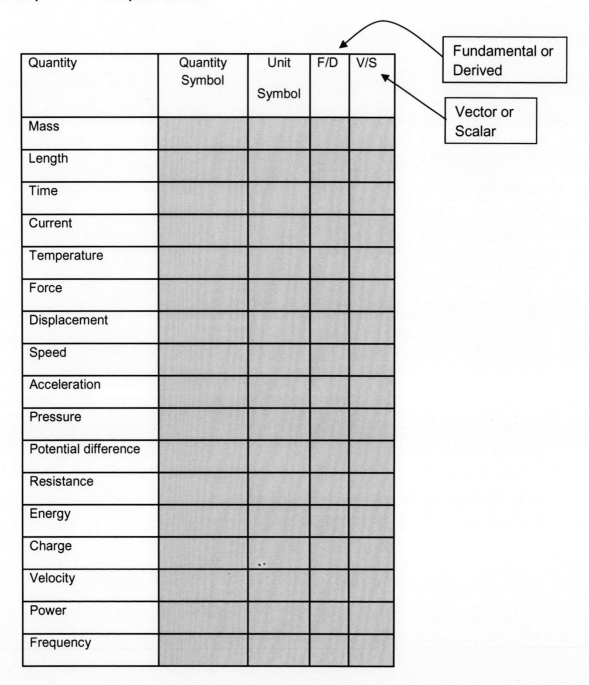

Quantity	Quantity Symbol	Unit Symbol	F/D	V/S
Mass				
Length				
Time				
Current				
Temperature				
Force				
Displacement				
Speed				
Acceleration				
Pressure				
Potential difference				
Resistance				
Energy				
Charge				
Velocity				
Power				
Frequency				

Fundamental or Derived

Vector or Scalar

Example T 1.2

Show that the kilowatt hour (kWh) and the joule (J) are both derived from the same fundamental (or base) units:

❖ Scientific notation and metric multipliers

It is convenient to express very large or very small quantities using prefix multipliers. The common multipliers used are as follows:

Example T 1.3 – complete the table

Name	Multiplication factor	Example	Conversion to S.I. units (using scientific notation)
nano (n)	10^{-9}	300nm =	
micro (μ)	10^{-6}	0.6 μs =	
milli (m)	10^{-3}	500 mV =	
centi (c)	10^{-2}	0.3 cm =	
kilo (k)	10^{3}	101 kPa =	
mega (M)	10^{6}	23.4 MN =	

❖ Significant figures

In Physics, numbers representing quantities have implied uncertainties. The uncertainty corresponds to half the next significant digit on the number.

For example, 45 N $\Rightarrow 45 \pm 0.5$ N. 45.67 N $\Rightarrow 45.67 \pm 0.005$ N

When we do a calculation in Physics we should always state the answer to the same number of *significant digits* as the *least significant digit* number in the data used in the calculation.

For example, $distance = 3.85m, time = 1.2s \; speed = \dfrac{distance}{time} = 3.208 m/s \; answer: 3.2 m/s$

Note that answers should be *written* to the appropriate number of significant digits, but the more "accurate" numbers should be used for further calculations, to avoid rounding errors. [Use the memory buttons on your graphic display calculator for this purpose].

❖ Orders of magnitude

In the physical world, many quantities are too large or too small to write down on a piece of paper using the "normal" number system. We therefore commonly use scientific notation in Physics. It is sometimes useful to get an idea of the approximate size of a quantity without needing to know the exact number. For this, we can use a concept known as "order of magnitude". The order of magnitude of a quantity is simply the power of 10 in the scientific form notation. We either state quantities "to the nearest order of magnitude" – ie. to the nearest power of 10 – or we express ratios of quantities as differences of orders of magnitude.

> ➢ **Worked example:**

(a) State the (rest) mass of an electron to the nearest order of magnitude (get data from data book or text).

(b) State the ratio of the rest mass a proton to that of an electron as a difference of orders of magnitude.

> ✓ **Solutions**

(a) The mass of an electron to the nearest order of magnitude is 10^{-30} kg (mass = 9.11×10^{-31} kg – this rounds to 1×10^{-30} kg or simply 10^{-30} kg)

(b) $\frac{m_p}{m_e} = \frac{1.673 \times 10^{-27}}{9.11 \times 10^{-31}} = 1.8 \times 10^3 \approx 10^3$

❖ Estimation

As physicists, we need to be able to estimate figures, particularly when a calculator or computer is not available.

> ➢ **Worked example:**

Estimate the volume of water on Earth (the radius of the Earth is 6400km).

> ✓ **Possible solution:**

Surface area of sphere = $4\pi r^2$

Take $4\pi \approx 10$
Take $r \approx 6000km$

Then $4\pi r^2 \approx 10 \times 6 \times 6 \times 10^3 \times 10^3 = 360 \times 10^6$

Assume that the ocean occupies $2/3^{rd}$ of the surface of the Earth and that the average depth of the oceans is 1km.

Volume of water on Earth $\approx \frac{2}{3} \times 360 \times 10^6 \times 1 = 240 \times 10^6 km^3$

So we get an answer of approximately 240 million cubic kilometres.

(According to some quick checking on the internet, the volume is in fact about four times as much as this, but the approximate figure is in the right ball park).

1.2   Uncertainties and Errors

❖ Random and systematic errors

A **random uncertainty** is an unpredictable and largely uncontrollable uncertainty. Examples include human reaction time and other forms of human measurement. Random uncertainties can be reduced by taking the average of repeated measurements.

A **systematic error** is an error that occurs on all measurements. An example is a zero error on a newton meter (spring balance). Systematic errors can often easily be detected on a graph of the measurements versus a related (dependent) variable – the whole curve, for example, will be this error distance too high – and will miss the origin when it should pass through it. Systematic errors are not reduced by taking repeated measurements.

❖ Absolute, fractional and percentage uncertainties

An **absolute uncertainty** is the actual uncertainty of a given measurement

A **fractional uncertainty** is the absolute uncertainty divided by the measured quantity (average)

A **percentage uncertainty** is the fractional uncertainty expressed as a percentage.

Example T 1.4

The time take for an object to fall to the ground from a height of 1.2m is recorded as follows:

Minimum recorded time (s):   0.40

Maximum recorded time (s):   0.50

Average time (s):   0.45

(a)   What is the absolute uncertainty in time?
(b)   What is the fractional uncertainty in time?
(c)   What is the percentage uncertainty in time?
(d)   Write down the time measurement with its absolute uncertainty
(e)   Write down the time measurement with its percentage uncertainty.

Propagation of uncertainties:

If two or more uncertain measurements are used to calculate another quantity that quantity will also involve an uncertainty. The uncertainty of the calculated quantity can be found by finding the maximum possible value, minimum possible value, and then (if necessary) calculating the percentage uncertainty. However, the following method is usually used to make things simpler:

If quantities are multiplied together (e.g. F = ma) or divided (e.g. speed = distance/time) then the percentage (or fractional) uncertainty of the product (e.g. of F) is obtained by adding the percentage (or fractional) uncertainties of the individual quantities, If quantities are added or subtracted (e.g. perimeter = length + length + width + width) then the absolute (actual) uncertainty is obtained by adding the absolute uncertainty for each measurement.

Hints:

- A constant does not affect the percentage uncertainty in a calculated quantity
- When squaring a quantity, its percentage uncertainty doubles
- When square rooting a quantity, its percentage uncertainty halves
- When finding the propagated uncertainty in a calculated quantity, start by rearranging the relevant equation to make the calculated quantity the subject.

Example T 1.5

The height (h) of an object dropped from rest is related to the time taken for it to fall (t) and the constant acceleration, a, of the object by the equation $h = \frac{1}{2}at^2$.

(a) Assuming that the acceleration is known to be $9.8ms^{-2}$ and that the time taken for an object to fall is measured as $0.80s \pm 0.05s$ calculate:
  (i)   The percentage uncertainty in time
  (ii)   The percentage uncertainty in height
  (iii) The calculated height, with absolute uncertainty.

(b) Now, assuming instead that the height is measured as follows:
  Initial release height (above ground): $3.34m \pm 1cm$
  Final height (above ground): $20cm \pm 3cm$

  Calculate:
  (i)   The distance the object fell, with absolute uncertainty
  (ii)   The percentage uncertainty in distance (height)
  (iii) Using this data for height and the time date given in (a), find the calculated value for acceleration, with percentage uncertainty.

❖ Error bars

Error bars show the maximum and minimum measured values on a graph. The length of the error bar is therefore twice the size of the absolute uncertainty.

❖ Uncertainty of gradients and intercepts

When constructing a straight line of best fit the following principles should be used:

The line should pass through all error bars. The slope (gradient) of the line should be found by taking two points that lie "on the grid" as far apart as possible. The maximum and minimum slopes and intercepts should be found by first constructing maximum and minimum slope lines by passing each line through the extreme ends of the first and last error bars on the graph.

Example T 1.6

The graph below shows the mass (in grams) of some pebbles versus the measured radius of the pebbles cubed (r^3 in cm^3).

This was done since mass versus produced a non-linear graph, and the students wanted to test the relationship: $mass \propto volume \Rightarrow mass \propto radius^3$.

Two points are provided for the line of best fit and for the maximum and the minimum slope lines.

Using graph and the lines and points provided:

    (i)   Write down the radius^3 of the heaviest pebble, together with its uncertainty
    (ii)   Calculate the percentage uncertainty of the radius^3 of this pebble
    (iii)   Hence, calculate the percentage uncertainty in the measured radius of the pebble
    (iv)   Hence, find the measured radius together with its absolute uncertainty
    (v)   Find the slope of the line of best fit for the graph and, using this, write down an equation relating the masses and the radii of the pebbles
    (vi)   Find the maximum and minimum slopes
    (vii)   Hence, state the equation for the line including uncertainties in slope and intercept
    (viii)   Given that the mass of a sphere of radius r cm and density ρ g/cm^3 is given by the equation: $m = \frac{4}{3}\pi\rho r^3$ find a range of possible values for the density of the pebbles.

Graph

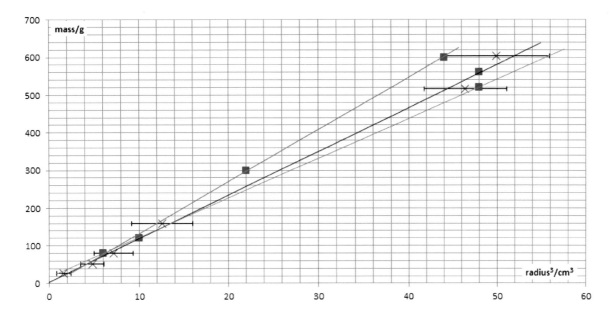

1.3   Vectors and Scalars

❖ Vector and scalar quantities

A vector quantity is a quantity that has both size (magnitude) and direction.

In Physics, vector quantities are represented using arrows. The length of the arrow represents the magnitude of the quantity and the direction of the arrow, the direction of the quantity. Solving vector problems can then be done either using mathematical geometry or scale diagrams.

❖ Combination and resolution of vectors

Unlike scalars, which are just treated like numbers when added, direction must be taken into account when adding vector quantities. They are added by summing head-to-tail vectors, then either by direct measurement of scale drawing or by using geometry.

The vectors are drawn, in any order, the head of one joining the tail of the next. The resultant vector is the vector that joins the tail (start) of the first vector to the head (end) of the last vector.

Any vector can be considered as a sum of several vectors. It is common and useful to consider single vectors as two perpendicular vectors. These are called component vectors. The process of splitting a vector into two perpendicular components is called resolution (vector has been resolved).

The process of combining two or more vectors into a single vector is called vector summation or vector addition (finding the resultant vector).

Example T 1.7

(a) A 5kg mass has forces acting on it as shown in the diagram. By scale diagram, or otherwise, find the resultant force acting on the mass:

Note: The diagram is not drawn to scale

The 3N force is perpendicular to the 4N force

The 7N force is at 45° to the 4N force

(b) Resolve the weight of a 25kg mass on a slope at 30° to horizontal into components parallel and perpendicular to the slope.

(c) Find the resultant speed of a man walking due East at 1.3 m/s across a flat lorry trailer if the lorry is moving due north at 3.2 m/s.

Topic 2: Mechanics

Summary Checklist

2.1	Motion
	Distance and displacement Speed and velocity Acceleration Graphs describing motion Equations of motion for uniform acceleration Projectile motion Fluid resistance and terminal speed
2.2	Forces
	Objects as point particles Free-body diagrams Translational equilibrium Newton's laws of motion Solid friction
2.3	Work, Energy and Power
	Kinetic energy Gravitational potential energy Elastic potential energy Work done as energy transfer Power as rate of energy transfer Principle of conservation of energy Efficiency
2.4	Momentum and Impulse
	Newton's second law expressed in terms of rate of change of momentum Impulse and force-time graphs Conservation of linear momentum Elastic collisions, inelastic collisions and explosions

Equations Provided (in IB databook) & Explanations

$v = u + at$	a is the constant acceleration,
$s = ut + \dfrac{1}{2}at^2$	u is the initial velocity,
$v^2 = u^2 + 2as$	v is the final velocity, $\quad\big\}\quad$ after time t
$s = \dfrac{(u + v)t}{2}$	s is the displacement
$F = ma$	Where a is the **acceleration** of mass m when a net (**resultant**) **force** of F is exerted on the mass.

$F_f \leq \mu_s R$	The **static friction** between an object and a surface is less than or equal to the product of the **coefficient of static friction** (for the object/surface) and the **normal force** (contact force) between them. (for objects not sliding/not in motion relative to each other)
$F_f = \mu_d R$	The **dynamic friction** between an object and a surface is equal to the product of the **coefficient of dynamic friction** and the **normal force** between them. (for objects sliding over each other)
$W = Fs\cos\theta$	The **work done** by a force moving an object is equal to the product of the **displacement** of the object and the component of the **force** parallel to the displacement/movement (is this component).
$E_k = \frac{1}{2}mv^2$	The **kinetic energy** of an object is equal to half the product of the **mass** of the object and its **speed squared**.
$E_p = \frac{1}{2}kx^2$	The (elastic) **potential energy** stored in a spring is equal to half the product of the **spring constant** and the **extension** of the spring **squared**.
$\Delta E_p = mg\Delta h$	The increase in **gravitational potential energy** of an object is equal to the product of the **mass** of the object, the **gravitational field strength** in the location of the object and the **increase in height** of the object.
$power = Fv$	The instantaneous **power** of a force (machine) moving an object is equal to the product of the **force** and the **speed** of the object.
$Efficiency = \frac{useful\ work\ out}{total\ work\ in}$ $= \frac{useful\ power\ out}{total\ power\ in}$	The fractional **efficiency** of a machine (or force) is the ratio of **useful work** done by the machine to the **total work** done by the machine. This can also be equated to the ratio of **useful power** produced by the machine to its **total power**.
$p = mv$	The (linear) **momentum** of an object is equal to the product of its **mass** and its **velocity**.
$F = \frac{\Delta p}{\Delta t}$	The **net force** on an object is equal to the **rate of change of its momentum**.
$E_k = \frac{p^2}{2m}$	The **kinetic energy** of an object is equal to the ratio of its **momentum** squared to **twice its mass**.
$Impulse = F\Delta t = \Delta p$	The **impulse** imparted (given) to an object is equal to the product of the **net force** applied and the **time** that it is applied for – this also equals the **change in momentum** of the object during that time.

2.1 Motion

❖ Distance and displacement

Distance travelled   length of path taken

Displacement   the position of an object relative to a defined starting position.

(distance and direction from the starting point)

❖ Speed and velocity

(Instantaneous) speed   rate at which distance is covered/changes (with time)

$$\textit{Average speed} = \frac{total\ distance\ travelled}{total\ time\ taken}$$

Average speed can also be thought of as the constant speed in the given time to cover the same distance as that actually covered in that time.

Velocity   rate at which displacement changes (with time)

Velocity is also referred to as "instantaneous velocity" since it is a measurement at an instant in time, rather than over a period of time. The (instantaneous) velocity of an object is always the same as the speed, but direction of motion must also be included.

$$\textit{Average velocity} = \frac{total\ displacement}{total\ time\ taken}$$

Average velocity can also be thought of as the constant velocity in a given time to cover the same displacement as that actually covered in that time.

Relative velocity   the velocity of one object as seen from another

Relative velocity of A as seen from B = $V_A - V_B$ where V_A and V_B are the velocities of A and B.

❖ Acceleration

Acceleration   rate at which velocity changes (with time)

Strictly, direction of acceleration should also be given, and in linear motion + represents velocity increasing in the "forwards" direction and − represents velocity increasing in the "reverse" direction. So it is important to note that it is incorrect to suggest that a negative acceleration implies that an object is slowing down or that a positive acceleration implies speeding up.

Example T 2.1

A particle moves at constant speed in a anticlockwise semicircle, radius 12m, taking 3.5 seconds to travel to a point due north of the starting point.

    (a) Find the average speed
    (b) Find the average velocity
    (c) Find the speed and velocity after 1 second
    (d) Is the object accelerating?

❖ Graphs describing motion

Graphs provide a very powerful way of describing any type of motion, whether it be uniformly accelerated, starting-and-stopping, or any other kind.

In all cases:

- The *gradient* of a *displacement* versus time graph at any point in time gives the *velocity* of the object
- The *gradient* of a *velocity* versus time graph at any point in time gives the *acceleration* of the object
- The *area under* a *velocity* versus time graph from one point in time to another gives the *displacement* of the of the object at the second point relative to the first (it is often more useful to find area from t=0 to any particular point in time – to give displacement from starting point)
- The *area under* an *acceleration* versus time graph from one point in time to another gives the *change in velocity* of the of the object at the second point relative to the first.

These simple rules lead to the derivation of the equations of uniformly accelerated motion (done later).

The following diagram summarises the rules:

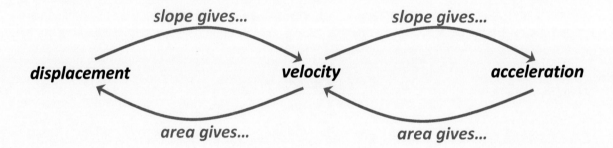

slope gives...   slope gives...

displacement   **velocity**   **acceleration**

area gives...   area gives...

Example T 2.2

The graphs below (labelled A to O) give information about the motion of 15 different objects. It represents time, s represents displacement, v; velocity and a, acceleration. Use the graphs to answer the question that follows.

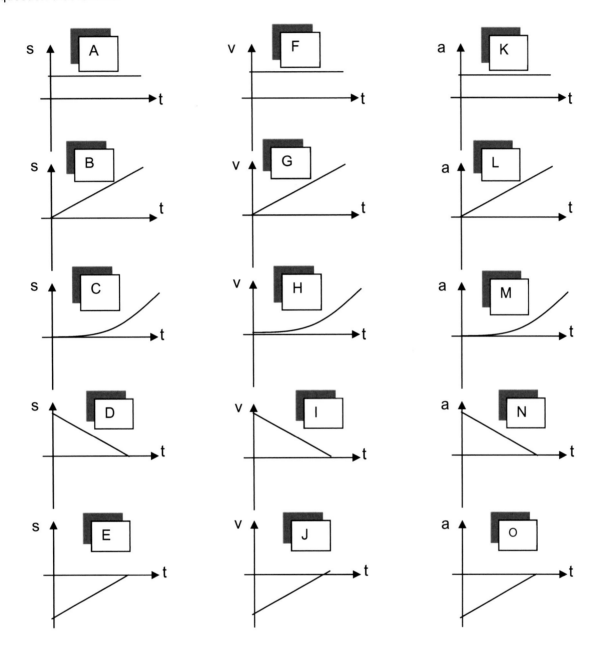

Example T 2.2 continued

Complete the table below by inserting 0 or $+$ or $-$ in the sign columns – to show the sign of the displacement, velocity or acceleration throughout the time on the graph and ↑ (for increasing) or ↓ (for decreasing) or C (for constant) in the change columns, to show how displacement, velocity or acceleration change as time elapses.

(For the velocity graphs (F-J), assume that the object starts (when t=0) at zero displacement and for the acceleration graphs (K-O), assume that the object starts at zero displacement and velocity.)

graph	Displacement		Velocity		Acceleration	
	sign	change	sign	change	sign	change
A						
B						
C						
D						
E						
F						
G						
H						
I						
J						
K						
L						
M						
N						
O						

❖ Equations of motion for uniform acceleration

These equations (given in data booklet) apply only to motion that is uniformly accelerated.

Consider a general example of such motion:

Initial velocity (at time t = 0) = u

Final velocity (at time t = t) = v

Acceleration = a (constant, over all time)

Displacement = s

The velocity versus time graph for such motion

would look as in the diagram on the right:

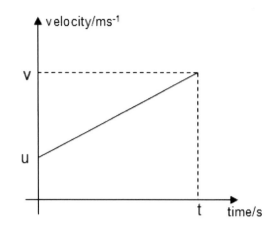

Example T 2.3

Derive the equations of motion from the graph shown above.

Hint: start by finding the gradient (slope) and noting that acceleration = slope, then find area (=displacement). Then find the other two equations by eliminating the appropriate variable.

Falling Objects

When solving problems involving objects falling under the influence of the Earth's gravitational field, we usually assume:

- That the gravitational field strength, g, (which is equal to, and also called, acceleration due to gravity) is constant (and taken to be $9.81ms^{-2}$)
- That the weight of the object is the only force acting on it.

If these two conditions do indeed apply it means that the acceleration of the object is constant and the object is said to be in free-fall:

$$weight\,(F) = mg$$

$$F = ma \Rightarrow a = \frac{F}{m} = \frac{mg}{m} = g$$

So, for objects in free fall $a = g = 9.81ms^{-2}$ (on surface of Earth).

Example T 2.4

A stone is projected vertically into the air, from the ground, at 25 ms^{-1}.

(a) Find the maximum height reached

(b) Find the total time taken to hit the ground.

❖ Projectile motion

Some initial concepts explained

Projectile motion is motion under the influence of a uniform field. In this course we study projectile motion in a uniform gravitational field. A uniform field is one which is the same size everywhere and is always in the same direction. We assume a uniform gravitational field at and around the surface of the Earth.

Gravitational Field strength is the force per kilogram acting on a mass when placed in the field – on Earth the gravitational field strength is known to be $9.81 N kg^{-1}$

It can be shown that g also measures acceleration due to gravity and thus can also have units of acceleration – hence, we also know g as $9.81 ms^{-2}$.

Notes

> Avoid the use of the word "gravity" in Physics
- If you mean "the force of gravity" use instead the word "weight" (measured in newtons; N)
- If you mean g (=9.81N/kg) use the words "gravitational field strength".

Projectiles

A projectile is a mass moving through a uniform (gravitational) field. This type of motion only commences once the mass has departed from the contact force causing its projection.

The path taken by a projectile is called a trajectory. It can be shown that all trajectories are parabolic in shape (except when the projectile is thrown vertically upwards or downwards).

The essence of projectile motion is that, regardless of the direction and speed of a projectile, the force acting on it is constant (since the mass is constant and the field strength is constant) and $F = mg$.

So any object "flying through the air" only has one force acting on it: its weight, acting vertically downwards. This, of course, assumes zero air resistance, which is not completely accurate but serves as a means for quite accurate velocity and displacement calculations provided that the mass is fairly dense and therefore air resistance forces are small compared with its weight.

To solve projectile problems we use the following method – we split the motion into horizontal and vertical motion and we take horizontal motion to be at uniform speed and vertical motion to be at uniform acceleration. Thus:

For horizontal motion the only equation we can use is: $speed = \dfrac{distance}{time}$

For vertical motion we use the equations of motion and (assuming we are on the surface of the Earth) that acceleration, g is equal to $9.81 \, ms^{-2}$.

The time for the horizontal motion is always the same as the time for the vertical motion for any trajectory.

Example T 2.5

A ball is projected horizontally from a point 5.0 metres above the ground at a speed of $8.0ms^{-1}$ What is the range of the ball and what is its speed as it makes initial impact with the ground. State any assumptions.

Example T 2.6

What is the optimum angle from the horizontal in order to maximize the range of a projectile, assuming negligible air resistance?

Example T 2.7

An experiment is carried out, projecting a ball from one building to another. The angle of projection and speed of projection can be varied. The following diagram illustrates the situation:

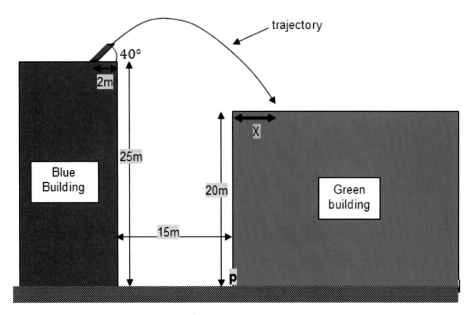

The ball is projected 2m from the edge of the blue building, at an angle $40°$ from the horizontal. Assume that the green building is very wide and that the height from which the ball is projected is at the top of the blue building (the projector is not raised above the roof of the blue building).

(a) If the ball is projected at 40° to the horizontal, at a speed of $12ms^{-1}$:

    i) Find the maximum height above the ground reached by the ball
    ii) Find the value of X , giving the position where it hits the green building
    iii) Find the speed at which it hits the building.

(b) At the same angle (40°), find the speed that the ball should be projected in order for it to land just at the base of the green building, labelled **P** on the diagram.

❖ Fluid resistance and terminal speed

In the above calculations we have assumed (i) gravity is constant (ii) weight is the only force acting. These conditions do not strictly apply in reality. The first condition is very close to true for objects very close to the surface of the Earth (within a few km, certainly). However the second condition ignores air resistance – a force whose magnitude (size) depends upon:

- The size, shape and texture of the surface
- The speed of the object.

As the speed of an object increases the air resistance also increases until at a certain speed, the force of air resistance is equal to the weight of the object, the resultant force is then zero and so the object no longer accelerates. The constant speed reached is called terminal speed or terminal velocity.

Example T 2.8

If an iron ball and a plastic ball are dropped in air from the same height, explain what would be observed and whether the equations of motion would be useful in each case.

Example T 2.9

A tennis ball is dropped from the top of the Eiffel Tower (about 300m tall), in Paris.

Describe how:

(a) Air resistance changes as the ball drops
(b) Acceleration changes as the ball drops
(c) Velocity changes as the ball drops.

2.2   Forces

❖ Objects as Point Particles

When solving problems in Physics we often do not consider the forces within the object, nor the rotation of the object. We consider the object as a point particle, with all the mass at the one point.

❖ Free Body Diagrams

A free body diagram shows all the forces acting on the body (and NOT the resultant force). The resultant force acting on the body is thus the vector sum of all these forces.

Example T 2.10

Draw free body diagrams for the following, showing relative size, direction and names of forces.
1) A woman standing on the floor

2) A man falling through the air, ignore air resistance

3) A mass sliding down frictionless slope

4) A parachutist falling at terminal speed.

❖ Translational equilibrium

A body is said to be in translational equilibrium if the vector sum of all the forces acting on the body is equal to zero. This means that such a body is moving at constant velocity.

Example T 2.11

A fish with a mass of 35g is moving at a constant velocity of 1.4m/s. Water resistance acting against the motion of the fish is 0.04N. What is the resultant force acting on the fish?

❖ Newton's laws of motion

Newton's first law

A body will continue in its current state of motion (velocity) unless acted on by a resultant force.

So, we can write: $If\ F_{net} = 0\ then\ a = 0\ (and\ v\ is\ constant)$

If it is known that the resultant force on an object is zero, we can therefore conclude that the acceleration of the object is zero and if acceleration is zero, then the resultant force is zero.

Example T 2.12

A 10 kg mass is on a slope elevated at 40° to the horizontal. The mass remains stationary.

    (a) Draw a free body diagram for the mass
    (b) Resolve the weight of the mass into components perpendicular to the slope
    (c) State the size and direction of the frictional force acting on the mass.

We should note that zero acceleration does not imply that a body is motionless – only that its velocity (speed and direction) is constant (unchanging). However, if a body is (and remains) motionless this does imply that the resultant force acting on the body is zero. We need to be very careful here. If a body stops momentarily, it can be in a state of acceleration (i.e. speeding up, in a certain direction) – and the resultant force on the body in this case is not zero.

Example T 2.13

A 5 kg mass is thrown vertically into the air. The table below describes its state of motion immediately after it is thrown, half way up during its ascent, at the highest point, half way down during its descent and just before it hits the ground. Complete the table by writing + (positive), – (negative) or 0 (zero) to show the direction of displacement, velocity, acceleration and force at each stage. Take the ground level as zero displacement and take the upwards direction as positive direction.

Motion	Displacement	Velocity	Acceleration	Force
Immediately after thrown (assume at ground level)				
Half - way up				
At highest point				
Half - way down				
Just before hits ground				

Newton's second law

The acceleration of a body is proportional to the resultant force acting on the body (and is in the same direction).

i.e.: $\quad \sum F = ma \quad$ ($\sum F$ = sum of forces or resultant force). Also written: $\quad F_{net} = ma$

Example T 2.14

If the slope in example T2.12 were frictionless, calculate the resultant force on the mass and acceleration of the mass, whilst on the slope.

An important follow-on from Newton's second law is that not only is the size of the acceleration proportional to the resultant force, but also that the direction of the acceleration is the same as the direction of the resultant force. To find the direction of acceleration, it is often useful to first find the direction of the resultant force – i.e. to deduce acceleration from force rather than from change in velocity (thinking about velocity and direction of motion often confuses direction of acceleration. For example, in Example T 2.13, finding direction of acceleration is easy if you simply consider the direction of resultant force: weight).

Example T 2.15

Mark on with arrows the direction of the acceleration of an object oscillating on a spring (as shown in the diagram below) at positions A, B and C. The object is shown at the highest position – position A. Position B is the position where the object will eventually come to rest and position C is the lowest position of the object.

Position A

Position B

Position C

Newton's third law of motion

When two particles interact, they always exert equal and opposite forces on each other.

Forces are therefore often described as (equal and opposite) pairs ("Newton's 3rd law pairs"), since it is not possible to have an unpaired force.

Note that Newton 3rd law pairs are always:

- ✓ Equal to each other in size – so if one changes, the other must change also
- ✓ The same type of force (so if one is tension, so must the other be etc.)
- ✓ Acting on two different objects - ie. Not on the same object (since they are the forces on the two particles when the two particles interact) (so the weight of a brick and the normal reaction force acting on it, whilst equal and opposite, do not constitute a newton's 3rd law pair).

Example T 2.16

Jessica attempts to lift a 500N weight off the ground by applying an upwards force of 300N to a string attached to the weight. Draw a free-body diagram of the weight and identify/describe all the (Newton's 3rd law) pairs of equal and opposite forces.

❖ Solid friction

Solid friction is the frictional forces between two solid objects or surfaces. There are two types of solid friction: static friction and dynamic friction.

Static friction is the force between the object and the surface that attempts to prevent the movement of one relative to the other. Static friction is variable, always matching the applied force, this preventing movement.

Dynamic friction is the force between the object and the surface that attempts to reduce the movement of one relative to the other. Dynamic friction is constant. Dynamic friction is less than maximum static friction.

According to research, the only factors that affect friction are:

  (i)   The nature of the two surfaces (measured with a coefficient)
  (ii)   The contact force between the two surfaces.

  • The contact force can be calculated.
  • The coefficient must be found experimentally: it cannot be found using theory alone.

Equations:

$F_f \leq \mu_s R$ μ_s is the coefficient of static friction

$F_f = \mu_d R$ μ_d is the coefficient of dynamic friction

$\left. \right\}$ R is the contact force, F_f is friction

Example T 2.17

A student attaches a Newton meter to a wooden block with a mass of 300g and places the block on a horizontal surface. She gently applies a horizontal force to the block using the newton meter and finds that the maximum force she can apply without the object moving is 1.1N. She then pulls the object along at a steady speed with the newton meter and finds that it takes 0.75N:

  (a) Calculate the coefficient of static friction for the wooden block/surface
  (b) Calculate the coefficient of dynamic friction for the wooden block/surface
  (c) If she applies a force of 1.5N to the wooden block, calculate its acceleration.

She now places four 100g masses on top of the wooden block:

  (d) Calculate the force required to produce an acceleration of 2.4ms^{-2} on the block
  (e) If the mass is placed on a slope and the slope inclined, at what angle does the slope need to be lifted in order that the mass just begins to slide?
  (f) How much force is needed to pull the wooden block and 4 masses along the surface (upwards) at a steady speed if it is inclined at 20° to horizontal (force applied parallel to slope)?

Example T 2.18

Jennifer is carrying out an experiment to investigate static friction. She uses a newton-meter (spring scale) to pull a block along the surface, as shown in the picture:

She pulls the block with the newton-meter *until the point where if just moves* and then she records the weight of the block (with weights) and the pulling force. She repeats several times for each different total weight.

The graph below shows how the pulling force varies as the weight of the object varies:

(a) Write down, in the form $a \pm b$, the pulling force required to just pull the 11N weight
(b) Add a line of best fit to Jennifer's graph
(c) Calculate the gradient of this line
(d) Explain the significance of this number (the gradient)
(e) Calculate the likely pulling force required to just move a the block if its total weight is increased to 20N.

2.3 Work, Energy and Power

An object possesses energy if it is either active in some way or able to be active.

Being active can be:

- Moving, vibrating, releasing radiation or releasing sound.

Able to be active can be:

- Stretched or squashed (and able to "spring back")
- Able to react, chemically (with release of thermal energy or perhaps light)
- Able to undergo a nuclear change (with release of thermal energy or another type or radiation)
- Able to fall, due to the pull of gravity and the height (causing increased movement).

The nine generally accepted forms of energy can be memorised with the mnemonic GREENSICK, as follows:

G   gravitational

R   radiation (including thermal/infra-red, light, etc.)

E   electrical (a form of potential energy that charged objects have, when in electric fields)

E   elastic (stretched or squashed objects that have elastic properties and can spring back)

N   nuclear (caused by the possibility of nuclear change due to instability)

S   sound

I   internal (KE + PE of particles, determining state and temperature of a substance)

C   chemical (caused by the possibility of chemical change or instability)

K   kinetic (movement of objects: can be rotational, vibrational or translational)

The action energies are highlighted yellow and the stored/potential energies are highlighted blue

The amazing thing is, we can quantify all types of energy and find that a certain quantity of one form of energy can be converted into another.

All forms of energy are scalar quantities, measured in joules.

❖ Kinetic energy

The kinetic energy of an object is half the product of the mass of the object and the speed of the object squared.

Thus: $E_k = \frac{1}{2}mv^2$

Example T 2.19

(a) Calculate the kinetic energy of a ball with a mass of 68g and speed of 3.5m/s
(b) If all the kinetic energy of this ball is transferred to another ball with mass 120g and speed 2.4m/s, what will the new speed of the second ball be after the transfer?

❖ Gravitational potential energy

The additional gravitational potential energy "stored in" an object due to it being raised through a certain height is the product of the mass of the object, the gravitational field strength of the field that it is in and the height it is raised.

Thus: $\Delta E_p = mg\Delta h$

[Note: on a more advanced level, we define zero potential energy as what objects have when they have escaped from a planet's gravitational field and when they "fall" towards and given planet they release kinetic energy, so have negative gravitational energy!]

Example T 2.20

    (a) Calculate the gravitational energy that an object with a mass of 5.8kg gains if it is raised through a height of 1.8m
    (b) Assuming that if the object falls back down again (thus reducing its height by 1.8m), state the KE is must have and therefore calculate the speed of the object
    (c) Using a relevant suvat equation (equation of motion), calculate the speed of an object when dropped from rest through a height of 1.8m.

❖ Elastic potential energy

An object has elastic properties if, when a distorting force is applied, a restoring force opposes this. Consequently, when the distorting force is removed, the object will self-restore and return to its original size and shape. It has taken energy to distort the object (squash it or stretch it) but this energy is transferred to elastic potential energy which can be released again when the object self-restores.

The energy stored in a stretched spring is equal to half the product of the spring constant (also known as stiffness constant) and the extension squared (extension is the amount it has been stretched from original length).

Thus: $E_p = \frac{1}{2}kx^2$ Note: $F_{restoring} = kx$ (not given)

Example T 2.21

A spring has a stiffness constant 5.0N/cm. A 1.25kg object is suspended vertically from the spring.

    (a) What will the extension of the spring be?
    (b) How much elastic energy is stored in the spring?
    (c) If the spring is held stretched then used to propel the object along a horizontal, smooth surface, calculate the speed that the object is launched.

❖ Work done as energy transfer

Work is said to be done whenever energy is converted from one form to another.
For example, if an electric light-bulb converts 100J of electrical energy into light and thermal energy, we can say that the bulb has done 100J of work.

However, it is more common that "work done" refers to mechanical work. Mechanical work is done by a device that is able to apply a force to move an object. Note that the force must be at least partly acting in the direction of the movement (displacement).

Mechanical work done (also simply called "work done") is equal to the product of the displacement and the component of the force parallel to the displacement of the object.

Thus: $W = Fs\cos\theta$

The diagram below shows the set up:

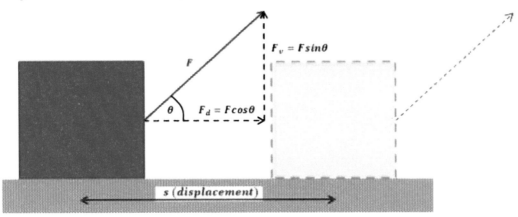

Example T 2.22

A 28N force is applied to an object of mass 64kg, as in the above diagram. The angle that the force makes with the horizontal is 35°.

    (a) Calculate the work done by the force if the object moves a distance of 3.2m
    (b) Given that the surface is smooth, state the kinetic energy of the block at this point and hence calculate its speed.

❖ Power as rate of energy transfer

Power is defined as the **rate** at which work is done, which is the same as the rate at which energy is transferred.

Thus: $Power = \frac{work\ done}{time\ taken} = \frac{energy\ converted}{time\ taken}$ (this equation is **NOT** provided)

Note: Power is measured in watts (W).

If we are taking about mechanical work being done, we can calculate the power of the force-device as the product of the force and the speed of the object.

Thus: $power = Fv$

Example T 2.23

Calculate the power of the device applying the force in example T 2.22 after the object has moved:
    (a) 1m
    (b) 2m
    (c) 3.2m

Example T 2.24

Calculate the average power of the device in T 2.22

    (a) Over the first 1m
    (b) Over the first 2m
    (c) Over the full 3.2m.

Example T 2.25

A man of mass 90 kg walks along a horizontal road, covering a distance of 3 km. Find the work done by the man in covering this distance.

❖ Principle of conservation of energy

When an object slows down, its kinetic energy is decreased. The principle of conservation of energy infers that for this to happen, some other form of energy must be increasing, since energy cannot be lost. The amount of energy in the universe is constant.

The principle is stated as follows: "Energy cannot be created or destroyed, only converted from one form to another".

Example T 2.26

Referring again to example T 2.22, the 28N force is applied over 3.2m but the speed of the object at this point is 1.2m/s.

(a) Calculate the kinetic energy of the object as this point
(b) Using this and your answer in T 2.22, calculate the transfer of work to thermal energy.

❖ Efficiency

The efficiency of a device is the ratio of the energy converted to what is deemed to be a useful form of energy to the total energy converted by the device.

Since power = energy/time, we can also measure efficiency as the ratio of useful power to total power.

Thus:
$$Efficiency = \frac{useful\ work\ out}{total\ work\ in} = \frac{useful\ power\ out}{total\ power\ in}$$

Example T 2.27

Calculate the efficiency of the device using the information in T 2.22 and T 2.26.

Example T 2.28

A 2kW electric motor is used to run a water pump and in 3 hours pumps approximately 100 tonnes (1 tonne=1000kg) of water, lifting the water into a canal 5m higher.

(a) Find the work done by the pump in this time
(b) Find the potential energy gained by the water in this time
(c) Calculate the efficiency of the pump and explain how the principal of conservation of energy applies in this example.

2.4   Momentum and Impulse

Linear momentum is defined as the product of the mass of an object and its velocity.

The impulse imparted to an object is defined to be the product of the net force applied to an object and the time for which it is applied, i.e. $Impulse = F_{net}\Delta t$.

The impulse imparted to an object is found to be equal to the change in momentum of the object, as the following shows:

Change in momentum, $\Delta p = \Delta mv = m\Delta v = m(v - u)$

By Newton's second law, $F_{net} = ma = m\frac{\Delta v}{\Delta t} = m\frac{v-u}{\Delta t} = \frac{m(v-u)}{\Delta t}$

Hence, $F_{net} = \frac{\Delta p}{\Delta t}$ and $F_{net}\Delta t = \Delta p$ i.e. Impulse = change in momentum.

❖ Newton's second law expressed in terms of rate of change of momentum

As the above algebra shows, we can write Newton's second law as:

$$F_{net} = \frac{\Delta p}{\Delta t}$$

Which can be expressed as: "the net force on an object is equal to the rate in change of its momentum"

Example T 2.29

A road vehicle has a mass of 1.2 tonnes (1,200 kg) and is initially stationary. The engine imparts an impulse of 14.4kNs on the vehicle.

   (a) At what speed is the vehicle moving after the engine force has been applied?
   (b) If the acceleration of the vehicle was 0.8ms^{-2}, find the force exerted by the engine
   (c) Find the time taken for the vehicle to reach the speed calculated in part (a).

❖ Impulse and force–time graphs

If force is not constant, the impulse (change in momentum) can be found in two possible ways. Either use impulse = average force x time or find the impulse from the area under a force versus time graph (but note that the force units must be newtons and the time must be seconds).

Example T 2.30

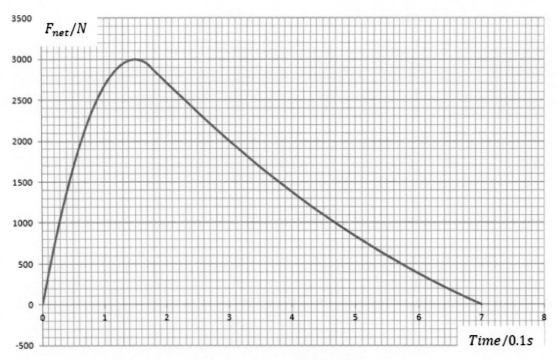

A large container of sand with a mass of 102kg is dropped onto the ground. The above graph shows the net force acting on the bag of sand as it hits the ground (horizontal axis shows tenths of a second, vertical shows newtons. Assuming air resistance is negligible, calculate the height that the container must have been dropped from.

Hints: First determine impulse from area, hence find change in momentum and initial velocity before collision with ground, then use "suvat" to find height.

❖ Conservation of linear momentum

The principle of conservation of momentum states that the total momentum of objects in an isolated system remains constant.

Notes
- Isolated means that nothing outside the system can apply a net force on the objects in the system
- Momentum is a vector quantity, so to find total momentum, vector addition must be used.

Example T 2.31

A boy with a mass of 68kg is riding on roller-skates at a speed of 1.8m/s towards a girl with a mass of 52kg who is riding directly towards the boy at a speed of 1.1m/s. For fun, they collide by embracing each other.

(a) Find the momentum of the boy and the momentum of the girl before they collide
(b) Hence, find the total momentum of the boy and the girl before they collide
(c) By applying the principle of conservation of momentum, find the common velocity of the boy and the girl immediately after the collision.

❖ Elastic collisions, inelastic collisions and explosions

Types of collision
Momentum is conserved for all types of collision, as long as the system is isolated

Elastic kinetic energy is also conserved.

objects bounce without conversion of kinetic energy to other forms (speed of approach = speed of separation).

Inelastic there is a maximum loss of kinetic energy.

(but the momentum must still be conserved).

objects stick together on impact.

Partially there is some loss of kinetic energy, but objects do not

Inelastic stick together on impact

momentum, as always, is still conserved.

Explosion like a collision, where momentum is conserved, but energy is converted from an external source (to cause the explosion) into kinetic energy. Objects move away from each other, rather than towards each other.

Example T 2.32

Each example below shows two-body collisions. Complete the diagrams by drawing labelled velocity vectors (not to scale) on the bodies where they are incomplete. (Masses of objects are omitted on the right – they are the same as masses before collision!) By calculating the kinetic energy before and after each collision, indicate in each case whether the collision is elastic, inelastic or partially elastic.

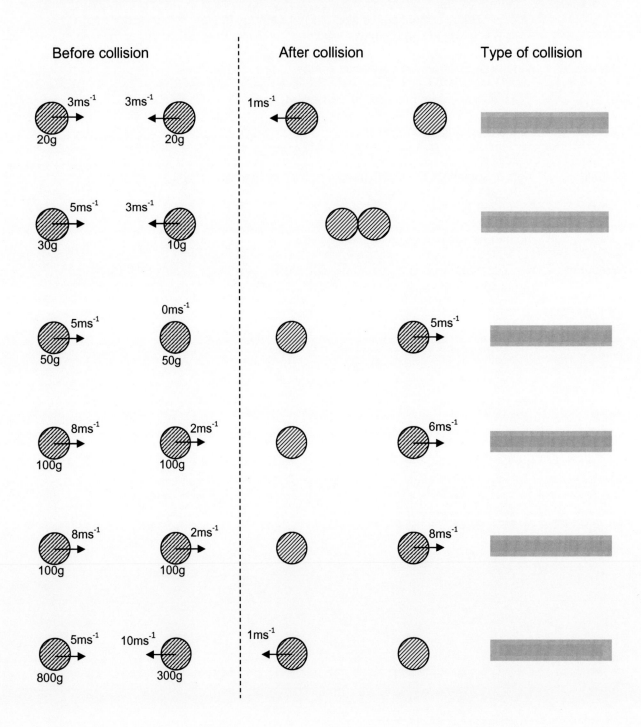

Topic 3: Thermal Physics

Summary Checklist

3.1	Thermal Concepts
	Molecular theory of solids, liquids and gases Temperature and absolute temperature Internal energy Specific heat capacity Phase change Specific latent heat
3.2	Modelling a Gas
	Pressure Equation of state for an ideal gas Kinetic model of an ideal gas Mole, molar mass and the Avogadro constant Differences between real and ideal gases

Equations Provided (in IB databook) & Explanations

$Q = mc\Delta T$	The **thermal (kinetic) energy increase** (when a substance increases in temperature) is equal to the product of the **mass** of the substance, its **specific heat capacity** and its **temperature**.
$Q = ml$	The **thermal (potential) energy increase** (when a substance changes state) is equal to the product of the **mass** of the substance and the **specific latent heat** (of fusion or vaporisation) of the substance.
$P = \dfrac{F}{A}$	The **pressure** exerted (by a gas or solid object) is equal to the ratio of the contact **force** exerted by the object (or collective gas particles) to the **area** over which the contact is spread.
$n = \dfrac{N}{N_A}$	The **number of moles** of a substance is equal to the ratio of the **number of particles** of the substance to **Avogadro's constant**.
$PV = nRT$	The product of the **pressure** of an ideal gas and its **volume** is equal to the product of the **number of moles** of the gas, the **molar gas constant** and the **absolute temperature** of the gas.
$\bar{E}_K = \dfrac{3}{2}k_B T = \dfrac{3}{2}\dfrac{R}{N_A}T$	The **average kinetic energy** of a particle of a gas is equal to $\frac{3}{2}$ times the product of **Boltzmann's constant** and the absolute **temperature** of the gas. This is also equal to $\frac{3}{2}$ times the product of the ratio of the **molar gas constant** to **Avogadro's constant** and the **absolute temperature** of the gas.

3.1 Thermal Concepts

❖ Molecular theory of solids, liquids and gases

The molecular theory of matter assumes that matter is made from small, spherical particles and the nature of solids, liquids and gases can be described and explained by considering the forces (bonding) between particles and the movement of the particles, as follows:

Solids

Particles are quite strongly attracted to each other so that they can vibrate but not move. Solids thus contain a regular and fixed arrangement of particles that overcome gravitational forces and maintain their bulk shape:

Particles have vibrational movement (and KE) but no translational movement. All particles in a solid are continuously vibrating

Liquids

Particles are weakly attracted to each other so that they can move past each other. Liquids contain an irregular and fluxional (moving) arrangement of particles that, due to gravity, fall to the bottom of a container changing their bulk shape:

Particles now have have translational as well as vibrational movement (and KE). All particles in a liquid are continually moving

Gases

Particles are not attracted to each other so they are able to move about freely past. Their weight is insignificant compared to their movement, so they tend to fill the container they are placed in, despite gravity:

Particles now have have translational movement (and KE). All particles in a gas a continually moving about, randomly and rapidly – coll ing with the walls of the container and each other

---

Example T 3.1

(a) Explain why liquids fill a container from the bottom up, whilst gases fill a container evenly
(b) Explain the difference between solids, gases and liquids in terms of forces and energy.

❖ Temperature and absolute temperature

Temperature

Temperature is the degree of hotness of a substance. On a microscopic level, temperature is a measure of the average kinetic energy of the particles within a substance.

Equation: $\bar{E}_K = \frac{3}{2}k_B T$

Example T 3.2

Find the approximate average kinetic energy of a molecule in the air. We can therefore say that if a substance is hotter then each particle will (on average) have a greater kinetic energy (so gas particles will be moving – or vibrating – faster).

This kinetic energy can be vibrational motion, in the case of solids, or translational motion, in the case of liquids or gases.

Thermal contact

Two objects are said to be in thermal contact if it is possible for thermal energy to be transferred directly from one object to the other as a result of the **temperature difference** between the two objects.

Temperature Scales: Absolute temperature

The two common temperature scales are the Celsius temperature scale and the kelvin temperature scale. The kelvin scale is also referred as the absolute temperature scale. The absolute (kelvin) temperature scale starts at the lowest possible temperature – zero kelvin (0 K – degrees word and sign is omitted).

This equates to a temperature of -273 °C. Since an increment of 1°C is the same as an increment of 1 K, converting from °C to K or visa versa is very easy.

To convert from °C to K: Add   273

To convert from K to °C: Subtract   273

Examples:

0 K	=	-273 °C
0 °C	=	273 K
100 °C	=	373 K
150 K	=	-123 °C

❖ Internal energy

Internal Energy = Potential Energy + Kinetic Energy

The potential energy of a substance increases if the attractive bonds between the atoms are weakened (by increasing the average distance between adjacent molecules).

Note: internal energy and thermal energy are not the same.

Internal energy: Sum of KE + PE of particles

Thermal Energy: The non-mechanical transfer of energy resulting from a temperature difference

Temperature: A measure of the average KE of particles in a substance.

Example T 3.3

Container A has 10kg of a substance which is at a temperature of 85°C
Container B has 10g of the same substance which is at a temperature of 125°C
Container C has 8g of the same substance which is at a temperature of $250K$

    (a) Describe the three containers and their substances in terms of their internal energies and temperatures

    (b) If container A was placed in thermal contact with container B, explain any thermal processes that would occur.

❖ Specific heat capacity

The energy required to increase the temperature of 1 kilogram of a substance by 1 °C varies from one substance to another. This property is known as the specific heat capacity of the substance.

Equation: $$c = \frac{Q}{m \times \Delta T}$$

$c = specific\ heat\ capacity$

$Q = energy\ required\ /\ released\ as\ a\ consequence\ of\ temperature\ change\ (joules)$

$m = mass\ of\ substance\ (kilograms)$

$\Delta T = temperature\ change\ (°C)$

Example T 3.4

27 KJ of energy is needed to warm up 3 kg of a substance by 12 °C.

Find its specific heat capacity.

Example T 3.5

When 500 grams of water cools down by 5°C it is found that approximately 10.5kJ of energy is given out – heating the cooler surroundings. Find an approximate value for the specific heat capacity of water.

Example T 3.6

Ice has a specific heat capacity of 2100 $Jkg^{-1}°C^{-1}$. How much energy is needed to increase the temperature of a block of ice with a mass of 7.5kg from –18°C to –5°C?

Variation in Specific Heat Capacity

Different substances have different specific heat capacities because, per kilogram, they contain different numbers of molecules and because the chemical (bonding) properties are different for different substances.

Water has an extremely high specific heat capacity. This makes it a very useful substance for cooling systems for car engines and other machinery. One kilogram of water will absorb a lot of energy whilst only increasing by a small temperature. (4200 J for 1 kg to increase by 1°C).

❖ Phase change

solid ↔ liquid
$$\left(\begin{array}{l} solid \rightarrow liquid = "melting" \\ liquid \rightarrow solid = "freezing" \ or \ "solidification" \ or \ "fusion" \end{array} \right)$$

Energy is required to change the state, or phase, of a substance from a solid to a liquid, and energy is released when a substance changes from a liquid to a solid.

$liquid \leftrightarrow gas$ liquid > gas = "vaporization"

gas > liquid = "condensation"

Energy is required to change the state, or phase, of a substance from a liquid to a gas, and energy is released when a substance changes from a gas to a liquid

❖ Specific latent heat

The specific latent heat of fusion is the energy needed to melt one kilogram of a substance at constant temperature. (This quantity is equal to the energy released when one kilogram of the same substance, in its liquid phase, freezes at constant temperature).

Note: Fusion is another word for freezing

Equation $Q = ml$

$Q = energy \ needed \ to \ melt \ the \ substance$
$(or \ energy \ released \ when \ substance \ freezes)$
$m = mass \ of \ substance \ changing \ state$
$l = specific \ latent \ heat \ of \ fusion$

Example T 3.7

An electrical heater is used to melt 5 Kg of ice, which has already been warmed up to its melting point (0°C). It is found that 1.7 MJ is needed. Find the specific latent heat of fusion of water using this information.

The **specific latent heat of vaporization** is the energy needed to vaporize one kilogram of a substance at constant temperature.

(This quantity is equal to the energy released when one kilogram of the same substance, in its gas phase, condenses).

Equation: $Q = ml$

$Q = energy \ needed \ to \ vaporize \ the \ substance$
$(or \ energy \ released \ when \ substance \ condenses)$
$m = mass \ of \ substance \ changing \ state$
$l = specific \ latent \ heat \ of \ vaporization$

Example T 3.8

Given that the latent heat of vaporization of water is 2.26×10^6 Jkg^{-1} how much energy is needed to vaporize 500 grams of water?

The graph below shows how the temperature of 150g of a substance changes as it is heated with a 100W heater.

Example T 3.9

The graph below shows how the temperature of 150g of a substance changes as it is heated with a 100W heater. Important coordinates are included.

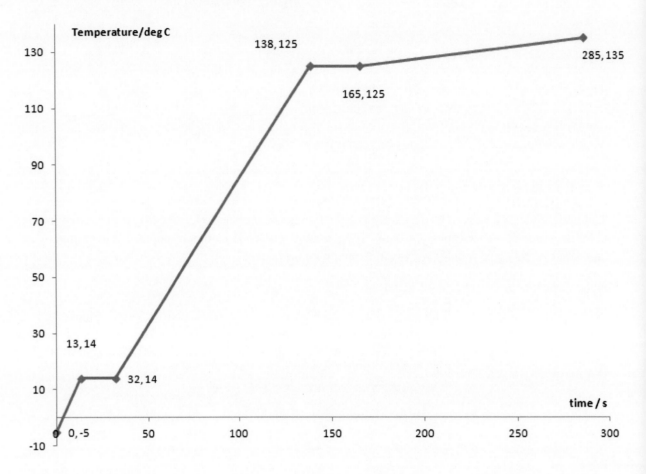

(a) Label on the graph when the state of the substance is solid (S) liquid (L) or gas (G) and any combination of these.

(b) Calculate or state the following:

   (i) The melting point and boiling point of the substance

   (ii) The specific heat capacity of the solid, liquid and gas phase of the substance, respectively

   (iii) The specific latent heat of fusion and specific latent heat of vaporization of the substance.

3.2 Modelling a Gas

❖ Pressure

Pressure is defined to be force per unit area ($P = \dfrac{F}{A}$)

Gas pressure can be explained by the average force of all collisions exerted on the walls of a vessel containing the gas.

Using this model it is easy to see that pressure is increased by:

- Increasing the speed of the particles
- Increasing the mass of the particles
- Decreasing the area of the collision surface, by decreasing the volume of the gas (whilst maintaining the number of particles).

It also explains that for a fixed mass of (an ideal) gas:

Increasing volume at constant temperature	$\Rightarrow$	pressure decreases
Increasing temperature at constant volume	$\Rightarrow$	pressure increases
Increasing temperature at constant pressure	$\Rightarrow$	volume increases

---

Example T 3.10

Suppose n particles collide with an area A of the walls of a container and the average time between each collision is t seconds. Suppose also that each collision exerts an average force of x newtons on the wall. What is the pressure caused by the gas particles?

❖ Equation of state for an ideal gas

An ideal gas is one that obeys the equation of state. i.e.

$PV = nRT$ where $P = pressure\ of\ gas\ (Pa)$

$V = volume\ of\ gas\ (m^3)$

$n = number\ of\ moles\ of\ gas$

$R = molar\ gas\ constant\ (8.31\ JK^{-1}mol^{-1})$

$T = absolue\ temperature\ of\ gas\ (K)$

For a fixed mass of such a gas:

- Pressure α temperature at constant volume (α means "is proportional to")
- Volume α temperature at constant pressure
- Pressure α $\dfrac{1}{volume}$ at constant temperature.

(Temperature is absolute (Kelvin) temperature in each case – see below.)

Example T 3.11

A 15 litre (1000 litres = 1m³) cylinder contains carbon dioxide gas at 220 kPa. Given that the temperature of the gas is 28°C, find:

Find the number of moles of carbon dioxide gas in the cylinder.

❖ Kinetic model of an ideal gas

The kinetic model of an ideal gas is a model that explains the macroscopic (bulk) properties of a gas, like temperature, pressure and volume.

The assumptions of the model are:
- Molecules are point molecules – they occupy no space
- Molecules have random motion – so they tend to spread out evenly in a container
- Collisions between pairs of molecules and between the walls of the container are elastic – so that the total kinetic energy of a gas left undisturbed will remain constant.

These assumptions apply to an "ideal gas" – one that behaves perfectly. In reality, under normal conditions of temperature and pressure, gases do approximate closely to these assumptions and behave in a very similar way to an ideal gas.

❖ Mole, molar mass and the Avogadro constant

Gas pressure does not depend on mass of particles, but rather, the number of particles of a given gas. For example 1000 molecules per cubic metre of hydrogen gas at room temperature will exert the same pressure as 1000 molecules per cubic metre of oxygen molecules – even though oxygen molecules are some 16 times more massive than hydrogen molecules.

The above example uses simple, but unrealistic numbers. At room temperature and pressure, one cubic metre will contain about 2.5×10^{25} molecules! We use a more convenient unit to measure "number of particles" – the mole.

One mole of particles is the same number of particles as there are atoms in 12g of carbon-12 (one of the isotopes of carbon).

This number is called the **Avogadro constant**, N_A, where:

$N_A = 6.02 \times 10^{23} mol^{-1}$

Molar mass is the mass of one mole of a particular substance.

Example T 3.12

Referring to example T 3.9

(a) Find the number of particles (molecules)
(b) Without calculation, explain how the answer would differ if hydrogen, a much lighter gas, were used instead (same pressure, volume & temperature).

Example T 3.13 (Using the equation of state of an ideal gas):

By assuming that air is made up of pure nitrogen gas, find an approximation of the mass of air in a container measuring 25cm x 50cm x 50cm at normal atmospheric pressure and room temperature. Use the following data:

Normal atmospheric pressure	= 101 kpa
Room temperature	= 25°c
Gas constant, R	= 8.31JK^{-1} mol^{-1}
Molar mass of nitrogen gas	= 28g

❖ Differences between real and ideal gases

Deviation from ideality

In general, most gases approximate closely to ideal gases. To behave as ideal gases:

- The particles themselves occupy zero volume
- There are no intermolecular forces between particles.

Gases deviate from ideality under conditions of very high pressure (above critical pressure) and/or very low temperature (below *critical* temperature).

Note that ideal gases cannot be liquefied, unlike real gases.

Topic 4: Waves

Summary Checklist

4.1	**Oscillations**
	Simple harmonic oscillations Time period, frequency, amplitude, displacement and phase difference Conditions for simple harmonic motion
4.2	**Travelling Waves**
	Travelling waves Wavelength, frequency, period and wave speed Transverse and longitudinal waves The nature of electromagnetic waves The nature of sound waves
4.3	**Wave Characteristics**
	Wavefronts and rays Amplitude and intensity Superposition Polarization
4.4	**Wave Behaviour**
	Reflection and refraction Snell's law, critical angle and total internal reflection Diffraction through a single-slit and around objects Interference patterns Double-slit interference Path difference
4.5	**Standing Waves**
	The nature of standing waves Boundary conditions Nodes and antinodes

Equations Provided (in IB databook) & Explanations

$T = \dfrac{1}{f}$	The **time period** of an oscillating system is equal to the reciprocal of the **frequency** of oscillation.
$c = f\lambda$	The **speed** of a wave is the equal to the product of the **frequency** of the wave and its **wavelength**.
$I \propto A^2$	The **intensity** (power per unit area) of a wave is proportional to the **square of the amplitude** of the wave.
$I \propto x^{-2}$	The **intensity** of a wave is proportional to the **reciprocal** of the **square of the distance** from the wave point source.
$I = I_0 \cos^2\theta$	The **intensity** of a plane polarised wave after it has passed through a polaroid filter is equal to the product of the **initial intensity** of the wave and the **square of the cosine of the angle** between the plane of polarisation of the wave and the axis of the filter.
$\dfrac{n_1}{n_2} = \dfrac{sin\theta_2}{sin\theta_1} = \dfrac{v_2}{v_1}$	The ratio of the **refractive indices** of two transparent materials, 1 and 2, is equal to the reciprocal of the **ratio of the sine of the angles** made with the normals in materials 1 & 2, and to the reciprocal of the **speeds of the waves** in materials 1 and 2.
$s = \dfrac{\lambda D}{d}$	The **separation/distance between successive bright (or dark) fringes** formed on a screen after light passes through a pair of double slits is equal to the product of the **wavelength** of the light and the **distance from double slits to the screen** divided by the **distance between the centres of the two slits**.
Constructive interference: $path\ difference = n\lambda$	When two coherent waves meet at a point the **path difference** between the length of the two paths of each wave from their origin to the point must be a **whole number of wavelengths** for constructive interference to occur at the point.
Constructive interference: $path\ difference = \left(n + \frac{1}{2}\right)\lambda$	For destructive interference to occur at the point the **path difference** must be a **whole number of wavelengths plus a half-wavelength**.

4.1   Oscillations

❖ Introduction

This topic is concerned with the nature and application of waves. Waves are one means by which energy is transferred from one place to another. Although a wave is defined as a transfer of energy, not matter, wave-transfer always involves oscillations – and these oscillations can be oscillations of an electromagnetic field (in the case of electromagnetic radiation (EMR) waves, such as light, x-rays etc. or oscillations of particles, such as water waves and sound waves.

In this guide, we shall refer to the oscillations in waves as "particle" oscillations – but must recognise that they can be particle or field oscillations.

Examples of oscillations:

- A mass bouncing up and down on a spring
- A girl bouncing on a trampoline
- A teacher pacing back and forth across the room
- A boy swinging on a playground swing
- The air molecules as a sound wave passes
- The molecules in any solid material.

❖ Simple Harmonic Oscillations

Simple harmonic motion is a type of motion that accurately describes the oscillating motion of the "particles" in a wave. It is important to realise that SHM is not merely oscillating motion: it is a specific kind of oscillating motion. Not all the examples of oscillations listed above are described by SHM

SHM involves motion where the acceleration of the particle is always proportional to and in the opposite direction to the displacement of the particle.The first, fourth and fifth examples on the list above are common examples of SHM. **All waves involve SHM oscillations**.

An easy way to visualise SHM is to consider a pendulum. Pendulum bobs swing with approximate SHM (the longer the string and the lower the angle, the better the approximation).

The central position of the bob (where it hangs when left to stop) is the equilibrium (zero displacement) position. When the pendulum is set in motion, as it swings outwards its displacement increases, its velocity decreases and the force pulling it back to the centre increases. This force tells us that the acceleration is always acting towards the centre.

The motion of particles in a wave is exactly the same. A cork on the surface of a water wave moves up and down (showing direction of "particles" the same way that a pendulum bob swings back and forth.

❖ Time period, frequency, amplitude, displacement and phase difference

Some definitions

Oscillation

- The term used to describe the movement of a "particle" (can also be field) from a position "to and fro" back to its original position. Vibration is an alternative term.

Medium

- The "material" through which a wave travels (can also be a vacuum, for light and other forms of electro-magnetic radiation).

Displacement

- The distance of a particle from its undisturbed (equilibrium) position
- Usually determined by y axis position on wave graph/diagram
- Measured in metres (but not normally stated or calculated).

Amplitude

- The maximum displacement of a particle from equilibrium position
- Represented by height (from middle/equilibrium position) of wave diagram
- Measured in metres, although not a normally useful measurement.

Period

- The time taken for one complete oscillation of a particle ie. Time taken for production of one complete wave
- Measured in seconds
- Symbol for period is t.

Frequency

- The number of waves/oscillations produced/observed per second
- Measured in hertz
- Symbol for frequency is f
- Note that $f=1/t$.

Phase difference

- The phase difference between two particles along a wave is the fraction of a cycle by which one moves behind the other
- The phase difference between two sources is the fraction of a cycle by which one
- Source moves behind the other
- One cycle corresponds to 2π radians or 360°.

Example T 4.1

The following passage is a description of a sound wave. Re-write the passage but you must use each of the above definitions at least once.

"Sound waves consist of particles (air molecules) that vibrate forwards and backwards, typically several hundred times per second – and so the time for a single particle to move back and forth would then be of the order of a hundredth of a second (both these quantities are very variable). Since they require particles to transfer energy, sound waves require a material to travel through such as air, water or a solid (like the ground). As the sound wave passes through a material, the particles in a material are shifted away from their usual position. This shift changes from one direction to another and the maximum shift is dependent on the power of the sound source and will affect the intensity and loudness of the sound. If we look at a line of particles in a sound wave, all along the direction that the wave is travelling in, we find that each subsequent particle is slightly out of synchrony with the next until, after a certain distance, we find a particle in synchrony with the first and the cycle is repeated".

❖ Conditions for simple harmonic motion

SHM is defined as motion where the acceleration of the particle is proportional to but in the opposite direction to the displacement of the particle.

i.e. $a \propto -x$ where: $a = acceleration,\ x = displacement$

The defining condition for simple harmonic motion is as follows:

$a \propto -x$ where: x s the displacement of a give particle over time

You must learn this condition; it is not given in the data booklet.

Meaning: Think of a pendulum bob. Zero displacement (equilibrium) is the position where the bob is at the lowest. If the bob moves forwards, it is being pulled backwards (so it will turn around and come back). If the bob moves backwards, it is being pulled forwards etc. Being pulled backwards means accelerating backwards (since F=ma), being pulled forwards means accelerating backwards.

Example T 4.2

A pendulum is set in motion so that it swings back and forth, from A through B to C, then back through B to A and so on, as shown in the diagram shown below. Other information is given on the diagram. We shall assume that it does not lose any energy as it swings, so it keeps swinging to equal amplitudes.

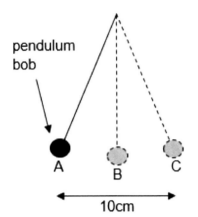

The pendulum bob is timed and it takes 1.25 seconds to move from A→B→C→ B→A→B→C→B→A→B→C, so that it has moved a total distance of 50cm in this time.

As shown, the "swing distance" is 10cm

(a) What is the amplitude of the motion of the bob?
(b) What is the period?
(c) What is the frequency?
(d) In order to demonstrate that the motion of the bob is simple harmonic motion, what must we show? Briefly describe what we could do to show this, experimentally.

The above examples could be applied exactly the same way as a particle in a sound or water wave, or any other wave.

Example T 4.3

The graph below shows how the velocity of a nitrogen molecule (in air), describing SHM, changes as a sound passes:

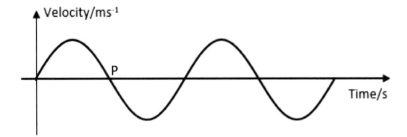

(a) Mark on the diagram with the letter A, positions where the displacement of the molecule is zero
(b) Mark on the diagram with the letter B, positions where the acceleration has maximum magnitude
(c) Explain how the displacement can be found from the graph
(d) Explain how the acceleration can be found from the graph at any point in time
(e) Explain how the graph shows that the motion is (i) oscillating (ii) SHM
(f) What does the area under the graph from the origin to point P represent?

Energy Changes in Simple Harmonic Oscillation

An undamped oscillating system is one where the total energy remains constant. For simple harmonic oscillations, the energy moves back and forth; from potential to kinetic to potential etc. The nature (type) depends on what is oscillating. For example, for a mass on a vertical spring, the potential energy can be gravitational (when mass is at top) or elastic (when mass is at bottom).

For a vibrating atom it would be KE→electrostatic potential energy→ KE etc. The electrostatic potential is, provided by the force of attraction between atoms.

Example T 4.4

Referring to the pendulum bob in example T 4.2, describe the energy changes as the bob swings back and forth (assume no energy loss due to heat/sound as a result of resistance to motion).

4.2   Travelling Waves

❖ Travelling Waves

Waves may be categorised into two groups: **standing waves** and **travelling** (or **progressive**) **waves**. Travelling waves are the means by which energy is transferred. All waves also involve oscillations.

❖ Wavelength, period, frequency and speed

To help understand the concepts of wave motion and particle motion within a wave, consider a side view of part of a water wave with a cork floating on it, as follows:

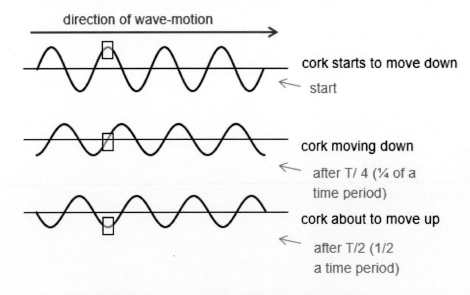

direction of wave-motion

cork starts to move down

start

cork moving down

after T/ 4 (¼ of a time period)

cork about to move up

after T/2 (1/2 a time period)

The waves shown is moving from left to right but the oscillations are "up down"

- The wave shows 4 complete cycles, or oscillations
- Wavelength is the total horizontal length of the wave shown divided by 4
- The wave is moving from left to right – this can be noted by the position of the crest that starts at the same position as the cork, and has moved forwards half a wavelength on the third wave shown
- The straight horizontal lines show the equilibrium position of the wave – this corresponds to the position of undisturbed water
- The energy movement corresponds to the wave movement: from left to right
- The motion of the particles (water molecules) is up and down – shown by the movement of the cork

- If the next 3 corresponding diagrams are drawn (as above) the wave would have moved forwards by one complete wavelength. The cork would have also moved through one complete oscillation (up and down). Hence, a wavelength corresponds to an oscillation of the vibrating particles
- This (water wave) is an example of a transverse wave.

Some definitions/descriptions

Wavelength

- The distance along the axis of the wave from one part of the wave to the next occurrence of this part (e.g. Crest to crest or trough to trough)
- Measured in metres
- Symbol for wavelength is λ.

Wave speed

- The speed that a wave travels: can be found by finding the speed of a particular point on a wave – e.g. crest for a water wave. Can also be found by finding the rate at which energy is transferred – e.g. sound waves: measure how fast the sound travels

Crest

- The point on a wave with maximum positive displacement

Trough

- The point on a wave with maximum negative displacement

Intensity

- Term used to describe the energy of a wave
- More intense light is brighter; more intense sound is louder
- $intensity\ \alpha\ amplitude^2$ so, if the amplitude of a wave doubles, the intensity (energy) of the wave multiplies by 4 (increases by a factor of 4).

The Wave equation

$c = f\lambda$ where c is $wave-speed$, f is $frequency\ of\ wave$, $\lambda = wavelength$

Derivation:

- Distance travelled by wave per second = number of waves passing a point per second x length of each wave
- But speed of wave = distance travelled by wave per second
- Speed of wave = number of waves passing a point per second x length of each wave (wavelength)
- But number of waves passing a point per second = frequency
  speed of wave = frequency x wavelength.

Example T 4.5

    (a) Calculate the frequency of gamma rays with a wavelength of $3.8 \times 10^{-13} m$

    (b) Calculate the speed of sound in air given that the wavelength of a middle c note has a frequency of 256hz and a wavelength of 1.30m

    (c) A canoeist riding waves is at one moment at the peak of a wave and 0.4 seconds later is at the next trough of the wave. Given that the wave peaks are 2.5 metres apart, calculate the speed of these waves.

❖ Transverse and longitudinal waves

1) **Longitudinal**: "particle" oscillations (vibrations) are parallel to direction of wave.

2) **Transverse**: "particle" oscillations are perpendicular to direction of wave motion

Note – particles are:
        - Air atoms/molecules in case of sound waves (in air)
        - Water molecules in case of water waves
        - Electromagnetic field in case of electromagnetic radiation.

Wave models (graphs):

The conventional sine-curve shaped wave is actually a mathematical graph showing the displacement of the particles within a wave, as follows. Pay particular attention to the description of the horizontal axes of each of the four graphs shown.

Transverse Waves

We should be familiar with two different graph representations:

This wave shows how **displacement** varies along the wave at an **instant in time**. It is a good visual representation of a real transverse wave – for example, a water wave. Horizontal distance from peak to peak gives **wavelength** and the maximum height of the wave, from the wave axis (x

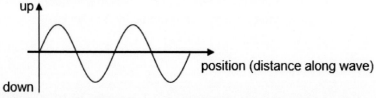

axis on graph) gives us the **amplitude** of the wave – which corresponds to the maximum displacement of the particles in the wave. A picture of a water wave would give us this graph – with correct displacement; distance coordinates, measured directly off the picture.

This wave shows how displacement at a single point on the wave varies as time progresses. It is therefore not a good visual representation of the wave – since if we can see the particles (e.g. water wave) we see the whole wave, not just a single point on the wave. This type of wave can easily be misinterpreted – horizontal "distance" from peak to peak on the graph does not give wavelength – because it is not a distance, it is a time. The time from peak to peak therefore gives the period of the wave and, as before, the maximum height of the wave, from the wave axis (x axis on graph) gives us the amplitude of the wave – which corresponds to the maximum displacement of the particles in the wave.

<u>Longitudinal Waves</u>

Again, we should be familiar with two different graph representations:

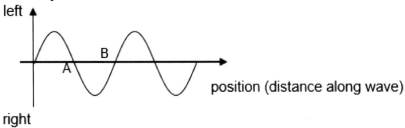

displacement – at one instant in time

This wave shows how displacement varies along the wave. It is a not a good visual representation of a real longitudinal wave – for example, a sound wave – since the graph shows left displacement upwards, visually and right displacement down, visually. In reality we would see the particles moving to the left and right, parallel to the axis of the wave, and not up and down, perpendicular to the direction of wave propagation. Distance from peak to peak gives wavelength and the maximum height of the wave, from the wave axis (x axis on graph) gives us the amplitude of the wave – which corresponds to the maximum displacement (left or right) from the usual equilibrium position of the particles in the wave.

Longitudinal waves are often called compression waves because they consist of a series of compressions – where particles are closer together than usual, (compressed) – separated by rarefactions. In the wave-graph above, point A, where the graph first crosses the x-axis, corresponds to a rarefaction, since particles to the left are displaced leftwards (as shown by the upwards part of graph) and particles to the right are displaced to the right (as shown by the downwards part of graph). Using a similar explanation, point B corresponds to a compression, as does the origin point of the graph.

displacement – at one position on the wave

This wave shows how displacement at one point on the wave varies as time progresses. Using similar arguments to those used in the previous two graphs, it is a not a good visual representation of a real longitudinal wave. Distance from peak to peak gives period and the maximum height of the wave, from the wave axis (x axis on graph) gives us the amplitude of the wave – which corresponds to the maximum displacement (left or right) of the particles in the wave.

<u>Wave Relationships</u>

One wavelength on a displacement / time graph represents the period of the wave

One wavelength on a displacement / position graph represents the wavelength of the wave.
For all waves: wave speed   =   frequency   x   wavelength.

❖ The Nature of Electromagnetic Waves

The Electromagnetic Spectrum (EMS) is a group of waves that are all forms of electromagnetic radiation: rather than oscillating matter, they consist of oscillating electric and magnetic fields. All waves in the EMS travel at the same speed (speed of light, c) ie. $3.0 \times 10^8 ms^{-1}$ (in a vacuum).

You can use the mnemonic: GAXUVIMR to remember the waves in order of wavelength, shortest first

$10^{-15} m$	Ga	gamma rays
$10^{-12} m$	X	X rays
$10^{-9} m$	U	Ultra-Violet radiation
$10^{-7} m$	V	Visible radiation (light)
$10^{-5} m$	I	Infra-red radiation
$10^{-2} m$	M	Microwaves
$10m$	R	Radio waves

It should be noted that each type of wave in the list above actually has a range of wavelengths. The different wavelengths, for example, of visible light give us the different colours of the visible spectrum (ROYGBIV).

Example T 4.6

Using the fact that audible sound has a wavelength range of around 1.5cm to 20m and travels at 330ms⁻¹ and using the data given above, do some calculations and to describe how sound wave frequencies compare to those of waves in the EMS.

❖ The nature of sound waves

Sound waves are generated by vibrating objects. The object then exerts a series of push-pulls on air particles. This causes regular pulses of high pressure air (compressions) and low pressure air (rarefactions) to move through the air, and they do so at over 300m/s (speed depends on air pressure, temperature and density).

Compression (maximum pressure)

- Term used to describe region where particles (e.g. Air molecules) are closer together than they would be in their normal equilibrium state.

Rarefaction (minimum pressure)

- Term used to describe region where particles (e.g. Air molecules) are further apart than they would be in their normal equilibrium state.

The frequency of the soundwave is a measure of the pitch of the sound, and the amplitude of the sound; the intensity, therefore loudness.

Example T 4.7

(a) An object vibrates at a frequency of 8500 oscillations per minute. Given that sound travels at 330m/s, calculate the distance between centres of successive rarefactions and compressions in the sound wave created

(b) In terms of the vibrating object, explain how (i) the pitch (ii) the loudness of the sound could be increased.

4.3   Wave Characteristics

❖ Wavefronts and rays

A wavefront shows a line of points all in phase with each other (so, they could all part of a 2 dimensional wave-peak, or a wave-trough.

Therefore the distance between two successive wavefronts is equal to the wavelength of the wave; the number of wavefronts passing a point per second can be used to determine the frequency of the wave and the time taken for two successive peaks to pass a point, the time period.

A ray simply shows the direction of the wave: a ray is always perpendicular to the wavefronts.

Example T 4.8

The following incomplete diagram shows wavefronts (in blue) on a water wave (not drawn accurately to scale).

(a) On the diagram, draw a ray showing the wave-direction
(b) From the information given, calculate the wavelength of the wave
(c) Given that the frequency of the wave generator is 50Hz, calculate the speed of the wave.

❖ Amplitude and intensity

Intensity

Intensity is a term that relates to any kind of radiation (e.g. light) or sound. It is a measure of the energy striking a surface, or passing through a surface of air, per second per square metre.

Hence, the equation is: $I = \frac{P}{A}$ where P is power, in watts and A is area, in square metres. Intensity is logically measured in watts per square metre.

If we assume that a source of power is a point source and that the energy is being dispersed (spread) around in all directions, then we can find the intensity at any distance, r, from the source by taking the surface to be a sphere of area: $4\pi r^2$.

Hence, we get: $I = \frac{P}{4\pi r^2}$

This tells us that if the distance from a point source (e.g. sound or light) doubles, then the intensity is ¼ the initial value (i.e. the intensity is quartered).

The equation above is referred to as an "inverse square law", since $P \propto \frac{1}{r^2}$

The connection to amplitude

It can be shown that the intensity of a wave is proportional to the amplitude of the wave squared.

i.e. $I \propto A^2$

Example T 4.9

    (a) Calculate the intensity of a sound being produced by a 2.0W speaker 3m away from the speaker, stating any assumptions

    (b) Explain why your answer in (a) may in fact be more or less intense

    (c) This sound is picked up on a microphone and converted to an electronic signal on a CRO (cathode ray oscilloscope), showing the following trace:

        The y axis of the trace shows displacement (arbitrary units) and the x axis shows time.

        Add on the diagram above the trace that would be expected if the microphone picked up sound from the same distance away from a 4.0W speaker.

❖ Superposition

Principle of Superposition

When two or more waves (have to be the same type of wave) meet, the total displacement at any point is the sum of the displacements that each individual wave would cause at that point.

To illustrate this, imagine sound is being observed at a single point. Over time, repeated rarefactions and compressions will be observed (the sound wave). Consider the waves from each source individually:

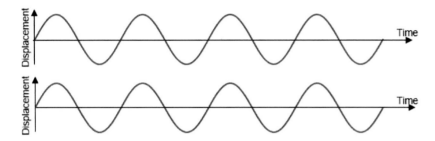

At all points in time the two waves are in phase (i.e. crests occur at the same time, as do troughs). This results in constructive interference, as follows:

The red coloured curve shows the displacement of both the individual waves (they are on top of each other, so they appear as one). The thick blue curve is obtained by applying the principle of superposition – the displacement at each point along the wave is obtained by adding together the displacements of each red wave. The amplitude (maximum displacement) of the resultant wave is thus double that of either red wave so this is constructive interference.

Now consider two waves that are out of phase (a crest from one source is observed at the same time as a trough from the other):

The blue wave is found by adding the individual displacements of the red and green waves – and since they are always of opposite sign (and equal magnitude) they cancel – the result is a "null" wave – no sound would be observed.

The first example showed two (red) waves 0° out of phase (i.e. in phase). The second example showed a green and a red wave 180° out of phase (the maximum amount two waves can be out of phase). The next example T 4.10 shows two waves that are between these two extremes, 90° out of phase.

Example T 4.10

Draw in the blue line, using the principle of superposition.

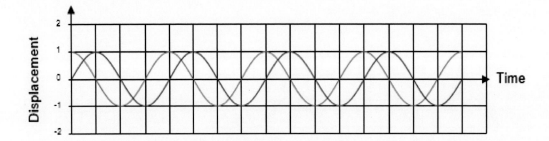

The blue wave is the result of the simultaneous existence of the red and the green wave. Consider time 0: green wave displacement+ red wave displacement = 1 + 0 = 1 Therefore resultant displacement at time, 0 is 1.

At time corresponding to 1 unit on the graph: green displacement = 0, red = 1 therefore total =1, and, after 2 units of time total displacement = –1 (green) + 0 (red) = –1, etc. Note that maximum resultant displacement is greater than either individual displacement, so we have constructive interference

This effect (and principle) applies to all types of wave, for example light, water, and sound.

❖ Polarization

Light is a member of the family of the electromagnetic spectrum.

Like all members of this family, it is an energy form that propagates (travels) at approximately $3 \times 10^8 ms^{-1}$ and consists of oscillating electric and magnetic fields. The oscillating electric field creates an oscillating magnetic field at right angles to the electric field, and the magnetic field creates an electric field and so on. This happens at "the speed of light". Both fields oscillate at right angles to the direction that the wave is travelling in – hence electromagnetic waves are classified as transverse waves.

The diagram below shows a simplified view of an electromagnetic wave:

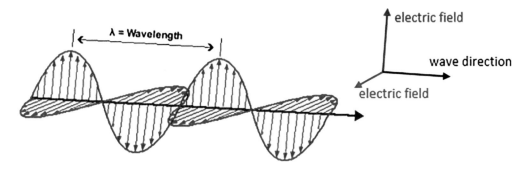

However, the diagram in fact shows an electromagnetic wave that has been plane polarized. A natural electromagnetic wave (e.g. light coming from a hot filament) consists of an infinite number of electric field oscillations in *all* directions perpendicular to the wave direction, and hence magnetic field directions are similarly distributed.

The following diagram shows some possible oscillations, to help illustrate this:

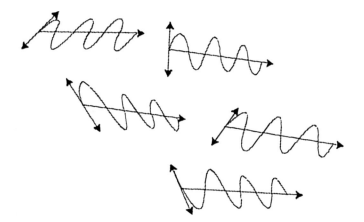

Note that the diagrams only show the electric field oscillations ("vectors") – the magnetic ones would be perpendicular, as shown in the previous diagram. Light (or any other electromagnetic radiation) that has been polarized has all but one plane of the electric field oscillations (and all but one plane of the magnetic field oscillations) removed.

Special materials, called filters (polaroid filters) can do this – if light is passed through them it emerges as plane polarized light, as the following diagram shows:

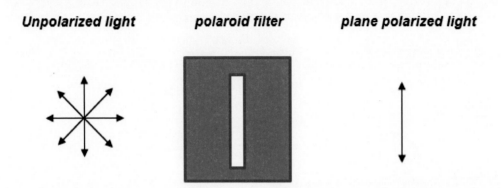

| *Unpolarized light* | *polaroid filter* | *plane polarized light* |

The diagram above is a schematic (simplified) illustration of the polarization process.

<u>Malus's Law</u>

If plane polarized light is passed through a Polaroid filter such as the above one, it passes through unaffected if the filter is orientated in the same plane as the light. Referring to the above diagram, if a second filter is placed in front of the one shown all the light will pass through unaffected (with unchanged intensity) as long as the second filter is still in line with the plane of the polarized light (so the "**transmission axis**" remains vertical). If the second filter is rotated through 90° it will completely stop the light. At other angles, the light will be reduced in **intensity** but not stopped.

The second filter in this example is referred to as an analyzer, since it can be used to analyse/identify the plane of polarization of the light.

Malus's Law allows us to predict the intensity of such a beam of plane polarised light of initial intensity I_0 if the transmission axis is at an angle θ to the plane containing the electric field. The intensity of the transmitted light is given by I, where:

$I = I_0 cos^2 \theta$ Malus' Law

Malus's Law can also be used to show that a Polaroid filter reduces the intensity of natural unpolarised light by 50%.

Polaroid sunglasses are therefore a useful way of reducing the glare and intensity of bright sunlight.

Example T 4.11

Vertically polarized light falls on a polarizer that has its transmission axis at 30° to the vertical. By what percentage has the intensity of the light reduced in passing through the polarizer?

<u>Polarization by reflection</u>

When unpolarized light meets a surface such as water, where the light can both reflect and refract, the reflected ray is polarized to an extent. For example, the glare from the sea contains partially polarized light and this glare can be reduced by wearing Polaroid (polarizing) sunglasses. Depending on the angle of the sunglasses and the way that the light reaches the lens, the intensity of light can thus be cut down.

Brewster's Angle

I have stated that the reflected light is partially polarized. This means that more than one plane of the electric oscillation is still left. The extent of polarization depends on the angle that the incident ray makes with the reflecting surface. Brewster's angle gives the incident angle of the light required in order that the reflected light is totally polarized (i.e. plane polarized – all but one plane of electric field oscillations removed).

Brewster's angle occurs when the refracted ray is at 90° to the reflected ray, as shown in the diagram below:

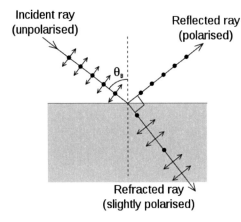

$$tan\theta_B = n$$

$$where\ \theta_B\ is\ Brewster's\ angle$$

$$and\ n\ is\ the\ refractive\ index\ of\ the\ medium$$

Example T 4.12

Calculate the angle between horizontal and a light ray incident on water if the light ray is to be totally polarized on reflection, given that the refractive index of water is 1.5

Optically active substances

Some substances are able to rotate the plane of plane polarized light. Such substances are called optically active substances. There are many optically active substances, including sugars and sweeteners. Light can be passed through solutions of such substances. The direction of the rotation depends on the chemical bonding in the substance and can be used to help identify the substance. The extent of the rotation depends on the concentration of the solution, and can thus be used to determine concentration (the angle of rotation of the plane polarized light is measured).

Stress Analysis

Materials under stress can also exhibit optical activity. Thus, if polarized light is shone on structures (such as metal tools, car windscreens) the way that the light is reflected can reveal stress points and possible weaknesses – in design or as a result of overstress due to loading.

LCD screens

Liquid Crystal Display (LCD) screens also make use of the polarisation of light.

Each liquid crystal forms a pixel on the screen. Plane polarized light is passed through the liquid crystal. These crystals have the special property that they rotate the plane of polarised light by 90° but, if a voltage is applied to the crystal, they do not. Analyser filters are placed in front of the liquid crystals, so that only light that has the same axis of polarization as the incident light passes through. The crystals with no voltage applied rotate the light will therefore not allow the light to pass through and the crystals with voltage applied will allow light to pass through. It is not difficult to imagine that arrays of these crystals can be arranged to form digits (say, 0 to 9) and by applying the right voltage combinations any number can be illuminated.

4.4   Wave Behaviour

❖ Reflection and Refraction

Reflection   when a wave meets a surface it may be reflected

angle of incidence = angle of reflection

wave can be reflected, transmitted or absorbed by a medium

the wave may refract as well as reflect on entering the new medium.

Refraction   wave enters a new medium

speed changes

wavelength changes

frequency remains the same

direction changes (unless incident angle = 0°).

If wave enters a medium in which it travels slower:

- Its speed decreases
- Its wavelength decreases
- Its frequency remains the same
- It bends towards the normal.
-

Example – light passing through air, then a glass prism:

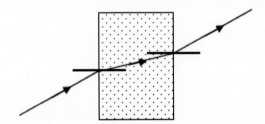

Notes

- The light bends towards the normal (line perpendicular to surface-boundary) as it enters the "slower" medium (glass)
- Waves never bend past the normal line
- The amount of bending (ie. the angles) can be calculated using Snell's Law (covered later)
- The light bends away from the normal as it passes from the glass to the "faster" medium (air)
- The ray entering the glass prism is parallel to the ray emerging from the prism because the two faces of the prism are parallel and the amount of bending at the first surface is the same as the amount of "unbending" at the second.

❖ Snell's law, critical angle and total internal reflection

Refractive Index

The refractive index of a (transparent) material is a number that tells us how fast light travels in that material. It is the ratio of the speed of light in a vacuum to the speed of light in the material.

We write this as:
$$n_{material} = \frac{c_{vacuum}}{c_{material}} = \frac{3.00 \times 10^8}{c_{material}}$$

Where n is the refractive index and c is the speed of light.

(the speed of light in a vacuum is always $3.00 \times 10^8 ms^{-1}$, as provided in data booklet)

Unless told otherwise, we assume that the speed of light in air is the same as that in a vacuum.

Example T 4.13

The speed of light in a certain type of glass is $2.2 \times 10^8 ms^{-1}$. What is the refractive index of that substance?

Snell's Law

Snell's law connects the speed, wavelength and direction of an incident wave with that of the same wave once it has been refracted. Snell's Law states that, for a certain boundary (e.g. air → glass) the following ratios are always the same, whatever the incident angle:

Speed in medium 1 : speed in medium 2

Wavelength in medium 1 : wavelength in medium 2

Sine of angle in medium 1 : sine of angle in medium 2

It follows (from the first ratio above) that each of these ratios is the reciprocal of the ratio of refractive indices of the substances. We can therefore write:

$$\frac{n_1}{n_2} = \frac{sin\theta_2}{sin\theta_1} = \frac{v_2}{v_1} \; (give \; in \; data \; book) \qquad = \frac{f_2\lambda_2}{f_1\lambda_1} = \frac{\lambda_2}{\lambda_1}$$

The following diagram illustrates this:

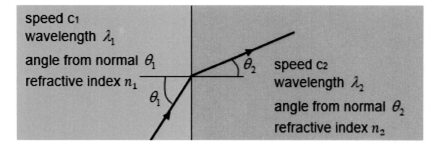

So we can use the ratio of refractive indices and one of the speeds, angles or wavelengths to find the other speed, angle or wavelength.

Note that we take the refractive index of air or a vacuum to be 1.

Example T 4.14

Light is shone into a glass block (prism) at an angle of 47° to the normal (i.e. angle of incidence = 47°). It emerges at 29° to the normal.

  (a) Find the refractive index of the glass used in the prism
  (b) Find the speed of light in this glass
  (c) If the wavelength of light in the glass is 600nm, calculate the wavelength of the light in the air
  (d) Calculate the frequency of this light in air
  (e) Calculate the frequency of this light in the glass.

Example T 4.15

Light travels at 3.00×10^8 ms^{-1} in air and 2.07×10^8 ms^{-1} in glass. If a light ray is shone into a glass prism at 30° to the surface of the prism (as shown), find the angle of the light ray inside the prism, and draw and label this ray on the diagram.

Refraction and Reflection at a medium: the wavefront model

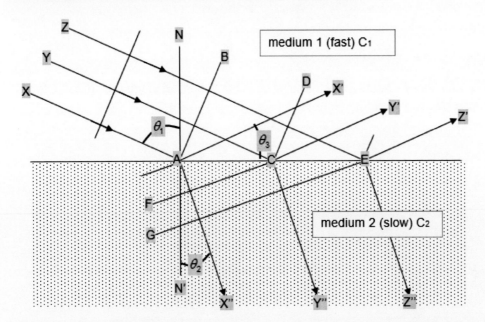

The above diagram shows a wave travelling in medium 1 and approaching a new medium, medium 2. The wave travels slower in medium 2 than in medium 1. As the wave enters medium 2 it refracts, slowing down and bending towards the normal. It also reflects, bouncing back into medium 1 at an equal speed and the angle of the reflection is equal to the angle of incidence.

This wave could be any kind of wave: water, sound or light, for example.

The new medium for water would be, for example, a shallower section of water (where it travels slower). For light the boundary may be air, then glass or perhaps air then water, for example. For sound, the boundary could be air then water (say, in a swimming pool) or warm air, then cold air)

A wave can be considered as a beam. Three rays are shown on this beam: X, Y and Z.

Wavefronts are lines that move forward with the wave, perpendicular to the wave direction (ray). The incident wave has wavefronts AB and CD, for example. The wavelength is the distance between consecutive wavefronts.

The wave reflects, emerging at X', Y' and Z' and the angle of incidence, θ_1, is equal to the angle of reflection, $90° - \theta_3$.

The wave also refracts when the rays meet at A, C and E, emerging at X'', Y'' and Z''. The angle of refraction is θ_2.

Refraction and Reflection at a boundary; Total Internal Reflection

We usually get both refraction and reflection at a surface – the diagrams below illustrate this.

- The incident ray is shown as a solid black arrow
- The refracted ray is shown as a solid red arrow
- The partially reflected ray is shown as a dashed green arrow

The blue medium is the denser of the two media (the other medium, shown as blank, is usually air).

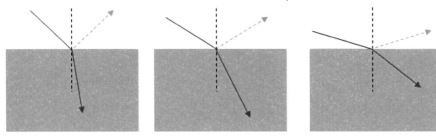

Note that:

- Angle of incidence = angle of refraction
- The ray always refracts towards the normal in the denser medium, when the ray slows down

If we reverse the direction of the ray, the ray is traced along the same lines, as follows:

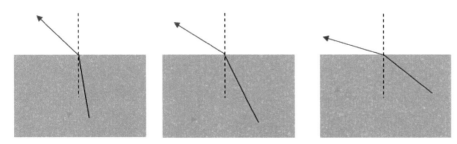

However, here we can see that the incident angle cannot get much larger, since the refracted angle has reached almost 90°.

If we increase the incident angle just enough for the ray to emerge along the boundary between the two media, the incident angle is called the critical angle, as follows:

$\theta_c = critical\ angle$

Note that this only happens when the incident ray is in the slower medium

If we further increase the angle of incidence, all the (light) reflects. This is called total internal reflection:

If $\theta > \theta_c$:

Total internal reflection occurs.

This only happens when the incident ray is in the slower medium

---

Example T 4.16

Glass has a refractive has a refractive index of approximately 1.4, and diamond has a refractive index of twice this value. Determine the critical angles for glass and for diamond and comment on how this can be used to explain why diamond glistens with light.

(Hint: for critical angle problems, take the angle of refraction to be 90°)

❖ **Diffraction through a Single Slit and around Objects**

Diffraction

When a wave meets the edge of a solid object it may be deviated from its path. Diffraction is most noticeable when a wave passes through a gap in a solid object and the effect is more pronounced when the gap is about the same size as the wavelength of the waves (can be greater or smaller than wavelength, there is no precision here).

Examples of Diffraction

i) Sound waves passing through a doorway, or past the corner of a building, can be heard "around the corner" (as well as in the expected regions!)

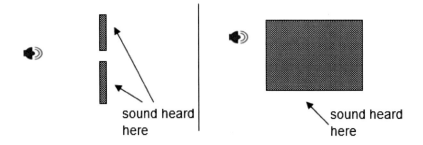

ii) Water waves – ripples show wavefronts and wave-direction

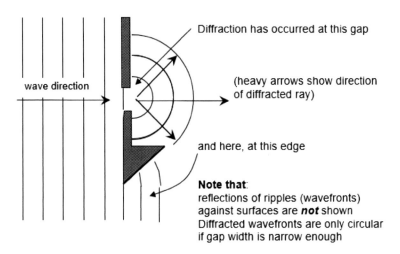

iii) Light passing through a narrow slit

Example T 4.17

Explain why lower frequency radio waves are more easily able to be easily picked up in buildings and around objects that high frequency radio waves

❖ Interference Patterns

Phase angle and phase difference

One cycle of an oscillation is taken to be equivalent to a "phase angle" of 360°.

If two wave sources are creating waves so that as a crest is being produced by one, a crest is also produced by another, and they continue to produce crests and troughs together, the two sources are said to be in phase. The phase difference between the two sources is said to be 0°. If they are 360° out of phase they are also in phase, since a complete wavelength out of phase still means they produce crests together. If one source produces a crest whilst the other produces a trough, the two sources are said to be 180° out of phase.

If two waves arrive at a point in phase we get constructive interference (in accordance with the principle of superposition). The amplitude of the resultant wave will be the sum of that of the two individual waves ($A_1 + A_2$).

If two waves arrive at a point 180° out of phase they cancel each other and we get destructive interference. The amplitude of the resultant wave will be the difference of the amplitudes of the individual waves ($|A_1 - A_2|$): zero if the amplitude of both waves are the same.

If the phase difference between two sources remains constant then they are said to be coherent.

For sound waves, as long as the frequency of the two sources is the same they will be coherent.

For light (since light waves also behave as particles, called photons), the two sources have to have originated from the same source (so a single point source can be split into two, by diffraction).

Interference patterns

Two coherent sources of any kind of wave (e.g. water, sound or light) will produce an interference pattern. Thus, if an observer moves in a straight line opposite to the two sources, there will be alternating regions of maximum and minimum intensity.

Two-source interference of waves

When two waves are produced at the same time, they will interfere with each other (see principle of superposition, earlier in this chapter). For an interference pattern to be observed, the two sources must be coherent.

Coherent

This term refers to two sources of wave. The two sources are coherent if the time lapse between a wavefront (ripple/crest) being produced from one source and from the other source remains constant. In the case of sound waves as long as both waves are generated at the same frequency, they will be coherent.

Consider two water wave generators: S1 and S2, below. Each generator dips in and out of the water, making circular ripples, as shown in the diagram. The ripples (crests) from S1 are shown in red, and those from S2, in blue.

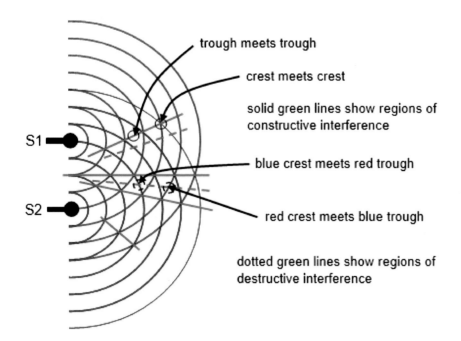

Whenever a crest from one source meets a crest from another source, or if a trough meets a trough, constructive interference will result – the amplitude of the resultant wave will be greater than that of either of the waves on their own. Whenever a crest from one source and a trough from another (or vice-versa) meet, destructive interference will result. Amplitude will reduce, possibly to zero.

Note that this effect is still observed if the two sources are still of equal frequency (waves per second) but do not produce peaks together, and troughs together. For example, if one source produces troughs, whilst the other produces crests, the two sources are still coherent, and an interference pattern is observed – the dashed green lines above would swap with the solid green lines.

Similar theory can be used to explain the interference pattern for sound waves and for light waves. The sound from two speakers, for example, can produce regions surrounding the speakers of particularly high volume or low volume sound.

Single Slit Interference

When light is directed towards a very narrow slit (like a single scratch on a painted glass slide) such that the width of the slit is of the order of only a few wavelengths of the light, it emerges in a particular way, due to diffraction. If the light is projected onto a screen a diffraction pattern is observed.

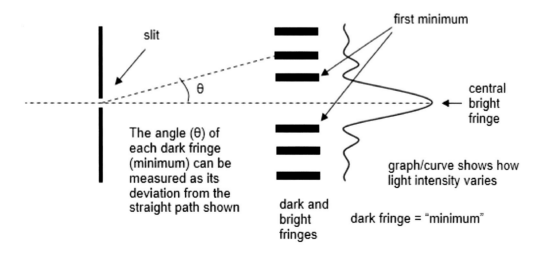

The light emerges in light and dark "fringes". The above diagram shows a simplified version of what is seen. The graph (usually see rotated 90° anti-clockwise) shows how the intensity varies with position. Thus, the central fringe has the greatest intensity and is the brightest.

It is possible to explain this pattern and to predict the positions of the dark fringes, as follows.

When a light wave enters the slit, the wave is not a single ray, but a beam. Each crest that passes through the slit is called a wavefront. (The wavefronts are at 90° to the beam).

Huygen's Principle tells us that we can consider a wavefront as a line of point sources of light. So effectively, when a wavefront enters the slit, we can think of this as an infinite number of light-rays.

These light rays can interact (interfere) with each other. At different positions along the screen there will be different types of interference.

In the centre a crest from one "point source" or ray will always be met by a crest from another, due to the symmetry. Similarly a trough from one wave at that point will be met by a trough from another. So in the centre constructive interference results. When two crests meet, a larger crest is formed; when two troughs meet, a larger trough is formed. The wave amplitude (and hence intensity) increases.

At a certain point a little way along from the centre, a crest from one wave will meet a trough from another, due to the slightly different distances the two waves have to travel and the asymmetry. Here there will be destructive interference and a dark fringe (minimum) will be observed.

❖ Double Slit Interference

<u>Interference of light and Young's double slits.</u>

For a qualitative discussion of two source interference, see "two source interference of waves", previously.

For two *light* sources to be coherent, there is a further condition. The light coming from the two sources must initially have come from the same source. This is because light is not emitted in a continuous wave-train. It is emitted in short bursts. The length and duration of each burst is essentially random. If two light sources of equal frequency are used, but from two separate bulbs, an interference pattern would not be observed.

The following set-up is used to observe interference with light. It is the Young's Double Slits experiment:

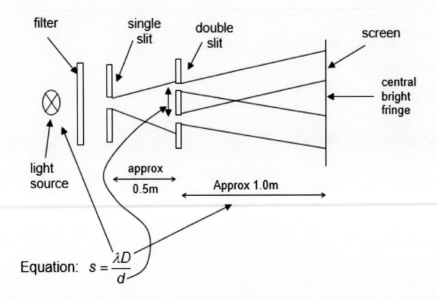

Equation: $s = \dfrac{\lambda D}{d}$

The double slit acts as the two light sources, and the interference pattern can be described exactly as in the case with water-waves as described previously. The following (fringe) pattern is observed on the screen:

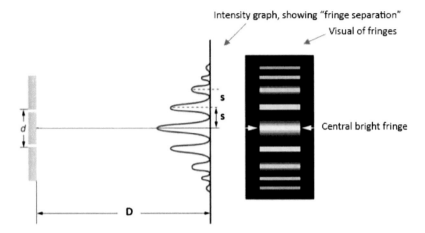

The fringe pattern at the screen is caused by interference between the two wave sources.

❖ Path Difference

Consider the position at the centre of the screen. A bright fringe is observed, as indicated on the diagram. There has been constructive interference between the two sources. This is because whenever a crest arrives at the screen from one of the sources, a crest from the other source also arrives. The two sources are in phase and have equal distances to travel to the screen – the difference in path length (path difference) between one light-path and the other equals zero, as the following diagram shows:

A little further down the screen (as viewed from the page), the two waves will be out of sync, because the wave from S1 has further to travel than the one from S2. Interference does occur, but it starts to

S_1 and S_2 are the two slits. P is the point on the screen being considered. In this diagram, P is at the centre of the screen. Path difference = $S_1P - S_2P$ = zero

become less constructive – the wave amplitude will not be quite double, as it is at the central position.

Destructive interference will occur when a crest from one source meets a trough from the other. Since both sources produce crests and troughs at the same time (the sources are in phase), this condition can be met if one wave has to travel half of a wavelength further than the other. This happens at the appropriate distance down the screen. The first dark fringe is observed when S1P–S2P is equal to one half of a wavelength. Destructive interference results.

It also follows that when the path difference between the sources is any whole number of wavelengths (λ), constructive interference results, and when the path difference is an odd number of half-wavelengths, destructive interference results.

The path difference required to meet these conditions will depend on the wavelength of the light and the fringe separation will depend on this path difference – the bigger the path difference required, the greater the fringe separation will be. But the movement along the screen required to produce a certain path difference also depends on the distance from the double slits to the screen (D) and the distance between the two double screens (d).

The following equation defines the relationship between these variables:

$$s = \frac{\lambda D}{d}$$

Example T 4.18

Yellow light of wavelength 589 nm strikes a double-slit, distance between slits is 0.75 mm. A screen is placed 1.38 m from the double slits.

(a) Calculate the fringe separation.

(b) Describe the effect of using blue light instead of yellow light.

4.5   Standing Waves

❖ The nature of Standing Waves

Standing waves are created by the interference of a wave and its reflection, and is another application of the principle of superposition. Water waves, waves on strings and standing sound waves in open or closed tubes are some examples of standing waves that can easily be observed.

With water waves for example, waves approaching a harbour can combine with waves that have reflected off the harbour wall to result in large waves that are approximately stationary.

If a rope or rubber tube is waved up and down with one end fixed, a standing wave may be produced. Standing waves are only formed at certain frequencies for certain strings (or pipes) at certain tensions. The wave produced by the lowest frequency is called the first harmonic.

The other frequencies are called second, third, fourth etc. harmonics.

❖ Boundary Conditions, Nodes and Antinodes

The boundary conditions of a standing wave refer to the two ends from which the wave reflects. We consider boundary conditions relating to waves on a string attached at both ends, waves in a pipe open at one end and closed at one end, and waves in a double open ended pipe, as follows:

Standing Wave on String

The diagram shows a string being vibrated rapidly up and down from the left end. At the appropriate frequency (which depends on string length, tension and string mass per unit length) the string vibrates as the diagram shows, with zero-amplitude positions (nodes) at each end and the maximum amplitude position (antinode) half-way along the string.

This is a side view of the string – note that at all points it is vibrating up and down – the three positions shown correspond to maximum positive and negative displacement and zero displacement. The diagram is a realistic picture of what is actually observed but if a snap-shot photograph is taken, the string would lie on a curve somewhere between these extremes – but only along one line (it is only one piece of string!)

Note that this wave section actually represents one-half of a complete wavelength. So, if the (horizontal) length of the string is l, $l = \frac{\lambda}{2}$ and so $\lambda = 2l$.

If the vibration frequency is changed slightly, no particular pattern is observed, and the amplitude is significantly reduced (resonance is no longer being achieved). However, other positions of resonance are achievable at higher frequencies. All such standing waves are called harmonics.

We shall now consider simplified diagrams showing some of the harmonics produced by a wave on a string of length l and consider the wavelength of standing wave produced for each.

To construct these harmonics simply remember that there must be a node at each end of the string. For a string of length l (as shown on diagram):

i) First Harmonic

$l = \dfrac{\lambda}{2} \Rightarrow \lambda = 2l$

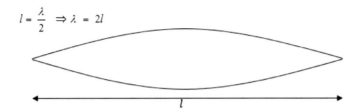

ii) Second Harmonic

$\lambda = l$

Example T 4.19

Draw the third harmonic. Label nodes, antinodes and state the wavelength in terms of the string length

Notes

* The wavelength of the successive harmonics decrease in a pattern, such that $\lambda = \dfrac{2l}{n}$ where

  n is the number of the harmonic (e.g. for first harmonic, $n = 1$, so $\lambda = \dfrac{2l}{1} \Rightarrow \lambda = 2l$

* Since the speed of the waves in the string (the waves moving along the string and interfering to form the standing wave) is constant for each set-up and string, the frequency is inversely proportional to the wavelength, (using the wave equation; $v = f\lambda$) so if, for example, the frequency of the first harmonic (fundamental) is f, then the second is $2f$, the third; $3f$ etc.

Standing Sound Wave in a Closed Pipe

If air is blown over an empty bottle at certain speeds, vibrations are set up inside the bottle and the resonant frequencies can be heard.

This is the situation with closed pipes: sound travels down the tube and reflects off the closed end, and back. At certain (resonant) frequencies standing waves are produced.

To construct these diagrams, just remember that there is always a node at the closed end and an antinode at the open end.

For a closed pipe of length l:

First harmonic   next harmonic (referred to as **3rd harmonic**)

$$l = \frac{\lambda}{4} \Rightarrow \lambda = 4l$$ $$l = \frac{3\lambda}{4} \Rightarrow \lambda = \frac{4l}{3}$$

          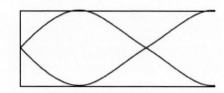

Note that the diagrams actually show how much the air particles are vibrating. At the open end of the tube, we can see that the air particles vibrate with maximum amplitude, and at the closed end, they are stationary. Note also that the air particles are actually vibrating, according to the diagram, left and right – since sound waves are reflected into and back out of the pipe. Sound waves are longitudinal and vibrate parallel to the direction in which the wave is travelling. The next harmonic is referred to as the third harmonic since it has 3 times the frequency of the first.

Example T 4.20

Draw the next harmonic and state expression for wavelength.

Standing Sound Wave in an Open Pipe

Similarly, resonance and standing waves can be set up in an open pipe – waves, surprisingly, can reflect off the open end. The important difference here is that there are antinodes at both ends. Hence:
For an open ended pipe of length l

First harmonic   **Second harmonic**

$$l = \frac{\lambda}{2} \Rightarrow \lambda = 2l$$ $$l = \lambda$$

Example T 4.21

Draw the **fourth** harmonic and state its wavelength in terms of the pipe length.

Notes: For double open-ended pipes:

General wavelength of n_{th} harmonic: $\lambda = \dfrac{2l}{n}$

In **all** standing wave situations:

Nodes are separated by a distance of $\dfrac{\lambda}{2}$ (this can be useful – e.g. in above example, there are 3 node-node spaces, making up $\dfrac{3\lambda}{2}$ wavelengths, add on two half node-node separations at the ends gives an extra $\dfrac{\lambda}{2}$. So total number of waves in the length shown is 2.

Hence $l = 2\lambda \Rightarrow \lambda = \dfrac{l}{2}$

Topic 5: Electricity and Magnetism

Summary Checklist

5.1	Electric Fields
	Charge Electric field Coulomb's law Electric current Direct current (dc) Potential difference
5.2	**Heating Effects of Electric Currents**
	Circuit diagrams Kirchhoff's circuit laws Heating effect of current and its consequences Resistance expressed as $R = \dfrac{V}{I}$ Ohm's law Resistivity Power dissipation
5.3	**Electric Cells**
	Cells Internal resistance Secondary cells Terminal potential difference Electromotive force (emf)
5.4	**Magnetic Effects of Electric Currents**
	Magnetic fields Magnetic force

Equations Provided (in IB databook) & Explanations

Equation	Explanation
$I = \dfrac{\Delta q}{\Delta t}$	The (electric) **current** through a point in a conductor (wire) is equal to the **rate that charge moves** past the point.
$F = k\dfrac{q_1 q_2}{r^2}$	The **force** between two (spherical or point) charged objects is equal to the **coulomb constant** multiplied by the **ratio of the product of the two charges** and the **square of the distance between the centres** of the two charged objects.
$k = \dfrac{1}{4\pi\varepsilon_0}$	The **coulomb constant** is equal to the **reciprocal of the product of four pi** and the **permittivity of free space** (a vacuum).
$V = \dfrac{W}{q}$	The (electric) **potential difference** between two points (in a circuit) is equal to the **ratio of the work done** (energy converted) by the charged particles moving from one point to the other and the total **charge** of the moving particles.

$$E = \frac{F}{q}$$	The (electric) **field strength** at a point in space is equal to the **ratio of the force** experienced by a charged object in the field and the **charge** of the object.
$$I = nAvq$$	The (electric) **current** at a point in a conductor is equal to the product of the **number density** of the charged particles in the conductor, the **cross sectional area** of the conductor, the **speed** ("drift velocity") of the charged particles and the **charge** of each charged particle.
$$\Sigma V = 0 \ (loop)$$	The **sum of all the potential differences** across points in a loop (clockwise or anticlockwise) within a circuit is equal to **zero.**
$$\Sigma I = 0 \ (junction)$$	The **sum of all the currents** meeting at a junction within a circuit is equal to **zero** (total current into point = total current out).
$$R = \frac{V}{I}$$	The (electrical) **resistance** between two points in a circuit, or across two points of a conductor is equal to the **ratio of the potential difference** between the two points and the **current** flowing from one point to the other.
$$P = VI = I^2 R = \frac{V^2}{R}$$	The (electrical) **power** of a component in a circuit is equal to the **potential difference** across the component and the **current** flowing in the component. This is also equal to the **product of the square of the current** and the **resistance** of the component and equal to the **ratio of the square of the potential difference** and the **resistance**.
$$R_{total} = R_1 + R_2 + \cdots$$	The **total resistance** of several components **in series** with each other in a circuit is equal to the **sum of the resistances** of each of the individual components.
$$\frac{1}{R_{total}} = \frac{1}{R_1} + \frac{1}{R_2} + \cdots$$	The **reciprocal of the total resistance** of several components in **parallel** with each other in a circuit is equal to the **sum of the reciprocals of resistance** of each of the individual components.
$$\rho = \frac{RA}{l}$$	The **resistivity** of a material is equal to the ratio of the product of the **resistance** of the material and its **cross sectional area** and the **length** of the material.
$$\varepsilon = I(R + r)$$	The **electro-motive force** ("voltage of source") of a battery/cell is equal to the **product of the current** flowing in the circuit and the **sum of the internal resistance** of the cell/battery and the **total external resistance** of the circuit.
$$F = qvB\sin\theta$$	The (magnetic) **force** on a charged particle moving in a magnetic field is equal to the **product of the charge** of the particle, the **speed** of the particle, the **magnetic field strength** of the field and the **sine of the angle** between the field lines and the direction of motion of the charged particle.
$$F = BIl\sin\theta$$	The (magnetic) **force** on a current carrying conductor (wire) in a magnetic field is equal to the **product of the magnetic field strength** of the field, the **current** in the conductor, the **length** of conductor exposed to the field and the **sine of the angle** between the field lines and the direction of the current in the conductor.

5.1   Electric Fields

❖ Charge

Charge is the property possessed by protons and electrons. There are two types of charge: positive and negative. Electrons have a negative charge; protons have a positive charge, exactly the same in magnitude as electrons, but opposite in sign (neutrons have no charge).

The amount of charge in the universe is constant (principle of conservation of charge). The charge of 1 electron is often written as e. This is known as the elementary charge.

Hence, the charge of 1 proton is also e ($-e\ for\ electron;\ +e\ for\ proton$).

- The S.I. unit for charge is the coulomb (C)
- The charge of 1 electron in coulombs is $-1.6 \times 10^{-19} C$
- The charge of 1 proton in coulombs is $1.6 \times 10^{-19} C$.

An object is said to be charged if it has, in any particular location, an unequal amount of electrons and protons. Generally, charge is given the symbol $q\ or\ Q$ but it can also be e.

Example T 5.1

In terms of e, what is the charge of:

(a) An electron?

(b) A proton?

(c) A helium nucleus (helium nucleus has 2 protons and 2 neutrons)

(d) An oxygen ion (O^{2-}).

Example T 5.2

Express each of the above in coulombs.

Example T 5.3

If an electron has a charge of -1.6×10^{-19}, how many electrons do you need to get 1 coulomb of charge?

❖ Electric field

An electric field is a place where a charged object will experience a force due to its presence in that place. Charged objects not only experience a force when in an electric field, but they will also create their own electric field. There will be an electric field around a proton, an electron, or a charged object.
Electric fields have a direction (by definition, the direction is the direction of the force that a proton – or small positive charge – would experience when placed in the field). Electric field strength is measured in either newtons per coulomb or volts per metre. Electric field strength is given the symbol E. Electric field strength is defined as the force experienced by a small positive charge placed in the field, per unit charge. Hence:

$$E = \frac{F}{q} \quad \text{and} \quad 1NC^{-1} = 1Vm^{-1} = \frac{1N}{C}$$

When a wire is connected to a battery, there will be an electric field concentrated in the wire. This field means that all the protons and electrons in the wire experience a force *(See next section for further equations for field strength).*

Example T 5.4

Predict the direction of the electric field in the following situations:

(a) Around a negatively charged sphere

(b) Around a proton

(c) Between two parallel plates; positive and negative.

Example T 5.5

Calculate the following field strengths, also stating the direction:

(a) A proton experiences a force of $4.0 \times 10^{-17} N$ to the left, when placed in the field

(b) An electron experiences a force of $7.68 \times 10^{-16} N$ upwards, when placed in the field

(c) A helium nucleus (He^{2+}) experiences a force of $3.84 \times 10^{-16} N$ downwards, when placed in the field.

❖ Coulomb's Law

The size of the force on a charged object depends on the size (strength) of the field and how charged the object is (the size of the charge).

Force = field strength x charge (we can see that units are consistent, i.e. N = N/C x C)

The force between two charges: q_1 and q_2, placed a distance r apart in a vacuum is given by the equation:
$$F = k\frac{q_1 q_2}{r^2}$$ (this equation is known as Coulomb's Law)

Where k is the coulomb constant, $k = 8.99 \times 10^9 Nm^2C^{-2}$ (* see below)

(This constant is a measure of how the field transmits and would be different for a material).

We can combine the above equation with the electric field equation to derive the following equation:

The field strength at a distance r from a point charge q is given by:

$$E = k\frac{q}{r^2}$$

Such fields, around point charges are non-uniform, since the field strength weakens as the distance from the charge increases (following "inverse square law"). The equation can also be used to calculate the field strength around a hollow charged sphere by assuming all the charge acts at the centre.

The field strength between oppositely charged parallel plates is uniform. At any position between such plates, the field strength is given by:

$$E = \frac{V}{d}$$ where V is the potential difference between the plates and d is the distance between the plates.

(This equation shows us that the alternative unit for field strength is volts per metre).

k is a constant which is derived from another constant, ε_0

where $k = \frac{1}{4\pi\varepsilon_0}$

ε_0 is called the permittivity of free space ("free space" = a vacuum)

If we were looking at situations not involving a vacuum, we would need to use a different constant (a different permittivity) in our equation. This is beyond this syllabus.

Example T 5.6

Calculate the force between:

(a) Two protons, placed 1.0nm apart in a vacuum

(b) Two electrons, placed 1.0nm apart in a vacuum

(c) An electron and a helium nucleus, placed $2.4 \times 10^{-12}m$ apart from each other in a vacuum.

Example T 5.7

Using the value for k given and the equation: $k = \frac{1}{4\pi\varepsilon_0}$, find the value of the constant ε_0. Check this against the value in your data booklet. Comment on what the constant represents.

Example T 5.8

(a) Given that the diameter of a helium nucleus is approximately $1.75fm$, calculate the approximate force between two protons within the nucleus, stating any assumptions.

(b) Given that the nucleus remains stable, suggest other forces that might exist in the nucleus.

Example T 5.9

Calculate the field strength (and state the direction):

(a) 2.5pm from the centre of a helium nucleus

(b) 12cm from the surface of a hollow sphere of radius 7.5cm, charged to $-4.8mC$

(c) At the two positions shown (i), (ii) between the following parallel plates:

❖ Electric current

Whenever charge moves there is said to be a current. Charge can be moved (i) manually: by physically moving a charged object (ii) using an electric field. Current can be increased by either increasing the amount of charge (coulombs) moving or by increasing the speed of the moving charge. Current is defined to be the rate of flow of charge. Current is measured in amps (or amperes), symbol, A, and the symbol for current is I

Hence: $I = \frac{\Delta q}{\Delta t}$ and $1A = \frac{1C}{s}$

We measure the current flowing **through** a wire or other conductor:

The amount of charge that moves depends on the amount of charge that each "charge carrier" has and on how many charge carriers there are.

Hence: $I = nAvq$ where: I is current in conductor/wire (A)

n is charge carrier density of conductor (m^{-3})

A is cross-sectional area of condcutor (m^2)

v is drift velocity (speed) of charge carriers (ms^{-1})

q is charge of charge carrier (C)

Note: for most applications of electricity, the charge carrier involved is the electron. This is because when we are dealing with metallic conductors (wires), the protons in the material are part of the nuclei: they cannot move. However, for conducting materials (metals), some of the outer electrons on each atom are free to move (referred to as "free electrons"). These electrons are the charge carriers mentioned above that are responsible for electric current.

Example T 5.10

If 1 amp flows if we have 1 coulomb of electrons passing a point per second, how many electrons must pass per second?

Example T 5.11

(a) What quantity of charge flows past a point in a wire per minute given that at that point the current flowing is a steady 1.8mA

(b) Given that 2.7×10^{17} electrons pass through a light bulb in a circuit every 5 seconds, calculate the current flowing through the bulb.

Example T 5.12

(a) Compare the drift velocity in a copper wire and an aluminium wire of equal diameter (1.4mm) if the current in each of the wires is 0.5A [density of free electrons in copper = $8.5 \times 10^{28} m^{-3}$, in aluminium: $6.0 \times 10^{28} m^{-3}$]

(b) Hence, comment on which of the two materials is the best conductor.

❖ Direct current (dc)

Electricity can be grouped into two basic categories:

Static electricity: involving stationary charged objects. If charge builds up sufficiently sparks can result, otherwise no current (charge movement) is involved.

Current electricity: involving the movement of charged particles, as described in the previous section. In most cases and practical applications, the moving charges involved are electrons.

There are two types of current electricity:

Direct current (dc): electrons flow only in one direction

Alternating current (ac): electrons flow backwards and forwards, in two directions.

Direct current is produced by dry-cell batteries (the ones you can buy for torches, radios, and toys, for example), and by lead-acid car batteries.

Alternating current is produced by power stations and bicycle dynamos. Household mains electricity is alternating current (changing direction, in Europe, at 50 times per second).

Example T 5.13

State the difference between ac and dc electricity.

❖ Potential difference

Potential difference (pd) is also referred to as voltage (the first is the better term!). Potential difference (voltage) has the symbol V and is measured in volts, also symbol V.

Potential difference is the **difference in energy** of **one coulomb** of charge carriers (usually electrons) at one point compared with another – as they move, they lose electrical potential energy. Potential difference is defined to be "**the work done per unit charge when charge moves from one place to another**".

Hence, equation: $V = \dfrac{W}{q}$ and hence $1V = \dfrac{1J}{C}$

So, when electrons move in a circuit, they often lose (electrical) potential energy and release it in other forms (e.g. kinetic or thermal/internal energy). Voltage can be applied across two points, by connecting to a battery.

We measure the potential difference (voltage) **across** two points in a circuit

Electro-motive Force (emf)

The potential difference of a cell or electrical source is referred to as the emf of the source. I shall explain this later, in more detail.

Example T 5.14

5C of electrons enter a bulb with an electric potential energy of 60J and by the time they have passed through the bulb filament, their total potential energy has dropped to 15J.

(a) How much work has been done by these electrons as they pass through the bulb?

(b) Describe the energy transfer taking place

(c) Calculate the potential difference across the bulb filament.

Example T 5.15

Calculate the energy delivered by each electron each time it passes around a circuit given that the circuit is powered using a 12.0V battery.

Example T 5.16

A bulb has 0.80A flowing through it and converts 240J of electrical energy into internal energy and light every minute. Calculate the potential difference across the terminals of the bulb.

Electronvolts

When dealing with very small energy changes we often use a different unit to the joule: we use the electron volt (eV). One electron volt is the work done by (or on) an electron as it travels through a potential difference of 1 volt.

Depending on which way through the potential difference the electron is moving, it will either accelerate (work is done on electron: it gains kinetic energy) or slow down (work done by electron: it gains PE and loses PE). If the electron is in a circuit, the usual energy change is electric PE → some form of kinetic energy (internal, movement, light etc.).

The above equation: $V = \frac{W}{q}$ rearranges to give $W = qV$, which gives us the work done when charge q moves through potential difference V.

If we use units of coulombs for charge, and volts for potential difference, we get the energy change (work done) in joules.

However, if we use units of elementary charge, e, for charge we get electron volts as a unit of energy, where: $\qquad 1eV = 1.6 \times 10^{-19} \times 1\,J = 1.6 \times 10^{-19}J$

Electron volts are not generally used in regular electric circuits, involving billions and billions of electrons. They tend to be used in electron beam and charged particle motion situations.

Example T 5.17

What type of quantity is the electron-volt: potential difference, energy or charge?

Example T 5.18

(a) An electron is accelerated through a potential difference of 100kV. What is the kinetic energy of the electron in (i) eV (ii) joules? What is its speed?

(b) A helium particle is accelerated through a potential difference of 100kV. What is its kinetic energy in eV? How does its speed compare with the electron above (no actual calculation: only reasoning required)?

(c) A proton is moving at a speed of $3.6 \times 10^5 ms^{-1}$. Calculate the speed of the proton by the time it has moved through a potential difference of 460V, in the opposite direction to the field.

5.2 Heating Effect of Electric Current

❖ Circuit diagrams

The following table shows some of the basic symbols used to draw circuit diagrams – the complete IB list is provided on page 4 of the IB Data Booklet.

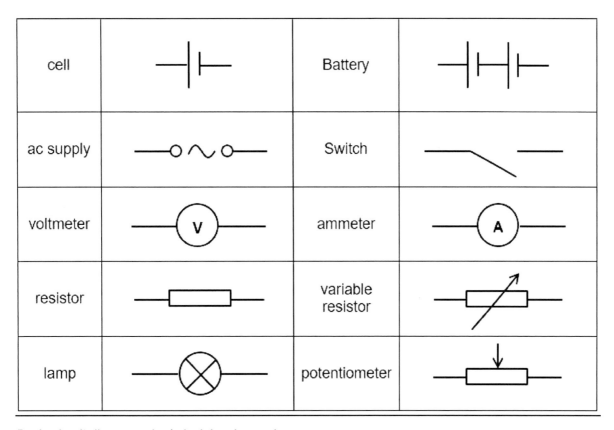

cell		Battery	
ac supply		Switch	
voltmeter		ammeter	
resistor		variable resistor	
lamp		potentiometer	

Basic circuit diagram rules/principles, in words:

- Connecting wires are assumed to have zero resistance (but this may be a point of discussion)
- Unless specified, we assume that the cell (or battery) has no resistance
- Current is shown as flowing from the positive terminal, around the circuit, to the negative terminal, and will always flow in this direction
- (To complicate things, we should also be aware that the actual electrons move in the opposite direction: the convention described above is a mistake of history!)
- When components are placed along the same line in a circuit, they are said to be "in series" with each other; when they are in different branches, they are described as "in parallel"
- There should never be a direct route from one of the battery/cell terminals to another without some form of resistance (lamp, motor, resistor etc.) along the route – this would be a "short circuit" and can damage the circuit wires and/or battery
- Ammeters should always be wired in series with the part of the circuit where current is to be measured
- Voltmeters should always be wired in parallel to the part of the circuit where the potential difference (voltage) is to be measured
- If wired correctly, (ideal) voltmeters and (ideal) ammeters do not affect the circuit in any way; they just measure it.

❖ Circuit diagram

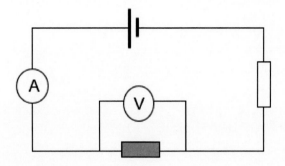

- An ideal voltmeter has infinite (in practice, very large) resistance
- An ideal ammeter has zero (in practice, very small) resistance
- Deviations from ideality lead to the meters changing the circuit they are measuring.

For example, the voltmeter in the above circuit is used to measure the potential difference across the grey resistor shown and the ammeter, to measure the current through the resistor.

If the ammeter was not ideal it would have significant resistance and reduce the current it is attempting to measure. Further, it would alter the potential difference across the resistor, since it would also take a share of the supply voltage.

If the voltmeter was not ideal it would have a relatively low resistance and would reduce the resistance between the points either side of the resistor. This would also reduce the potential difference that it is attempting to measure. Further, it would alter the current measurement made by the ammeter, since it would also allow current to flow (through it), increasing the current reading made by the ammeter.

Example T 5.19

Draw a circuit diagram showing a battery with two 2.0 volt cells connected to a lamp and resistor in series with each other. Include an ammeter and voltmeter wired correctly so as to measure the voltage across and current through the lamp.

❖ Kirchoff's circuit laws

These laws can be used to solve current and voltage circuit problems.

The first law (the "junction rule") states that, at any junction in a circuit, the current flowing in to the junction is equal to the current flowing out (so if "in" = + and "out" = − then we can say that the sum of currents at a junction is zero.

i.e. $\Sigma I = 0 \; (junction)$

The second law (the "loop rule") states that, in any complete loop in any part of a circuit, the sum of all the potential differences (voltages) across all components and power sources (cells/batteries) is equal to zero. For a typical circuit there is a voltage gain (electrons increase in energy) as current passes through a cell and a voltage drop as current passes through external resistors.

i.e. $\Sigma V = 0 \; (loop)$

> ➤ **Worked example**

Consider the following circuit, which has a resistor in parallel with a bulb and resistor that are in series with each other. The circuit is powered with a single 12V cell.

Given that the potential difference across the bulb is 4.0V, that ammeter 3 (A_3) reads 3A and ammeter 1 reads 5A, determine the readings on all the other ammeters and voltmeters.

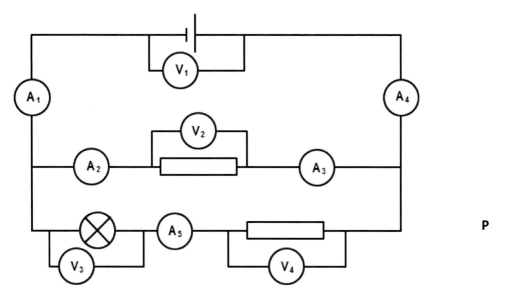

✓ Solutions/reasoning

Voltmeter 1 reads 12V, since it will record the cell voltage (assuming internal resistance is zero – explained later).

Voltmeter 2 also reads 12V – we can determine this using the loop rule: taking the upper loop (rectangle) as our loop and moving clockwise starting from the left of the cell: there is a voltage increase (from negative to positive terminal) $+12V$, then no other potential differences in the loop until we encounter the resistor, where there must be a voltage drop of $12V$, according to Kirchoff's "loop rule", so that the sum of potential differences in the loop is zero.

Voltmeter 3 must read 4V, since we are told that the potential difference across the bulb is 4.0V

If we now take the large loop/rectangle, which includes the cell, the bulb and the lower resistor, we can deduce that the potential difference across the resistor is 8V, since there must be a total voltage drop of 12V across both the bulb and resistor so that the sum of p.d.s in the large loop adds to zero, in accordance with the loop rule.

Hence, voltmeter 4 must read 8V

Ammeter 1 must read the same as ammeter 4, since they are are on the same line and taking any point along this line, passing from ammeter 1, through the cell, and then through ammeter 4 as the "junction" the same current comes out of the junction as that which goes in (i.e. 5A)

Hence both ammeter 1 and ammeter 4 read 5A.

Ammeter 2 and ammeter 3 must both give the same reading as each other for the same reason as above. Hence both ammeter 2 and ammeter 3 read 3A.

(Note that we assume no current flows through the voltmeters – as discussed later – so we also know that 3A must pass through this upper resistor).

We can now use the junction rule to deduce what ammeter 5 reads. Taking point p on the left of the circuit as the junction.

We know that the current out of the junction is the same as the reading on ammeter 1: 5A (current flows through the cell from left to right; conventional current always flows out of the + and into the − terminal).

The current flowing into this junction comes from ammeter 2, on the left wire and from the wire below, via ammeter 5.

Hence, using $\Sigma I = 0$, and taking "in" as −, "out" as +, we get $-3 + 5 + A_5 = 0 \Rightarrow A_5 = -2A$

So, ammeter 5 reads 2A and this current flows through the ammeter to the left, and up through the junction labelled p.

Example T 5.20

The circuit below shows two cells, each with an emf of 2V, connected to two bulbs (lamps) and two resistors, as shown. The current is known in two parts of the circuit and the potential difference, in one part, as shown by the non-highlighted meters. Determine the current and voltage readings in the highlighted meters.

❖ Heating effect of current and its consequences

If one small grain of course brown sugar represented one electron, the amount of sugar we would need to represent the number of electrons in a single small-value coin would be enormous. One would have to completely cover the surface of the Earth in sugar to around waist height! When a potential difference is applied across a conductor an electric field causes a similarly enormous number of electrons to flow – being repelled by the negative terminal and attracted to the positive terminal of the supply. The electrons moving between enormous numbers of atoms, all vibrating at around a trillion or so oscillations per second causing an energy transfer from electrical potential energy to internal energy, and a heating effect in the conductor.

In general, therefore, as current in a conductor increases, temperature increases. As we discuss later in this chapter, this causes an increase in the resistivity of the material, and in the resistance of the conductor (wire).

Resistance, expressed as $R = \frac{V}{I}$

The greater the resistance of a material, the more potential difference must be applied to produce a certain current. Resistance is this defined as the ratio of potential difference (voltage) across a conductor to the current flowing through the conductor. Resistance is measured in ohms (Ω) and 1 ohm is equivalent to 1 volt per amp.

Definition: $R = \frac{V}{I}$

Where R is the electrical resistance of a conductor, V is potential difference across the conductor and I, the current through the conductor.

Example T 5.21

A bulb is connected to a cell with an emf of 4.0V, with an ammeter and voltmeter in the circuit, as follows:

(a) Given that the voltmeter reads 4.0V and the ammeter reads 0.25A, calculate the resistance of the bulb

(b) Assuming that the resistance remains constant, calculate the ammeter reading if the bulb is connected to a 6.0V cell

(c) Explain why the assumption in (b) may not be accurate.

❖ Ohm's Law

"The current through a wire is proportional to the potential difference across it, provided the temperature is unchanged".

Ohm's law equation:

$$V = IR, \quad V \propto I \ (if \ T \ is \ constant)$$

Ohm's law effectively states that the resistance, R, is constant - and does not change if current (or voltage) is increased as long as the material is not allowed to heat up.

Generally, metallic conductors obey Ohm's Law.

Ohmic and non-ohmic behaviour

A conductor is said to be ohmic if the current flowing through the conductor is proportional to the potential difference across the conductor (i.e. one for which resistance remains constant).

An easy and effective way to observe this behaviour is to plot current versus potential difference for a range of voltages.

Examples:

The only graph for which $V \alpha I$ is the first. The wire is thus ohmic and the other two are non-ohmic. Note that if a very large current is forced through the wire, it will become non-ohmic (like the lamp).

A lamp is non- ohmic because the filament gets very hot as current is increased. This causes resistance to increase. The gradient of the IV graph hence decreases.

A diode is non-ohmic because if the potential difference is reversed, no current flows: resistance is infinite. For the wire and lamp the direction of the current (and potential difference) makes no difference to the way they behave, as conductors.

Semiconductor diodes generally have an **"effective resistance"** of zero at 0.3V.

<u>Resistance in series and parallel circuits</u>

<u>*Series circuits*</u>

Consider the following circuit, which has a cell with an emf of V_T volts, negligible internal resistance and is connected in series to 3 resistances, of R_1, R_2 and R_3 ohms respectively. Current, I, flows around the circuit, as shown:

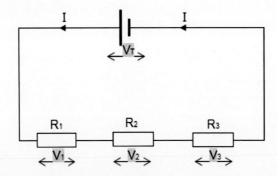

The same current, I, flows through all resistors.

Let the total resistance of the circuit be R_T.

The total voltage is therefore: $V_T = IR_T$

But also, the total potential difference (pd) across resistors in series is equal to the sum of the pds across the individual resistors, i.e.:

$$V_T = V_1 + V_2 + V_3$$

But, $V_1 = IR_1, V_2 = IR_2, V_3 = IR_3$

Hence, $V_T = IR_1 + IR_2 + IR_3 = I(R_1 + R_2 + R_3)$
$V_T = I(R_1 + R_2 + R_3)$

But, $V_T = IR_T$

e

Hence $\boxed{R_T = R_1 + R_2 + R_3}$

Parallel circuits

Consider the following circuit, which has a cell with an emf of V_T volts, negligible internal resistance and is connected to 3 resistances in parallel to one another, of resistance R_1, R_2 and R_3 ohms respectively. A current, I, flows around the circuit, as shown:

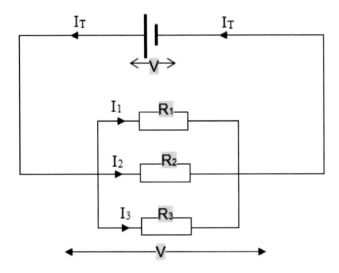

The potential difference across any branch of a parallel circuit is equal. Therefore, V(across R_1)= V(across R_2)=V(across R_3)=V(of cell). Let the total resistance of the circuit be R_T. The total voltage is: $V = I_T R_T$.

But also, the total current around the circuit (and through the cell) is equal to the sum of the currents through each branch of the parallel part of the circuit. I.e., $I_T = I_1 + I_2 + I_3$

But, $V = I_1 R_1, V = I_2 R_2, V = I_3 R_3$

$\Rightarrow I_1 = \dfrac{V}{R_1}, I_2 = \dfrac{V}{R_2}, I_3 = \dfrac{V}{R_3}$

$I_T = I_1 + I_2 + I_3 \Rightarrow I_T = \dfrac{V}{R_1} + \dfrac{V}{R_2} + \dfrac{V}{R_3}$

But also: $V = I_T R_T \Rightarrow I_T = \dfrac{V}{R_T}$ Hence: $\dfrac{V}{R_T} = \dfrac{V}{R_1} + \dfrac{V}{R_2} + \dfrac{V}{R_3} \Rightarrow$ $\boxed{\dfrac{1}{R_T} = \dfrac{1}{R_1} + \dfrac{1}{R_2} + \dfrac{1}{R_3}}$

Example T 5.22

Consider the following circuit, and complete the table below:

	5Ω	10Ω (a)	10Ω (b)	Total circuit
Voltage				
Current				
Resistance				
Charge passed in 1 sec				
Power				

Some tips to start you off!

- Start by finding the total circuit resistance
- Then find total circuit current (from total resistance and voltage)
- Next find pd across 10Ω resistance in series
- Find current through each of the two resistors in parallel, using v=ir
- Find power dissipated by each resistor using p=vi (or one of other formulae), charge passed using q=it.

(**Note**: there are usually many different ways of solving circuit problems – they all (obviously) lead to the same solutions!)

Potential dividers

A potential divider is a circuit that is able to vary (divide) the potential difference of the supply. This is particularly useful for students doing experiments involving varying the voltage (potential difference) when they do not have a variable voltage power supply.

A common potential divider circuit involves a rheostat (wound wire resistor) – as in the picture. The resistance is varied by changing the length of the wire that the current passes through via the sliding terminal in the middle.

The circuit below shows potential divider being used to vary the voltage across a bulb.

Rheostat (wire wound resistor) used as a potential divider

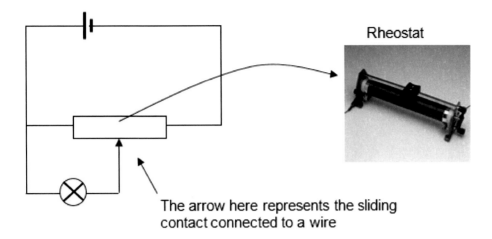

Rheostat

The arrow here represents the sliding
contact connected to a wire

Potential dividers as sense/response circuits

Potential Divider Circuits can also involve the use of two resistors in series, rather than using a rheo-stat. This set-up is useful for electronic sensor circuits – since one of the resistors is a sensor, and its resistance controls the split of the total potential difference across both resistors.

Example: LDR potential divider circuit

An LDR is a light dependent resistor: its resistance changes as the level of light changes. If light in-creases, the resistance of the LDR decreases, V_2 decreases and V_1 increases.

The fixed resistor, R_1, can be attached to a meter or can form part of an alarm system, or any other device. The essential point here is that the voltage across the fixed resistor, R_1 is controlled by the LDR. The sensor resistor could also be a temperature dependent resistor (thermistor) or strain gauge (resistance depends on physical strain-force).

❖ Resistivity

The rate at which charge flows (current) depends on the velocity of the charges. The velocity of the charges is called drift velocity.

For ohmic conductors, the speed (drift velocity) of electrons in a conductor depends on:

1) Cross-sectional area of conductor
2) Length of conductor   } Resistance of conductor
3) Material from which conductor is made
4) Temperature of conductor
5) Potential difference (voltage) across conductor
The resistivity of a material is a measure of the resistance of a certain material.

We can find the resistivity of various materials in data-books or on the internet and we can then find the electrical resistance of, for example, a wire made of this material using the following formula:

$$R = \frac{\rho L}{A}$$ where

$R = resistance\ (\Omega)$ $\rho("rho") = resistivity\ (\Omega m)$

$L = length\ (m)$ $A = cross\ sectional\ area\ (m^2)$

As we can deduce from above, resistivity is measured in ohm-metres (Ωm).

Example T 5.23

Given that copper has a resistivity of $1.72 \times 10^{-8}\ \Omega m$ at 20°C, calculate the resistance of a piece of copper wire with a diameter of 1.00mm and a length of 5cm at 20°C.

Note that, generally, as the temperature of a metallic material increases its resistivity (and therefore resistance) increases. This can be explained in terms of the atoms in the metal vibrating at an increasing rate at higher temperatures and hindering the progress of passing electrons.

❖ Power Dissipation

Power is defined as the rate of doing work.

$Power = \dfrac{work\ done}{time\ taken}$, assuming work is done at a constant rate.

But $work\ done, W = q\Delta V$, as stated earlier

Hence: Power = $\dfrac{qV}{t}$

but, for a constant current, $q = I t \Rightarrow$ Power = $\dfrac{I t V}{t} \Rightarrow$ Power = $I V$

So, electrical power delivered by a resistor (conductor) is equal to the product of the potential difference across the resistor and the current flowing through the resistor.

$$P = VI$$

Other expressions for power – derivations:

$P = V I,\ but\ V = I R,$

$\Rightarrow P = (I R)I = I^2 R$

$P = V I, but\ I = \dfrac{V}{R}$

$\Rightarrow P = V\left(\dfrac{V}{R}\right) = \dfrac{V^2}{R}$

Summary

$P = VI$

$P = I^2 R$

$P = \dfrac{V^2}{R}$

Note that any of these equations can be used in any situations. Sometimes one yields a quicker answer than another.

Example T 5.24

A circuit has a single 30Ω resistor connected to a 12V power supply.

    a) Find the current flowing through the resistor
    b) Find the power delivered through the resistor.

5.3   Electric Cells

❖ Cells

A battery is a collection of cells working together to form a single electrical power supply.

Wet cells and dry cells

Cells can be categorized as dry-cells or wet-cells.

The most common example of wet cells are those used in cars and motorcycles, to start up the engines. Car batteries consist of six 2-volt cells, each of which contains lead and lead oxide plates immersed in a solution of sulphuric acid. Due to chemical reactions and consequent electron movement, there is a potential difference of 2V across the terminals of each cell. As current is drawn from each cell (when connected to a device like a car starter-motor or headlights) chemical reactions take place. Chemical energy is thus converted into electrical (then into internal energy, kinetic energy, or whatever energy form the useful device utilizes).

Dry cells are those you buy in almost any supermarket or newsagent store. These also work on quite complex chemical reactions (there are several types of dry cell, for example, lithium ion, lithium polymer, zinc-carbon, nickel cadmium, etc.) and each involves a different set of chemical reactions. Dry cells usually only consist of one cell, even though they are usually referred to as "batteries".

❖ Primary and secondary cells

A **primary cell** is a disposable, non-rechargeable cell, whilst a secondary cell is rechargeable. Primary cells are cheaper and last much longer in a single use than a similar sized rechargeable secondary cell.

A **secondary cell** can be cheaper in the long term since it can be re-used over and over again.

The choice of which cell to use depends on several things, including the frequency of use and the sensitivity to voltage variation of the device being powered.

Terminal potential difference

In general, dry cells quickly lose their initial, fully charged voltage (potential difference), then remain approximately constant for most of their use-lifetime, then drop off rapidly to zero as the cell discharges.

The following graph shows a fairly typical voltage pattern for any dry cell, but this actual example relates to a lithium polymer cell with a nominal (fully-charged) voltage of 3.7V:

Notes

The initial potential difference is slightly above the nominal (stated fully charged) voltage value.

The cell terminal voltage soon drops to lower, but approximately constant value, which it sustains for most of its use-life. The above cell has become depleted at around 3V.

The terminal potential difference can be logged by simply connecting the cell to a high resistance voltmeter (i.e. any decent voltmeter) while it is discharging, as follows:

<u>Recharging cells</u>

To recharge a cell, an external potential difference is applied at a slightly higher voltage than the cell voltage so that current runs through the cell backwards. A battery charger is used for this purpose. Assuming the cell has been designed for this purpose then the chemical reaction in the cell will be reversed, so that the reactants are recycled. In this case we are converting electrical energy into chemical energy. The cell is then ready for the "forward" chemical reaction, and chemical to electrical energy conversion.

<u>Charge storage in cells and batteries</u>

The amount of "electricity" stored in a battery is measured in ampere-hours, or more often with dry cells, milli-ampere hours.

For example if a cell has a storage of 1500mAh, it means it can deliver 1500mA for 1 hour (or 15mA for 100 hours etc.). Total charge stored would be $1.5A \times 3600s = 5400C$.

Example T 5.25

A dry cell is rated at 1.5V, 900mAh:

(a) Assuming the terminal voltage remains at the nominal value, calculate how long the cell should last if connected to a 0.3W light bulb

(b) Discuss, in reality, how your answers are likely to differ.

Example T 5.26

Referring to the lithium polymer discharge curve above, given that the cell had an initial charge of 400mAh stored, estimate:

(i)   The approximate average current delivered over the duration of the discharge
(ii)   The total chemical energy converted into electrical energy.

❖ Electromotive Force (emf)

Refers to a source of electrical energy.

The emf of a source is equal to the electrical energy produced per unit charge inside the source. Unit: volt. Equation: $\varepsilon = \frac{W}{q}$, so energy converted by cell, $W = \varepsilon q$

In simple terms, the emf of a source is the maximum possible voltage of the source. Some of this voltage is "lost" because the source itself has a resistance – so the apparent voltage of the power supply, and the voltage across the external resistor, will be a little lower than the emf of the power supply (source).

So – not all energy is converted to electrical energy outside the source since some is lost inside the source due to internal resistance.

Internal resistance: the resistance of a source.

To solve emf/internal resistance problems, simply consider the internal resistance as an additional resistor in series with the source.

Example T 5.27

An 8.0V power supply is connected to a 12 Ω resistor. The voltage across the resistor is measured as 7.68V and the current; 0.64A. Explain the voltage drop, and explain (with any necessary calculations) what the emf is and what the internal resistance of the supply is.

Example T 5.28

A battery has an internal resistance of 10Ω and is connected to an external resistance of 100Ω. A voltmeter is connected across the external resistor, as shown below. It gives a reading of 10V:

(a) Find the current flowing in the circuit
(b) Find the potential difference across the internal resistance
(c) Hence, state the emf of the battery
(d) What assumption about the voltmeter have you made in your calculations?
(e) If a different voltmeter was placed in the circuit, and this new voltmeter had a resistance of 60Ω, what reading would the voltmeter now give?
(f) If a non-ideal ammeter was connected correctly in the circuit (at position P), but the ammeter was non-ideal, explain what effect this would have on:
    (i)   The potential difference across the external resistor
    (ii)   The current through the external resistor.

Notes

The internal resistance of a source is approximately constant, BUT the voltage "lost" across the internal resistance depends on the current flowing in the circuit and through the supply, which depends on the size of the total external resistance.

The smaller the external resistance, the greater the pd across the internal resistance. (for example, in the above example – (a) to (c), the emf of the supply is 11V, but only 10V is available to the external resistor. If however, the internal resistance is equal to the external resistance, only half the emf value would be available for the external resistor.

5.4   Magnetic Effects of Electric Currents

❖ Magnetic Fields

A magnetic field is a region in space (a place) where a *moving* charge experiences a force due to its presence in the field. The interaction between the moving charge and the field causes the force on the charge.

The moving charge referred to above can be:

- An electron (or beam of electrons), or other negatively charged object(s), flying through space
- A proton (or beam of protons), or other positively charged object(s), flying through space
- A current carrying conductor (the moving charges are electrons)

A bar magnet or magnetic material (electrons within the material are moving, and unbalanced).
Not only does a moving charge experience a force when placed in a field but a moving charge also produces a magnetic field.

Field lines

Magnetic field lines are the lines that plotting compasses or magnets align themselves to

Bar magnet

("magnetic lines of force (field lines)

always flow away from north")

Straight current-carrying conductor

Use "screw rule" to predict

the direction of the field lines

Note the X represents current

going into the page

To make a screw go into

page, turn screwdriver

clockwise – like field lines

Flat current-carrying single loop

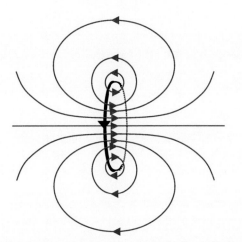

Notes

- The black circle represents the current-carrying wire and the blue curves; the field lines
- Only a cross-section of the field line pattern is shown. The field lines also go in and out of the plane of the paper, with the same pattern as shown in the diagram
- The power-source for the current carrying wire is not shown
- The field lines follow the same arrangement (but there are more, and closer together) if several coils of wire are used.

A current carrying solenoid (tubular coil of wire)

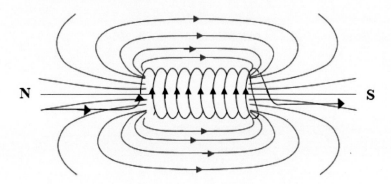

Note the similarity between (i) this diagram and the diagram for a flat, single coil (as previous) (ii) this diagram and the diagram showing the field pattern for a bar magnet. To determine direction of field lines (coloured blue) imagine looking down either end of the solenoid. Note whether current is flowing clockwise or anti-clockwise.

If **clockwise** $\Rightarrow$ S (the letter S has ends pointing in clockwise direction) $\Rightarrow$ South pole (and lines of force point AWAY from north – i.e. towards south).

If **anti-clockwise** $\Rightarrow$ N (the letter N has ends pointing in anti-clockwise direction) $\Rightarrow$ North pole (and lines of force point AWAY from north). Thus, on the above diagram there will be a north pole on the left hand end and a south pole on the right.

Strength of field from field lines

For all fields the strength of the field is indicated on the field line diagram by the spacing of the field lines: the greater the spacing the weaker the field.

❖ Magnetic Force

<u>Force on a conductor in a magnetic field:</u>

When a current carrying conductor (i.e. wire) is placed in a magnetic field, the conductor has its own magnetic field, so the two will interact. Depending on the orientation of the wire relative to the field there will therefore be a force on the wire and it will move, if allowed. There are three things to consider: the direction of the field in which the current is placed, the direction of the current in the wire and the direction of force (or motion). Two of these variables must be known in order to calculate the third. Fleming's **left** hand rule may be used, as follows.

Remember *FBI*

F for Force,

B for magnetic field (B is symbol

for magnetic field strength)

I for current

F Force

B B-field

I Current

Notes
- The blue lines are all orthogonal (at 90°) to each other
- Current is **conventional** current
- There are other rules you may have come across for making these predictions - it doesn't matter which one you use.

The size of the force (F) on a current (I) carrying conductor (length l) in a magnetic field (B), at an angle θ to the current is given by the equation:

$$F = BILsin\theta$$

Example T 5.29

(a) A wire is placed next to the north

end of a bar magnet, (see diagram)

Describe the direction of the force

experienced by the wire

N

current carrying wire

(b) Given that the wire has 2.5cm exposed to the field, carries a current of 1.4A and that the field strength is 1.8mT, calculate the size of the force on the wire.

<u>Force on a charge moving through a magnetic field</u>

A moving charge can also be considered to be a current, for this is how a current is defined. However, it is important to remember that conventional current is opposite to the direction that electrons move.

Therefore, in order to predict the direction of the force on a charge moving in a magnetic field, first consider whether it is a positive charge (direction = same direction as current) or a negative charge (direction = opposite direction to current) and then simply use Fleming's left hand rule, as before.

Note though, that the thumb gives the force on the charge (the motion will result from this force and from the motion it already has).

The size of the force (F) on a charge (q) moving with velocity (v) in a magnetic field (B), at an angle θ to the velocity vector is given by the equation:

$$F = Bqv\sin\theta$$

Example T 5.30

The following diagram shows two charges, an electron and a proton moving through a magnetic field, shown by the blue crosses. The proton is coloured red and the electron, black. The arrows drawn in already show the direction of motion of the two particles.

(a) Label each charge with an arrow, labeled F, showing the direction of force acting on it.
(b) Given that the speed of each particle is $2.4 \times 10^4 ms^{-1}$ and that the magnetic field strength is 4.6mT calculate the magnetic force acting on each charge
(c) Compare the effect of these two forces on these two particles.

Note:

Crosses are used for field lines or current to indicate that the direction is directly away – i.e. into the page. Dots are used (less commonly) to show that direction to be out of the page. Sometimes larger crosses are used, or even a large single cross.

Note that the two equations given for magnetic force involve $\sin\theta$, since if the current or the moving charge is *not* moving *perpendicular* to the magnetic field lines, we must take the component of the field that is perpendicular. To do this we replace B with $B\sin\theta$

Example T 5.31

The green lines below show a field, of strength 2.2mT and the blue line shows a wire carrying 1.8A current through the field. Calculate the force per cm exposed to the field acting on the wire, and state the direction of the force.

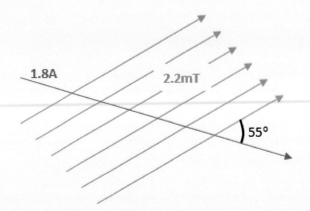

Topic 6: Circular Motion and Gravitation

Summary Checklist

6.1	Circular Motion
	Period, frequency, angular displacement and angular velocity Centripetal force Centripetal acceleration
6.2	Newton's Law of Gravitation
	Newton's law of gravitation Gravitational field strength

Equations Provided (in IB databook) & Explanations

$v = \omega r$	The (tangential) **speed** of an object describing a circle at constant speed is equal to the **angular velocity** multiplied by the **radius** of the circle being described.
$a = \dfrac{v^2}{r} = \dfrac{4\pi^2 r}{T^2}$	The **acceleration** (called centripetal acceleration) of an object describing a circle at constant speed is equal to the ratio of the **square of the speed** and the **radius**. It is also equal to the ratio of $4\pi^2$ **multiplied by the radius of the circle** and the **square of the time period**.
$F = \dfrac{mv^2}{r} = m\omega^2 r$	The **net force** (called **centripetal force**) on an object describing a circle at constant speed is equal to the **ratio of its mass multiplied the square of its speed and the radius of the circle**. It is also equal to its **mass** multiplied by the **square of its angular velocity** and the **radius** of the circle.
$F = G\dfrac{Mm}{r^2}$	The gravitational **force** between two objects is equal to the **universal constant of gravitation** multiplied by **the ratio of the product of the mass** of the two objects and the **square of the distance between the centres of the objects**.
$g = \dfrac{F}{m}$	The **gravitational field strength** at the position of an object is equal to the **ratio of the gravitational force on the object** and the **mass** of the object.
$g = G\dfrac{M}{r^2}$	The **gravitational field strength** at a certain distance from the centre of an object (usually planet) is equal to the **universal constant of gravitation** multiplied by **the ratio of the mass** of the object and the **square of the distance between the centres of the objects**.

6.1   Circular Motion

This topic deals with situations where an object moves in a circle at a constant speed. This is referred to as *uniform circular motion*.

For such motion:

- The acceleration is always directed towards the centre of the circle
- The acceleration is called centripetal acceleration
- The resultant force on the object must be towards the centre of the circle
- This resultant force is called centripetal force
- To describe circular motion there must be a centripetal force acting on the object
- The size of the acceleration depends on the speed of the object and on the radius of the circle described by the object.

❖ Period, frequency, angular displacement and angular velocity.

The **period**, T, of an object describing uniform circular motion is simply the time taken for one complete circle (compare with waves, where it is time for one *oscillation*).

The **frequency**, f, of an object describing uniform circular motion is the number of circles that the object moves through per second. It is intuitive that there is a reciprocal relationship between T and f:

$T = \frac{1}{f} \Leftrightarrow f = \frac{1}{T}$ (equation provided in data booklet for Topic 4 – Waves).

The **angular displacement**, θ, is the angle, in radians, that the object moves through in a given time.

The **angular velocity** (speed) is the rate of change of angular displacement of the object - i.e. the angle (in radians) through which the object moves as it describes the circle, per second.

Example T 6.1

A toddler is on a merry-go-round, sitting on a horse 3.4m from the centre. His mother times him with her stopwatch and she notes that he makes exactly 5 complete revolutions around the merry-go-round in one minute.

Assuming that she starts her stopwatch just as her child passes her, calculate the following:

(a) The period of rotation of the child
(b) The frequency of rotation of the child
(c) The angular displacement after 10 seconds
(d) The angular velocity of the child.

❖ Centripetal force and centripetal acceleration

The centripetal acceleration on an object describing uniform circular motion is given by:

$$a = \frac{v^2}{r}$$ where v is the speed and r is the radius

Since $v = \frac{distance}{time}$, if we take the distance as one full circle (circumference $2\pi r$), then the time will be one period, T.

Hence $v = \frac{2\pi r}{T}$

So we get another equation for acceleration:

$$a = \frac{\left(\frac{2\pi r}{T}\right)^2}{r} = \frac{4\pi^2 r}{T^2}$$

We can go on to find the net force acting on such an object, using Newton's 2nd law;

$F_{net} = ma$, and we get:

$$F_{net} = \frac{mv^2}{r} = m\frac{4\pi^2 r}{T^2}$$

We could also show that $v = \omega r$ and so another equation for acceleration and net force on an object describing uniform circular motion are as follows:

$a = \omega^2 r$

$F_{net} = m\omega^2 r$

Example T 6.2

A string is used to twirl a 300g mass in a horizontal circle of radius 25 cm, in zero gravity conditions, so that the mass moves at a speed of 2 ms^{-1}

(a) Find the tension in the string

(b) If the mass is now twirled in a vertical circle **with gravity** at the same speed, draw a free body diagram showing the mass at the lowest point and calculate the tension in the string at this point.

Note: This example illustrates the point that centripetal force is the required resultant force that must act on a mass if the mass is to describe a circle. This resultant force can be from a single force or the result of two or more forces.

Example T 6.3

An old fashioned record player plays a 12 inch record (radius 15cm) at 33⅓ revolutions per minute. A cork (mass 8.4g) is placed on the outside edge of the record, with its centre 2.0cm from the edge. It rotates with the record without slipping.

    (a) Calculate the period of oscillation of the cork
    (b) Calculate the angular velocity of the cork
    (c) Calculate the centripetal acceleration of the cork
    (d) Calculate the centripetal force acting on the cork
    (e) Describe all the forces acting on the cork (size and direction)
    (f) If a second cork with the same mass is placed exactly half the distance away from the centre of the record, how will each of the answers above change for this second cork moving in a circle of half the radius?

6.2   Newton's Law of Gravitation

❖ Newton's Law of gravitation

Newton's law of gravitation states that two objects will attract each other and that the force of attraction is proportional to the product of the masses of the two objects and to the reciprocal of the square distance between the masses. Note that the law relates to "point masses" but we apply the law to spherical masses by assuming that all the mass is concentrated at the centre (so we just consider the distance between the centres of the objects).

The size of the force on each mass is therefore given by the equation:

$$F = G\frac{m_1 m_2}{r^2}$$

where:
- G is the universal constant of gravitation
- m_1, m_2 are the values for the two masses
- r is the distance between centres of the masses

This is also written as: $F = G\frac{Mm}{r^2}$ (the capital M is taken to be the mass of the planet and the small m; the object in proximity of the planet)

This equation is known as Newton's universal law of gravitation. It can be applied to any two masses in the universe: all masses attract each other. The value of G is given in the data booklet: $6.67 \times 10^{-11} Nm^2kg^{-2}$.

Example T 6.4

Given the following data, complete the questions below:

Mass of Earth:	$5.97 \times 10^{24} kg$	Radius of Earth:	$6370km$
Mass of Moon:	$7.35 \times 10^{22} kg$	Radius of Moon:	$1740km$

Earth – Moon distance: $384,000km$:

(a) The gravitational force of attraction between an adult male, mass 85kg and the Earth, given that the male is standing on the surface of the Earth.

(b) The force of attraction between the same male and the Moon, given that he is standing on the surface of the Moon.

(c) The force between the Earth and the Moon.

(d) The force between two adult males, both with mass 85kg, embracing each other (assume the distance between "centres" is 30cm).

Note that this force of attraction is the force on both objects: equal in magnitude, in accordance with Newton's 3rd law.

Example T 6.5

The view below shows the Moon orbiting the Earth in a clockwise sense.

(a) Draw and label any forces acting on each body
(b) Using your answer in T6(4) above and a relevant circular motion equation (previous section), calculate the period of orbit of the moon about the Earth. Convert to days.

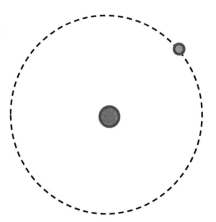

❖ Gravitational Field Strength

Gravitational field strength is a vector quantity.

The quantity is defined by the equation:

$$g = \frac{F}{m}$$

In words: the gravitational field strength (at a given position) is the force per unit mass experienced by a small mass placed in the field (at the given position).

The unit of gravitational field strength is the newton per kilogram (N/kg)

Example T 6.6

Bags of sand with various masses are used to test the surface gravitational field strength of various (made up) planets. A newton-metre is used to determine the gravitational force.

(a) For each, calculate the surface gravitational field strength:

Planet	Mass of sand-bag	Force on sand bag	Gravitational field strength
X	12kg	92N	
Y	200g	18N	
Z	460kg	230N	

(b) Determine the weight of a 65kg person standing on each planet

We can also calculate the gravitational field strength at a given position in the proximity of a point mass (or spherical mass), as follows:

$$g = G\frac{M}{r^2}$$

As explained in the table at the start of this topic, M is the mass of the object that causes the field and r is the distance from the centre of this object.

Example T 6.7

What can we say about planets X, Y and Z from the information calculated in T 6.6?

Example T 6.8

Using the data provided in T6(4) calculate the gravitational field strength:

(a) At the surface of the Earth
(b) At the surface of the Moon
(c) 1000km above the surface of the Earth.

If we consider being in the vicinity of more than 1 mass, we combine the field strength (they may add or subtract: field strength is a vector quantity)

Example T 6.9

Using the data provided in T 6.4 calculate the gravitational field strength:

(a) At the surface of the Earth nearest the Moon **due to the Moon**
(b) Explain what effect this will have on the net field strength at this point due to Moon and Earth
(c) At the surface of the Earth furthest away from the Moon **due to the Moon**
(d) Explain what effect this will have on the net field strength at this point due to Moon and Earth
(e) How does this explain why there are low and high tides on Earth?

Gravitational fields can also be described using gravitational field lines.

They are the lines followed by a small mass placed in the field.

It makes sense that gravitational field lines point in the same direction as gravitational field strength.

Gravitational Field for a point mass

Approximate Gravitational (Same for a planet)
field for a planet surface

radial field

uniform field

surface here

The strength of the field can be compared by how close together the field lines are: so if they are parallel, the field is uniform and if not, the field is non-uniform. The field close to the surface of a planet is considered to be approximately uniform (as the ground is considered to be flat).

However, if the bigger picture is considered it is clear that the field is non-uniform (and planets are spherical, not flat!).

Topic 7: Atomic, nuclear and particle physics

Summary Checklist

7.1	Discrete energy and radioactivity
	Discrete energy and discrete energy levels Transitions between energy levels Radioactive decay Fundamental forces and their properties Alpha particles, beta particles and gamma rays Half-life Absorption characteristics of decay particles Isotopes Background radiation
7.2	Nuclear reactions
	The unified atomic mass unit Mass defect and nuclear binding energy Nuclear fission and nuclear fusion
7.3	The structure of matter
	Quarks, leptons and their antiparticles Hadrons, baryons and mesons The conservation laws of charge, baryon number, lepton number and strangeness The nature and range of the strong nuclear force, weak nuclear force and electromagnetic force Exchange particles Feynman diagrams Confinement The Higgs boson

Equations Provided (in IB databook) & Explanations

$E = hf$	The **energy of a photon** of radiation is equal to **Planck's constant** multiplied by the **frequency** of the radiation
$\lambda = \dfrac{hc}{E}$	The **wavelength** of a photon is equal to the **ratio of the product** of Planck's constant and the **speed of light** ($3.0 \times 10^8 ms^{-1}$) to the **photon energy**
$\Delta E = \Delta mc^2$	The **energy change** (release or decrease) in a nuclear reaction is equal to the **change in mass** $(\lvert mass_{products} - mass_{reactants}\rvert)$ **multiplied by the square of the speed of light**. This equation is also used to calculate **binding energy** (ΔE) where Δm is the **difference between the total mass of the nucleons in a nucleus and the mass of the actual nucleus**.

Structure of matter (data provided in data booklet)

Charge	Quarks			Baryon number
$\frac{2}{3}e$	u	c	t	$\frac{1}{3}$
$\frac{1}{3}e$	d	s	b	$\frac{1}{3}$
All quarks have a strangeness number of 0 except the strange quark that has a strangeness number of −1				

Charge	Leptons		
−1	e	μ	τ
0	v_e	v_μ	v_τ
All leptons have a lepton number of 1 and antileptons have a lepton number of -1			

	Gravitational	Weak	Electromagnetic	Strong
Particles experiencing	all	quarks, leptons	charged	quarks, gluons
Particles mediating	graviton	w^+, w^-, z^0	Υ	gluons

7.1 Discrete Energy and Radioactivity

❖ Discrete energy and energy levels

It is now accepted that electrons occupy "shells" surrounding the nucleus. Each shell corresponds to a certain energy level that the electrons occupying the shell have. An energy level of zero corresponds to the electron escaping from the atom. Electrons "attached" to an atom have energy levels with negative values. The further away the electron from the nucleus, the higher the energy level.

❖ Transitions between levels

To promote an electron from one shell to a shell further from the nucleus, i.e. to move it from one energy level to a higher energy level, energy must be put in. Conversely, if an electron relaxes back, dropping to a lower energy level, energy is released.

Atomic emission and absorption spectra provide us with experimental evidence for these atomic energy levels.

Emission Spectra

When certain substances are excited by some external source of energy, e.g. heat, light or electricity, they can become illuminated. For example, Neon tubes glow when stimulated by electricity. Sodium lamps appear yellow. An emission spectrum is a spectrum showing wavelengths (and frequencies) of light emitted. The light emitted is usually split up (dispersed) using a prism or diffraction grating.

When tungsten is heated strongly it emits white light. White light consists of a continuous spectrum of all the colours in the visible spectrum (red, orange, yellow, etc). So if the light from a tungsten filament is dispersed using a prism and viewed on a screen, the following is observed:

The scale shows the how the wavelength of light varies with colour.

Sodium vapour in a gas discharge tube (vapour is excited by high voltage) results in the following **emission spectrum**:

If white light is shone through sodium vapour, the following **absorption spectrum** results:

The last two spectra above are called **line spectra**, because lines of light are emitted or absorbed. It is no coincidence that the lines for the two spectra above correspond to the same wavelengths – it is because they originate from the same energy level jump in the same atom. The wavelength is the wavelength of light emitted or absorbed when electrons jump from one particular energy level to another. If they jump to a higher level, they absorb the light; if they jump to a lower level they emit light (there are many other, less distinct and bright lines for sodium corresponding to jumps to and from different energy levels).

Different elements have different energy levels corresponding to particular "shells" and require different amounts of energy to jump from one level to the next. Therefore line spectra provide a very accurate way of identifying the presence of a minute amount of a particular element in a sample.

Photons

Experimentation shows that light behaves not only as a wave-like energy, but also as a particle beam. A particle of light is called a photon. In an emission line spectrum, for example, like the one shown above, only light photons with the exact same energy as the energy involved in the electron jump will be emitted. The energy of a photon depends on the frequency of light, and the colour of light depends on the frequency, so a line with a certain colour will be emitted.

Energy of a photon

The energy of a photon depends on the frequency (and, therefore wavelength). The higher the frequency (lower the wavelength) the greater the photon-energy.

$$E = photon\ energy\ (J)$$

Equation: $E = hf$ where $h = Planck's\ constant\ (6.63 \times 10^{-34}\ Js)$

$$f = frequency\ of\ light\ (Hz)$$

Example T 7.1

Calculate the energy of a photon:

(a) Of blue light, with a frequency of 650THz
(b) Of X-rays with a wavelength of 5.2nm.

Example T 7.2

Convert the above energies into electronvolts.

Example T 7.3

Calculate the wavelength of the photons emitted when an electron drops in energy level by 2.5eV

So, photon energy provides the link between the light emitted or absorbed when an electron changes from one energy to another. This model of the atom works well to explain the emission and absorption spectra for the hydrogen atom, as follows:

The lowest energy state for its electron is the first shell, called n=1

energy level diagram showing energy levels and transitions

conventional shell diagram for electron orbits (states)

energy levels or states

energy of each level/state in electron-volts (eV)

nucleus

This lowest, most stable energy state, is called the ground state.

In order to jump from the ground state to higher states, energy is needed. If hydrogen is illuminated with the whole spectrum of frequencies of electro-magnetic radiation, the photons with the correct energy to cause this excitation from the ground state to the next state (n=2) will be absorbed. Other photons will be absorbed when they pass on their energies to promote the electron between other energy states (shells). This is how the absorption spectrum arises.

The energy levels for the hydrogen atom are thus as follows:

Notes

- The blue lines represent some of the possible transitions from one state (or level) to another.
- Transitions can occur from any state to any other state
- States $n = 5, 6, etc$ have not been shown, for lack of space!
- $n = \infty$ corresponds to the electron entirely leaving the atom – ionization
- For a transition of the electron from $n = 1$ to a higher level, energy must be put in (absorbed from electromagnetic radiation, if available)
- If the electron drops, atom will emit energy (in the form of electromagnetic radiation)
- The type of electromagnetic radiation absorbed or emitted depends on the size of the energy transition (and hence frequency of photon)
- Different atoms have different energy levels – this is why absorption and emission spectra can be used to identify materials.

Example T 7.4

(a) Using the diagram above find the energy required, in joules, to ionize a hydrogen atom from its ground state.

(b) Hence, find the frequency of electromagnetic radiation to effect this transition.

Example T 7.5

A hydrogen line emission spectrum has a line of wavelength $1.78 \times 10^{-6} m$.

(a) Find the photon energy, in eV, of light emitted for this line.

(b) Using the energy level diagram above, identify the transition causing this line

The diagram below shows the emission spectrum for hydrogen. The lines are all in the visible range. They correspond to transitions to the level $n = 2$, from other levels. The highest energy light emitted is the blue light on the far left, and the lowest is the red (red has lower frequency than blue light). Hence the lines on the left correspond to larger electron transitions than those on the right.

<u>Emission spectrum for hydrogen</u>

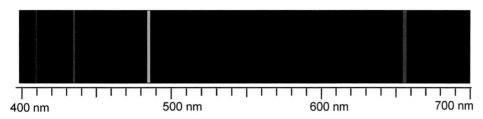

Example T 7.6

Using the energy level diagram for hydrogen, shown two pages previously, identify the transitions for two of the lines in the hydrogen emission spectrum shown above (do all for more practice, if you wish!!) [Note that the energy levels shown are approximate so your answers will not agree exactly to the lines shown on the emission spectrum].

Nuclear Structure

An atom is made up of a central nucleus and surrounding electrons. The nucleus is composed of protons and neutrons.

- The number of protons is called the atomic number (sometimes also called proton number)
- Nucleons is the collective term for protons and/or neutrons. So the number of nucleons in an atom is the total number (sum) of protons and neutrons.
- The number of nucleons (protons + neutrons) is called the mass number (also sometimes called the nucleon number)
- A nuclide refers to an atom with a particular nucleus configuration – referring simply to an atom is ambiguous because it could be one of two or more possible isotopes. It is common to refer to nuclides using their chemical symbol followed by their mass number. For example the nuclide with 53 protons and 74 neutrons is I-127 (Iodine 127).

General Symbol of the nuclide: $_Z^A X$ where

$X = the\ element$

$A = nucleon\ number\ (protons + neutrons)$

$Z = protons$

So neutron number N is equal to $A - Z$

Example T 7.7

Copper has the symbol **Cu**. A certain nuclide of copper has 29 protons and 34 neutrons. Show this nuclide using both methods above and explain why we can deduce the proton number from the method that does not give it directly.

❖ **Radioactive decay**

Chemical reactions involve the electrons within an atom. The nuclei of the atoms taking part in chemical reactions never change. Nuclear reactions, however, involve one or more nucleus changing.

Some nuclei are more stable than others. When an unstable nucleus disintegrates (breaks apart) to acquire a more stable state, radiations are emitted. This phenomenon is called radioactivity or radioactive decay.

❖ **Fundamental forces and their properties**

It may seem surprising that a nucleus stays together, given that it is composed only of positive and neutral particles. To understand why this is so, it is necessary to outline the forces that exist in a nucleus. Three types of force exist in a nucleus:

Gravitational force: an attractive force between particles with masses. Very weak compared to the other two

Electrical force: the repulsive force that the protons exert on each other. This force is immense compared to the gravitational force of attraction and would, without the existence of another attractive force, cause the nucleus to fly apart

Strong force: simply called "strong force" or "strong nuclear force" this force is about 100 times as strong as the electrical force in the nucleus. Unlike the electrical and gravitational forces, it has a very short range, reaching only as far as from one nucleon to its neighbour.

❖ Alpha particles, beta particles and gamma rays

Radioactivity is spontaneous and most commonly involves the emission of an alpha particle (α particle) or beta particle (β particle).

In both α emission and β emission the parent nucleus undergoes a change of atomic number and therefore becomes the nucleus of a different element. This new nucleus is called the daughter nucleus or the decay product. It often happens that the daughter nucleus is in an excited state when it is formed, in which case it reaches its ground state by emitting a third type of radiation called a gamma ray (γ ray)

❖ Beta decay

When a nuclide undergoes beta decay a β^- (beta minus) particle is always emitted (along with the daughter nucleus). A third particle is known to also be emitted: an antineutrino ($\bar{v}$). You must learn that whenever a beta minus particle is emitted, so is an antineutrino.

Example: The β^- decay of chlorine-36:

$$^{36}_{17}Cl \longrightarrow \,^{36}_{18}Ar + \,^{0}_{-1}\beta + \bar{v}$$

Balancing Nuclear Reaction Equations

Balancing chemical reactions involves balancing the number of each type of atom (element) on the left and right hand side of the equation. However, with nuclear reactions elements can change but the total mass (i.e. all mass numbers added up) and total atomic number are the same on both sides of the equation.

Example T 7.8

    (a) In the following decay reaction, find the values of *a, b, c, d, e, f*:
    (b) What kind of nuclear reaction is it?

$$^{a}_{b}Po \rightarrow \,^{c}_{d}\alpha + \,^{206}_{82}Pb + \,^{e}_{f}\gamma$$

Example T 7.9

Complete the following nuclear reactions by adding in any mass or proton numbers and any other products and classify each reaction.

a) $\quad ^{238}_{92}U \quad \rightarrow \quad Th \quad + \quad \alpha$

b) $\quad ^{14}_{6}C \quad \rightarrow \quad ^{14}_{7}N \quad +$

c) $\quad ^{60}_{27}Co \quad \rightarrow \quad Ni^* \quad + \quad \beta$
$$\downarrow$$
$$Ni \,+\, \gamma$$

❖ Half-life

The half-life of a radioactive substance is the time taken for the number (or mass) of radioactive nuclei present to fall to half its value. This length of time is constant at any point in time – showing that radioactive decay is exponential.

Example T 7.10

The half-life of a certain radioactive material is 6 minutes. What fraction of a sample of the material will decay in half an hour?

Example T 7.11

The following decay shows how the mass of a particular radioactive sample varies with time. Use the graph to find the half-life of the sample.

Note that to find the half-life from a decay curve, the time taken for the mass or activity of the sample to half is found – ANY starting point can be used. For example, try finding the time taken for the mass of the above sample to decrease from 10g to 5g – you should get the same answer, 8 days (approximately).

Radioactive decay curves such as the one above show exponential decay – the quantity reduces to half its value in constant time.

❖ Absorption characteristics of decay particles

The following table gives the properties and absorption characteristics of the three main decay particles:

Property	α-particle	β-particle	γ-ray
Symbol	$^4_2\alpha$	$^{\ 0}_{-1}\beta$	γ or $^0_0\gamma$
Production	loss of 2p+2n from Parent	Parent n → p+e (e emitted)	daughter nucleus relaxes → energy
Nature	Helium nucleus	Fast electron	EMR
Charge	+2e	-e	0
Rest Mass	4.0015u	.00055u	0
Velocity	≈ .06c	Up to 0.98c	c
Energy	≈ 6MeV	≈1 MeV	≈ 0.1MeV
Ionization power	≈ 10^5	10^3	10
Path through matter	straight	tortuous – (not at all straight!)	Straight
Deflection by a magnetic field	deflected	deflected strongly	not deflected
Penetration	≈ 5cm air	≈ 500cm air ≈ 0.1cm aluminium	≈ 4cm of lead reduces intensity to 10%

Notes

EMR = electromagnetic radiation

c = speed of light

u = unified atomic mass unit (average mass of 1 nucleon, $1.661 \times 10^{-27} kg$). See next section (7.2)

❖ Isotopes

Elements are defined by their atomic number. For any particular element, the atomic number does not change (for example, it is possible for an atom of the element oxygen to have 8 electrons or 10 electrons and it is possible for an atom of oxygen to have 8 neutrons, 9 neutrons or 10 neutrons, but, to be an oxygen atom, it must have 8 protons. An oxygen atom is defined to be an atom of the element with atomic number 8.

Some atoms of the same element have different masses. This mass difference is attributed to the fact that they contain different numbers of neutrons.

Atoms with the same atomic number (i.e. atoms of the same element) but different mass numbers are called isotopes. Two different isotopes of the same element therefore are different because they contain different numbers of neutrons.

Example T 7.12

Uranium is an element with chemical symbol U, and it has an atomic number of 92. Two common isotopes of uranium have 145 and 146 neutrons in their nuclei.

       (a) Name the two nuclides in this example
       (b) For the nuclide with the greatest atomic mass, state its atomic mass, nucleon number and how many protons and neutrons it has.

❖ Background radiation

Radioactive radiation versus electromagnetic radiation.

These two concepts are often confused in physics. Radioactive radiation is not the same as electromagnetic radiation. The confusion is not surprising since; first, they share the same name ("radiation") and; second, they do have some common overlap. Radioactive radiation is radiation that causes ionisation of material that is exposed to such radiation.

Examples include alpha and beta radiation (as discussed). Electromagnetic radiation is a form of wave that consists of a rapidly self-generating electromagnetic field that propagates (travels) at the speed of light. Light is one example of EMR. See topic 4 (Waves) for details of all members of the electromagnetic spectrum.

Examples of radiation that fit into both of the above categories are gamma radiation, electrons, X-rays, charged particles, neutrons, protons and many more.

Background radiation

Background radiation is radiation from sources all around us due to a multitude of sources occurring from within the background (on Earth). Anything radioactive is a potential source.

Almost all elements on the periodic table have several radioactive isotopes, so it is not surprising that we have a certain level of background radiation.

The following are common sources of background radiation:

Radon gas: this comes from the ground (especially rocks) and can be quite high in concentration in certain locations. It is the most prevalent form of background radiation at Earth surface level and is a cause of lung cancer.

Cosmic radiation: this is radiation from outer space and the sun and includes various radiations like X-rays, photons, alpha particles, electrons, protons and neutrons as well as several other particles. These radiations interact with Earth's atmosphere (which therefore protects us from the potentially very dangerous effects) and produce further secondary radiations emitted in all directions, including down to Earth's surface. Carbon-14 (a radioactive form of carbon), for example, is produced in the Earth's atmosphere and so a constant source of the isotope is (approximately) continually generated on Earth. Cosmic radiation becomes much more prevalent as altitude increases and is the major source of background radiation over a few kilometres above sea level.

Terrestrial ("from Earth") sources: uranium-238 occurs naturally in the Earth's core. Isotopes of Thorium, radium and potassium are other examples.

Food, organic matter: animal tissue (human bodies) account for part of the radioactive background count. Elements found naturally on Earth contain a certain proportion of radioactive isotope and this proportion cannot be separated chemically, so perpetuates within matter. Carbon-14 and potassium – 40 in the human body are two examples.

Man-made (artificial): medical (for example X-ray imaging, cancer gamma-therapy), smoking (radioactive polonium sticks to tobacco leaves), weapons testing, nuclear accidents.

Technically, background radiation should be taken into account when calculating half-life.

Example T 7.13

A students uses a geiger-muller counter (activity counter) to measure the activity of a certain sample. First, she measures the background count and times 19 counts in a minute (when she simply holds the counter in the air, before introducing the radioactive sample). Then she records the count with the sample and gets an initial reading of 65 counts per minute. What will the count rate be when one half life has elapsed?

7.2   Nuclear Reactions

❖ The unified atomic mass unit

In chemistry, masses of nucleons are expressed in atomic mass units. In physics, we need to be more precise (for example, we shall see that protons and neutrons have slightly different masses) and to use S.I. units for mass. Nucleons are therefore measured in terms of the unified atomic mass unit, u. The unified unit is defined to be exactly $1/12^{th}$ the mass of a crobon-12 atom. Hence 12u is the exact mass of a carbon-12 atom.

Masses of individual (isolated) electrons, protons and neutrons have been determined and can be expressed in terms of u, as follows:

Masses of protons, neutrons and electrons:

$$1u = 1.661 \times 10^{-27} \text{kg}$$

mass of an electron, $m_e = 0.000549u$

mass of a proton, $m_p = 1.007276u$ — all given in data book

mass of a neutron, $m_n = 1.008665u$

Example T 7.14

Calculate the mass of a carbon-12 atom in terms of u:

(i)   By using the definition of the unified atomic mass unit and the above data
(ii)   By adding the masses of the individual protons, neutrons and electrons.

The difference in your two answers, above, is dealt with in the following section.

❖ Mass defect and nuclear binding energy

Einstein's famous mass-energy equivalence principle (published 1905) explains that if a body increases in energy it also increases in mass.

This means that if you run faster, you are also getting heavier (but you would have to run extremely fast to increase in mass significantly). It also explains why, in Physics, the term "rest mass" is often quoted. Similarly, if an object gets hotter it has gained energy so it has also gained mass.

This concept is known as "mass-energy equivalence".

The quantitative relationship between mass and energy is described by Einstein's famous equation:

$$E = mc^2 \text{ where}: \quad E = \text{energy, in joules}$$
$$m = \text{mass, in kilograms}$$
$$c = \text{speed of light} = 3.00 \times 10^8 \, ms^{-1}$$

When energy is released, for example by a nuclear reactor, there is also a decrease in mass of the products, compared with reactants.

Example T 7.15

Calculate the amount of energy accompanying a 1.00 gram fuel mass-loss in a reactor.

Mass Defect and Binding Energy

Since energy is required to break up a nucleus into its constituent parts (protons and neutrons), energy must be added. This energy is called binding energy since it is the energy associated with the binding together of the nucleons – and numerically equal to the energy required to separate them. Using the above idea of mass energy equivalence, mass is also therefore added when energy is added.

It follows that the mass of a nucleus is less than the total mass of all the separate protons and neutrons making it up. This difference in mass is called the mass defect of the nucleus.

Mass defect (for a nucleus) = total mass of separate nucleons – mass of nucleus

Mass defect (for an atom) = total mass of separate nucleons + electrons – mass

of nucleus.

In this course we deal with nuclear binding energy, so the first concept above.

Example T 7.16

A helium nucleus has a mass of $6.6447 \times 10^{-27} kg$. Find the mass defect (in terms of u and kg) and the binding energy (in MeV and in J) of a helium nucleus.

❖ Nuclear fission and nuclear fusion

A useful measure of the stability of a nucleus is its binding energy per nucleon. This is the energy that needs to be supplied to remove a nucleon from the nucleus. Nuclides that have the largest binding energy per nucleon are therefore the most stable.

The following graph shows how binding energy per nucleon varies with the mass number (nucleon number).

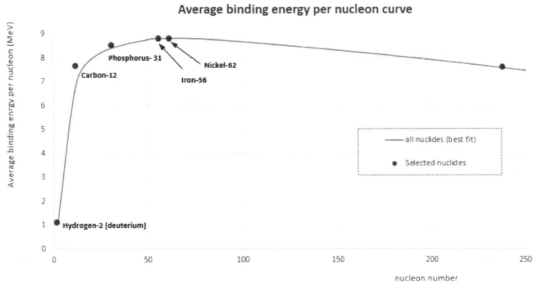

Notes

- Average binding energy per nucleon is calculated by $\dfrac{total\ binding\ energy\ of\ nucleus}{number\ of\ nucleons}$
- The blue line is a best-fit line. In reality the data (for all nuclides) would be scattered
- The higher the BE/nucleon, the more stable the nuclide
- Carbon-12 is above the best fit line, and is above C-13 and C-14 since it the most stable carbon isotope
- Nickel-62 is the most stable nuclide of all. Iron-56 is very closely behind
- The stability of Iron-56 explains why iron is so common on Earth (and other "spent supernova star fragments".

Example T 7.17

Iron – 56 has a binding energy per nucleon of 8.7922MeV.
Calculate the nuclear binding energy of this nuclide.

Further notes

Nucleons in iron-56 or nickel-62 have the most binding energy, so are the most stable. Therefore iron-56 and nickel-62 are the most stable nuclides. As can be seen from the graph, the further either side of nickel/iron you go, the less stable the nuclide. Nuclides therefore become more stable if they change in mass (nucleon number) closer to that of the mass of iron/nickel-62. Therefore nuclides heavier than iron/nickel tend to break apart (undergo fission reactions) and nuclides lighter than iron/nickel tend to join (fuse) with other light nuclides, undergoing fusion reactions. When nuclides undergo fission or fusion reactions to produce more stable nuclides, energy is always released. This can be a little confusing, so to explain, remember:
Binding energy = energy you have to put in to break nucleus apart

Hence: High binding energy nuclide → low binding energy nuclide
        (put energy in)
and   Low binding energy nuclide → high binding energy nuclide
                (energy is released)
This is the theory that allows us to release energy in nuclear reactions, e.g. in nuclear power stations.

Example T 7.18

Using the graph above, predict which is the most stable nuclide: Pb-206 or Po-210, and whether energy will be released or absorbed in the following reaction. Calculate the quantity of this energy.
$$^{210}_{92}Po \rightarrow {}^{206}_{82}Pb + {}^{4}_{2}He$$
Mass of $^{210}_{92}Po = 209.983u$
Mass of $^{206}_{82}Pb = 205.974u$
Mass of $^{4}_{2}He = 4.003u$
In order to make a nuclear fusion reaction take place, the reacting nuclei must approach each other at incredibly high speeds (to overcome electrostatic repulsion). One way of attaining these speeds is to use very high temperatures (about 100 million ºC) – **thermo**nuclear fusion reactions. So far, no one has managed to produce a controlled thermonuclear fusion reaction – bombs have been made using thermonuclear reactions – but these involve chain reactions, which are not controlled. The sun's energy comes from fusion reactions, and many heavier nuclei are produced from fusion of hydrogen nuclei.

7.3   The Structure of Matter

The structure of the atom and discovery of the nucleus

The currently accepted model of the atom is that it is spherical and composed of a central, very small and dense nucleus that is surrounded by "shells" of electrons, orbiting the nucleus.

The nucleus contains protons (positively charged) and neutrons (no charge – neutral), of approximately equal mass. The electrons are negative and are therefore attracted to the positively charged nucleus. This attraction, together with the momentum of the electrons, causes the electrons to orbit the nucleus in the same way that planets orbit stars. Electrons are virtually massless, and are considered to occupy no volume.

Evidence for this model was first provided by Geiger and Marsden, in the early 20th century.

Rutherford's/Geiger & Marsden's Alpha scattering Experiment

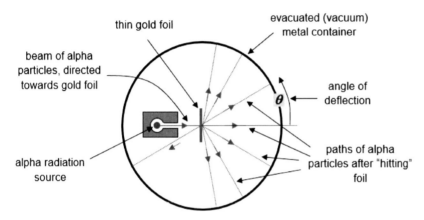

Note: *Alpha particles are helium nuclei (He^{2+}), which are very small, positively charged particles.*

Results:

1. Most particles passed straight through the foil, with no significant deflection
2. About 1 in 1800 particles was deflected by angles between 0° and 90°
3. About 1 in 8000 particles "bounced" backwards, at an angle greater than 90°.

❖ Explanation of results

1. Given that the foil was around 400 layers of gold atoms thick, from result 1 above, it was concluded that the atom must be composed mostly of space (calculations show that an atom is about 10,000 times larger than its nucleus: atomic diameter$\approx 10^{-10}m$, nuclear diameter$\approx$ ter$\approx 10^{-14}m$)

2. These deflections were attributed to the fact that the gold nuclei are positive, and so are the alpha particles – so, when an alpha particle passes close to a gold nucleus (not very often, due to 1, above) it is repelled, and deflected. The amount by which it is deflected depends on how close it passes by the gold nucleus

3. These deflections were explained by the fact that in a very few cases, the alpha particle actually collides with a gold nucleus, and therefore bounces back.

These observations and explanations can be summarized using the following diagram (which is worth drawing in most exam questions referring to this experiment).

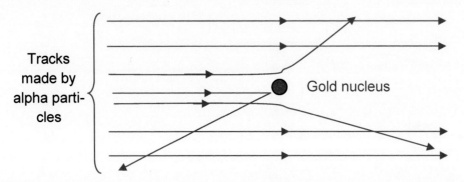

❖ Follow up calculations:

Size of atom: $\approx 10^{-10}\,m$

Size of nucleus $\approx 10^{-14}\,m$

Particle physics

Particle physics is concerned with particles the size of nucleons (protons / neutrons) or smaller. We shall see that some of these particles are made up of even smaller particles, but some cannot be broken down any further, and are called fundamental particles. All particles are therefore composed of the fundamental particles.

Anti-particles

All particles have antiparticles. Antiparticles are identical to their particle counterparts except, in the case of charged particles, antiparticles have opposite (but equal in magnitude) charges.

*   Antiparticles are not constituents of ordinary matter – they are created in high energy collisions (or by cosmic ray interactions with matter, or by radioactive decay of radioactive matter).

*   Antiparticles are stable in isolation but if they meet their particle counterparts, they become annihilated and cease to exist

*   All particles are represented with a single letter or symbol. Their antiparticles are usually represented with the same symbol but with a line on top. Example: neutrino (v), antineutrino ($\bar{v}$).

*   When a particle and its antiparticle meet they annihilate into pure energy.

Familiar Examples:

Particle Antiparticle	symbol	electrical charge	rest mass (MeV/c^2)
Electron	e^-	−1	0.511
Positron	e^+	+1	0.511
Proton	p	+1	938.3
Antiproton	$\bar{p}$	−1	938.3
Neutron	n	0	939.6
Antineutron	$\bar{n}$	0	939.6
Neutrino	ν	0	0
Antineutrino	$\bar{\nu}$	0	0

❖ Quarks, leptons and their antiparticles

Most observable matter is made from protons and neutrons. These are both made up from quarks.

There are 12 types of quark – called "flavours" and "antiflavours" (flavours = types!)

quark	symbol	electrical charge	antiquark	symbol	electrical charge
up	u	⅔	antiup	$\bar{u}$	−⅔
down	d	−⅓	antidown	$\bar{d}$	⅓
charmed	c	⅔	anticharmed	$\bar{c}$	−⅔
strange	s	−⅓	antistrange	$\bar{s}$	⅓
top	t	⅔	antitop	$\bar{t}$	−⅔
bottom	b	−⅓	antibottom	$\bar{b}$	⅓

Isolated quarks or antiquarks have never been observed – and it is strongly believed that they do not and cannot exist in isolation. There are a large number of quarks, due partly to the large combination of possible quark arrangements – ways of putting quarks together.

The remaining observable matter is made up from leptons. Unlike quarks, which only exist with other quarks (in groups), leptons exist in isolation. The best known lepton is the electron.

There are also 12 types of lepton, as follows:

lepton	symbol	electrical charge	antilepton	symbol	electrical charge
electron	e	-1	positron	e^+	$+1$
electron neutrino	ν_e	0	electron antineutrino	$\bar{\nu}_e$	0
muon	μ	0	antimuon	$\bar{\mu}$	0
muon neutrino	ν_μ	0	muon antineutrino	$\bar{\nu}_\mu$	0
tau	τ	0	antitau	$\bar{\tau}$	0
tau neutrino	ν_μ	0	tau antineutrino	$\bar{\nu}_\mu$	0

❖ Hadrons, baryons and mesons

As stated earlier, quarks never exist in isolation: they always exist in groups of 2 or 3 quarks. These groups of quarks are called hadrons. When quarks form hadrons it always results in a particle with net integer electric charge.

There are two types of hadrons: mesons and baryons. Mesons are formed from two quarks: one being a particle and the other, an antiparticle. Baryons are formed from three quarks.

Examples of baryons

Particle	Quark Content	Antiparticle	Quark Content
Proton	uud	antiproton	$\bar{u}\bar{u}\bar{d}$
Neutron	udd	antineutron	$\bar{u}\bar{d}\bar{d}$

The above are all hadrons and are all also classed as baryons. Hence, protons are made up of two up quarks and one down quark and neutrons are made up of one up quark and two down quarks

Baryons are made up of 3 quarks, and the net charge is always an integer value.

Examples of mesons

Particle	Quark Content	Antiparticle	Quark Content
Pion (π^+)	$u\bar{d}$	antipion	$d\bar{u}$
Kaon/K Meson (K^+)	$u\bar{s}$	antikaon (K^-)	$s\bar{u}$
K^0	$d\bar{s}$	$\overline{K^0}$	$s\bar{d}$

Mesons are made up of 2 quarks, one a particle and the other; an antiparticle

The net charge of a meson is always in integer value.

Example T 7.19

Which of the following are feasible hadrons, and if so, are they mesons or baryons? If not, why not?

       (a) csd
       (b) $b\bar{s}$
       (c) $t\bar{c}b$
       (d) $c\bar{c}$
       (e) ud

The conservation laws of charge, baryon number, lepton number and strangeness

In the same way that a nuclear reaction is only feasible if proton number and mass number are conserved, a particle interaction/reaction will only take place if baryon number and lepton number are conserved.

	baryon	antibaryon
Baryon number	+1	−1

	lepton	antilepton
Lepton number	+1	−1

Example T 7.20

Complete the following table, applying the conservation laws to deduce whether or not each interaction is possible:

Interaction	charge		lepton number		baryon number		interaction possible?
	left	right	left	right	left	right	
$n \rightarrow p + e^+$							
$p \rightarrow e^+ + n$							
$n \rightarrow p + e^- + \bar{\nu}$							
$p \rightarrow n + e^+ + \nu$							
$n + p \rightarrow e^+ + \nu$							
$e^- + p \rightarrow n + \bar{\nu}$							
$e^+ + e^- \rightarrow 2\gamma$							

Strangeness

Strangeness is another quantum number that is conserved during strong and electromagnetic interactions but not during weak interactions. The amount of strangeness can change in a weak interaction by +1, 0 or −1, depending on the reaction.

Strangeness is calculated by adding +1 for every antistrange quark and −1 for every strange quark in the particle.

Example T 7.21

Referring to the notes in this chapter, deduce the strangeness of the following particles:

      (a) A proton
      (b) A neutron
      (c) An electron
      (d) A k^+ meson
      (e) A k^0 meson
      (f) A k^- meson.

❖ **The nature and range of the strong nuclear force, weak nuclear force and electromagnetic force**

It may seem surprising that a nucleus stays together, given that it is composed only of positive and neutral particles. To understand why this is so, it is necessary to outline the forces that exist in a nucleus. Four types of force exist in a nucleus and, in general between particles.

Gravitational force: an attractive force between particles with masses. At short range this force is insignificant compared with the other 3 forces but range is infinite (force weakens with distance in accordance with the inverse square law).

Weak force: about 10^{32} times stronger than gravitational force when in range ($10^{-18}m$). This force acts between both quarks and leptons. It is very important in stellar reactions and in beta decay reactions.

Electromagnetic force: the force that charged particles exert on each other. This force is immense compared to the gravitational force of attraction and would, without the existence of the strong force, cause the nucleus to fly apart. This force is around 10^4 times stronger than the weak force at comparable ranges and the range of the electromagnetic force is infinite and in accordance with the inverse square law, like the gravitational force

Strong force: simply called "strong force" or "strong nuclear force" this force is about 100 times as strong as the electrical force in the nucleus. Unlike the electrical and gravitational forces, it has a very short range, reaching only as far as from one nucleon to its neighbour (maximum range is around $10^{-15}m$). The strong force only acts between quarks (not leptons), hence the importance of the weak force which acts on both these particles.

❖ **Exchange particles**

Particle physics can be used to explain all forces (attractive and repulsive) between particles.

Consider two particles adjacent (next to) each other.

If a particle (an "exchange particle") is ejected from one towards the other then, in accordance with Newton's 3rd law, the first particle will be forces backwards away from the first and, when the second particle receives this exchange particle, it will be forced backwards.

This is the thought experiment to demonstrate how an exchange particle is responsible for a repulsive force between two other particles.

To explain attractive force, consider that the first particle ejects the exchange particle directly away from the second particle and the exchange particle moves in a loop around and back to the first (rather like a ball on a string). Again, in accordance with Newton's 3rd law, both particles will experience forces towards each other: the first as it recoils back against the ejected exchange particle and the second as it receives the exchange particle.

The following table summarises the three types of force required for study in this syllabus: strong, weak and electromagnetic:

Type of force	Matter particles	Force carrier (exchange) particles	Reasoning/discussion
Electromagnetic	electrons and protons	photons	Matter must have charge to be affected by electromagnetic charge.
Strong	quarks	gluons	Matter must have "colour charge" in order to be affected by the strong force. Quarks and gluons have this property.
Weak	quarks and leptons	W^+, W^- and Z particles	The weak force explains the decay of more massive quark/lepton particles into smaller ones.

Example T 7.22

Name the exchange particles involved in:

(a) Weak forces
(b) Strong forces
(c) Electromagnetic forces.

Example T 7.23

Name the type of force(s) involved in the following instances:

(a) Normal force between an object and a surface
(b) Forces between nucleons in nucleus
(c) Friction
(d) Forces holding stars together in a galaxy
(e) The force between leptons
(f) The interaction force involved in beta decay of a neutron.

Example T 7.24

How many fundamental particles are known to exist? Name each group.

Example T 7.25

Identify each of the particles below as a particle class or type, and give the fundamental particles from which is composed:

(a) A proton
(b) A neutron
(c) An electron.

❖ Feynman diagrams

Feynman diagrams are a way of illustrating the interactions between particles.

It is important to correctly identify the axes, one of which will show time and the other; space.

The following rules apply to all Feynman diagrams:

The lines used on a Feynman diagrams are coded as follows:

———————— straight line represents matter particles

∿∿∿ wavy lines represent photons (exchange particles)

ℓℓℓℓ loopy lines represent gluons (exchange particles)

---------- dashed lines represent bosons (W, Z)

Note the above line coding is not always used, *so be careful* to also read the labels/symbols.

Each vertex (where the lines join each other) represents an interaction. Arrows show the progression of time for particles but are drawn in the reverse direction for antiparticles.

The following diagram shows the interactions involved when a nucleus undergoes beta emission:

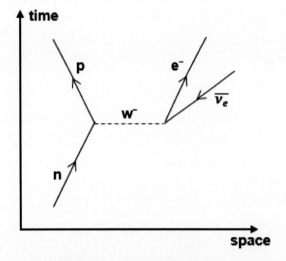

Key notes for the above diagram:

- We start with a neutron (since time starts at the bottom of the diagram)
- The arrow points in the direction of time since a neutron is a particle
- The neutron releases a W⁻ boson, which has virtual or brief existence (hence it happens at an instant in time, horizontally)
- We know that the virtual particle is a W⁻ boson because charge must be conserved at the interaction: a proton (+) is emitted from the nucleus, so the exchange particle must carry a negative charge
- The W⁻ boson then splits into a fast moving electron (beta minus particle/electron), and an antineutrino
- The electron and proton creation are shown with upwards arrows, since they are particles
- The antineutrino is shown with a downwards arrow, since it is an antiparticle.

Example T 7.24

    (a) Write down the equation for the above interaction
    (b) Explain why the boson must be a W^- boson (rather than a W^0 or W^+)
    (c) Show that the above interaction satisfies baryon number, lepton number and charge conservation.

Example T 7.25

Sketch a Feynman diagram to illustrate electron capture ($e^- + p \rightarrow n + v_e$) and describe the process (the virtual exchange particle is a W- boson, as before: why?).

❖ Confinement

Quarks are not possible to separate: they only exist in pairs or threes. They are therefore confined to groups, rather as separate entities.

This is because in trying to separate quarks, energy has to be put in. This energy provides sufficient mass to form additional quarks. So, for example, if two quarks are pulled apart two new quark-antiquark pairs are formed.

❖ The Higgs Boson

The Higgs boson is a theoretical particle whose existence was initially postulated in 1964. It provided a mechanism to explain mass in fundamental particles. The scientists hypothesized a new field and suggested that this new field would need a particle. They deduced (from a quantity called "spin") that this particle must be a boson and called it (after one of the scientists, Peter Higgs, who was on the team) the Higgs boson.

What was unclear at the time was the mass of this particle. However, it became apparent that if it existed it must be very massive. The more massive the particle, them more energy needed to create the particle and, at the time, the equipment was not good enough.

It was not until 2012 that scientists at CERN (Geneva) were able to report excellent evidence for a "Higgs like particle". Since the particle is so short lived, evidence could only come from its interaction decay products. This is how the mass of the Higgs boson was estimated: essentially from the mass/energy of the products observed from the subsequent decay that happened almost as soon as its (unobservable) formation.

Example T 7.26

According to current theory and understanding, each statement below is either true or false. Write T, for true and F for false for each statement. If you have written F, try to explain why, in the margin. Complete all the answers before checking them.

a) The proton and the neutron are fundamental particles
b) The electron has no antiparticle
c) The antiparticle always has a different charge to a particle
d) All particles (excluding antiparticles) are constituents of ordinary matter
e) Particles and antiparticles have the same mass and average lifetime
f) For annihilation to occur, the interaction must be between a particle and its antiparticle
g) In particle interactions, mass must be conserved, and so must energy
h) The observable fundamental particles are leptons, quarks and gauge bosons
i) Exchange particles are mediators of the fundamental interactions
j) Gluons, photons and the intermediate vector bosons are all exchange particles
k) Exchange particles are all gauge bosons
l) Gauge bosons are fundamental particles
m) Exchange particles are all quarks
n) An electron is a lepton
o) An electron neutrino is the antiparticle of an electron
p) Quarks come in 6 flavours
q) Protons and neutrons are made up from quarks
r) Isolated quarks have never been observed but they do exist in isolation
s) The observable fundamental particles are leptons, hadrons and gauge bosons
t) The uud is the particle from which protons are made
u) The udd is the antiparticle of the uud, from which neutrons are made
v) Hadrons are observable particles, made from quarks
w) Hadrons are fundamental particles
x) Mesons and baryons are the two subgroups of quarks
y) Charge, lepton number and baryon number are always conserved
z) Protons and neutrons are mesons.

Topic 8: Energy Production

Summary Checklist

8.1	Energy Sources
	Specific energy and energy density of fuel sources Sankey diagrams Primary energy sources Electricity as a secondary and versatile form of energy Renewable and non-renewable energy sources
8.2	**Thermal Energy Transfer**
	Conduction, convection and thermal radiation Black-body radiation Albedo and emissivity The solar constant The greenhouse effect Energy balance in the Earth surface–atmosphere system

Equations Provided (in IB databook) & Explanations

$$Power = \frac{energy}{time}$$	The **power** of any kind of energy conversion device or machine is equal to **the rate at which energy is converted** by the machine – if **total energy and total time** is used in the calculation this gives **average power.**
$$Power = \frac{1}{2}A\rho v^3$$	The **power** of a wind turbine is equal to ½ the product of the turbine **cross sectional area** (circular), the **wind density** and the **cube of the wind speed**.
$$P = e\sigma AT^4$$	The power of radiation emitted by a body (e.g. star or planet) is equal to the product of the emissivity of the body, the Stefan-Boltzmann constant, the surface area of the body and the 4th power of the temperature of the body.
$$\lambda_{max}(metres) = \frac{2.90 \times 10^{-3}}{T(kelvin)}$$	The **most intense wavelength** of radiation emitted by a body (e.g. star, planet) is equal to the ratio of the number 2.90×10^{-3} and the **temperature** of the body, in kelvin.
$$I = \frac{Power}{area}$$	The **intensity** of radiation received on a given surface is equal to the ratio of the **power** of radiation received on the surface and the **area** perpendicular to the direction of radiation projected onto the surface.
$$albedo = \frac{total\ scattered\ power}{total\ incident\ power}$$	The **albedo** of a surface is equal to **the power of radiation scattered** (reflected) by the surface to the **power of radiation received** by the (same area of) surface

8.1   Energy sources

❖ Specific energy and energy density of fuel sources

A given community will require a given average amount of energy on a daily basis. The rate at which energy is consumed is a measurement of power consumption:

$$Power = \frac{energy}{time}$$

We can therefore easily calculate the amount of energy a community requires over a given time if we know its average power consumption. More importantly, if we know the energy requirements we can calculate the approximate power of the delivery of energy.

On a national scale, this kind of pre-planning needs to take place when considering power supply. Especially with recent environmental concerns and pressures, the consideration of various different fuels is an important part of the planning process.

The specific energy is a measurement of a fuel and the equation/definition is as follows:

$$specific\ energy = \frac{energy\ available\ or\ released\ from\ fuel}{mass\ of\ fuel\ used}$$

This equation is not provided in the IB data booklet.

This equation allows us to consider efficiencies of fuel usage in terms of how much energy we can get from a certain mass of fuel. We can also consider the volume (or space taken up), using a measurement called energy density, as follows:

$$energy\ density = \frac{energy\ available\ or\ released\ from\ fuel}{volume\ of\ fuel\ used}$$

Again, this equation is not provided in the IB data booklet.

The following table gives some specific energies for a range of fuels:

Fuel	Specific Energy ($MJkg^{-1}$)
natural gas	50
crude oil	45
coal	25
water in a dam (100m high)	0.001
Uranium-235 (nuclear power)	88.25×10^{6}

Example T 8.1

Using the table above, calculate the energy available from 1.0g of:
(a) Natural gas
(b) Crude oil
(c) Coal
(d) Uranium – 235.

Example T 8.2

The approximate densities of natural gas, crude oil and coal and uranium are:
$0.75 kg/m^3$, $890 kg/m^3$, $850 kg/m^3$ and $18,800 kg/m^3$ respectively.

(a) What volume of uranium-235 gives us 1.0g of the fuel? Write your answer in cubic metres and cubic centimetres?

(b) Calculate the volume of the following fuels required to give the same quantity of energy as 1.0g of uranium-235:

    (i) Coal
    (ii) Crude oil
    (iii) Natural gas.

Power Stations

Fossil fuel (coal, oil, natural gas) and nuclear power stations basically work the same way. The key is that they use a source of energy that can be converted to thermal energy (the power station then converts this energy into electricity: a useful secondary source of energy for the consumer.

The following schematic diagram shows the basic sequence of how such power stations work:

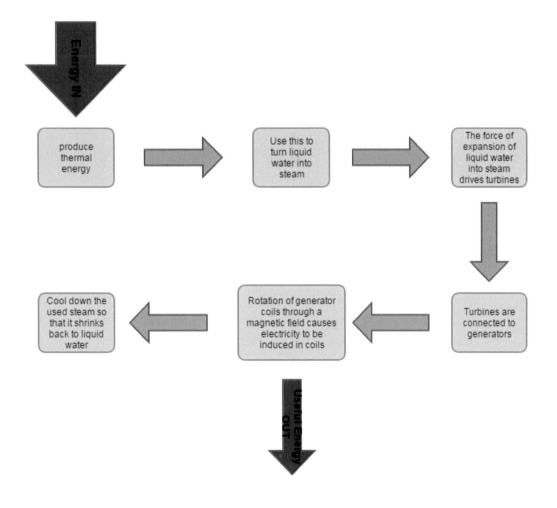

Example T 8.3

If necessary do some research (search terms: power station schematic diagram; how power stations work; energy losses in power stations) before answering part (b) of this question.

(a) Referring to the schematic flow diagram above, identify the major *useful* energy transformations taking place from start point to end point

(b) Discuss energy losses (i.e. wasted energy) from the system.

Fossil Fuel Power Production

It may be surprising to you, with all the focus these days on global warming and "greener fuels" that around three quarters of world energy production still comes from the burning of fossil fuels. The reasons are largely historical and geographical. Industrialisation led to a hugely increased rate of energy usage and industries were developed near to large deposits of fossil fuels.

If you do some internet research you will see many arguments suggesting that energy usage and power station efficiencies have not changed significantly over the last several decades and that this has much to do with short term economy and profit. The next decade or two will be very interesting times in seeing what changes are made and what new energy technologies are developed.

Power Station Efficiencies

The figures are similar for all three types of power station: Approximate maximum efficiencies are:

Coal fired power stations: 42%

Oil fired power stations: 45%

Natural gas fired stations: 52%

Typical power stations may run at between 5 and 10% lower than these efficiencies.

Example T 8.4

A particular power station has a power output of 400MW (a fairly typical value for a power station). Using any relevant information provided in this chapter so far, find the approximate mass of coal that would be needed to run such a power station for a week (assume that it runs 24 hours per day).

Environmental Problems associated with fossil fuel use in Power Stations

Pollution (acid rain, greenhouse gases), damaged environment when extracting, pollution when transporting large masses of fuels to power stations (increased traffic), non-renewable so will eventually run out.

Nuclear Power

Nuclear power is the power associated with energy produced as a result of nuclear reactions. When a nuclear reaction takes place an enormous amount of heat energy may be liberated (given out) so nuclear power is potentially very useful.

Nuclear reactions, unlike chemical reactions, involve nuclear changes. Atoms, thus, are not conserved. Total mass number and total proton number, however, are conserved (after the reaction, compared with before the reaction). There are two kinds of nuclear reactions: nuclear fusion and nuclear fission. Fusion is where two light nuclei come together to form a heavy nucleus. Fission is where a heavy nucleus breaks apart to form two (or more) lighter nuclei.

The Nuclear Fission Power Plant (Power Station)

A nuclear fission power plant works essentially in the same way as a fossil fuel power plant, as discussed earlier. The key difference is the fuel that is used to produce the heat: the energy source is nuclear rather than chemical. An isotope of uranium (u-235) is the most common nuclear fuel used. Polonium-239 is also used.

Some important terms:

- **(Nuclear) Chain reaction**: a nuclear reaction that causes one or more other nuclear reactions to take place

- **Fissionable**: a fissionable material is one that can undergo nuclear fission

- **Isotopes:** two or more nuclei with the same atomic number but different atomic masses. Uranium 235 and uranium 238 are isotopes of uranium. Most naturally occurring elements occur as a mixture of more than one isotope.

The following schematic flow diagram shows the basics of how thermal energy is extracted from a nuclear fuel in a power station.

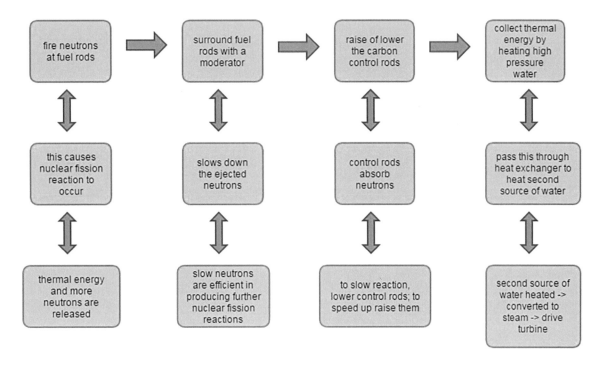

Example T 8.5

If necessary do some research (search terms: nuclear power station schematic diagram) and refer to the diagram above below and explanatory notes immediately following before doing this question.

(a) Why are the nuclear reactions taking place in the reactor of a nuclear power station referred to as chain reactions?

(b) Why are control rods necessary?

(c) What is the purpose of the moderator?

Moderation / Moderators

Slowing down the neutrons will increase the chance of achieving a critical chain reaction. This is because slowing down the neutrons increases the chance of them causing fission when they collide with a uranium atom. The material used for this slowing down process is called a moderator. Regular water is the most commonly used moderator.

Control Rods

If the chain reaction is left as it is, more and more neutrons cause more fissions and the chain reaction becomes uncontrolled. The heat produced is then explosive. Such chain reactions are how fission bombs work. Control rods are used to control fission chain reactions. Control rods simply absorb neutrons. So if the reaction is going too fast, control rods are inserted into the reactor to absorb more neutrons. If the reaction is going too slow, they are removed. Control rods can be made of many different materials. One example is boron.

Nuclear Reactor

A nuclear reactor is a device that contains, initiates and controls nuclear chain reactions at a steady and sustained rate. The purpose of a nuclear reactor is to convert nuclear energy into thermal energy (heat).

Risks of Nuclear Power

Thermal meltdown: this is the term used to describe a severe nuclear accident. A nuclear (or thermal) meltdown occurs when the reaction is not controlled properly and extreme heating occurs, which leads to the highly reactive fission products becoming overheated and melting and the possibility of containment failure. There have been several nuclear meltdowns in history, the most famous being the Chernobyl disaster in 1986. Due to cover-ups, it is not known how many died, but the overall cost of the disaster is estimated at 200 billion US dollars; the costliest disaster in modern history.

Radioactive nuclear waste: remains radioactive for millions of years. often buried in geologically secure sites.

Dangers of mining and transporting radioactive materials (uranium): mining is already dangerous. This has the added danger associated with radioactive materials.

Risk of inappropriate use for nuclear weapons.

Nuclear Fusion Power

If we could harness the energy of nuclear fusion, this would produce safe products, since fusion reactions are between light nuclei and results in the production of another light and radioactively inactive nucleus.

The problem with this kind of power is that such extremely high temperatures are required to initiate a fusion reaction and it is very difficult to maintain and confine a high temperature, high density plasma that would be produced.

Solar Power

Solar power is harnessed in two possible ways: using photovoltaic cells ("solar cells") or using solar panels.

Photovoltaic cells convert light energy (sun's radiation) into electrical energy. This form of energy collection requires a large surface area for a relatively small amount of electrical energy. Solar cells, therefore, are commonly used to power smaller devices or the electrical energy produced can be fed into the grid system.

Solar heating panels (solar thermal collectors) convert light energy (sun's radiation) into thermal energy (heat). Solar heating panels are used increasingly on house roofs to assist in the heating of water for central heating and washing use.

Hydroelectric Power

Hydroelectric power is power derived from gravitational potential energy of water: so, when water flows downwards, the gravitational potential energy is released and may be converted into electrical energy.

Energy Chain:

Hydroelectric power is the most widely used renewable energy resource. In 2005, hydroelectric power produced 19% of the world's electricity.

It is a clean and free fuel. Emissions are (usually) clean. Running costs and maintenance are low.

On the other hand, dam construction can damage the environment and enormous quantities of methane gas (a potent greenhouse gas) can be produced by rotting vegetation when an area of land is flooded. Population relocation can be socially unjust and there is always a risk of dam failure: a big safety hazard.

Pump storage: water is pumped from a low reservoir to a high reservoir. The idea is that the pumping occurs at low demand periods, ready to provide extra power in times of demand. Clearly this method is not energy efficient, since at least as much (and in fact more) energy is required to pump the water up than is released when it falls back down.

Wind Power

Wind turbines convert the kinetic energy of the wind into electrical energy. Note, though, that in accordance with the laws of thermodynamics, one can never convert all the energy from wind into mechanical, then electrical energy. The turbines have mechanisms to direct the turbine into the wind, to increase power and away if the wind is too strong (and could otherwise damage the turbines)

If the windspeed of air passing through the turbine blades is known, you can easily calculate the maximum power delivery of a wind turbine, as follows:

Maximum Power available $\qquad = \frac{1}{2} A \rho v^3$

Where: $\qquad$ A is the cross sectional area (πr^2) of the rotor blades (m^2)

$\qquad \rho$ is the density of the air (kg/m^3)

$\qquad v$ is the wind speed (m/s)

Do a quick internet search (search terms: wind turbines) for more construction details.

Example T 8.6

Calculate the radius of a wind turbine's rotor blades given that it has a maximum power output of 5kW and that the density of air is $1.2 kg/m^3$ and that it runs on a maximum windspeed of 10 m/s.

❖ Sankey diagrams

A Sankey diagram is an arrow representation of the flow of energy and its transfers and energy dissipations in the process from input to output. The relative thickness of each part of the arrow (shown with little arrows) corresponds to the amount (proportion) of energy involved in each stage. In a very visual way, the diagram gives an idea of the overall efficiency of the process by comparing the thickness of the useful energy output with that of the input (energy from fuel).

Example T 8.7

Estimate the efficiency of the above process and the power consumption of fuel given that the power output is 1.2MW. Note that the diagram is not very useful for making any precise measurements.

Note also that the Sankey diagram would be very similar for any thermal (heat producing) power station.

❖ Primary energy sources

A primary energy resource is some natural source of energy that can provide us with energy such as coal, oil, wind, solar, hydroelectric etc.

❖ Electricity as a secondary and versatile form of energy

Electricity is the major form of energy delivery across the globe. Power stations are used to transfer energy from primary sources to an electrical distribution network. Electricity has the benefit of being easy to distribute. Transport is convenient (through cables) and clean.

Once this secondary energy-form reaches the user it is then easily and conveniently converted to the required useful form.

One of the challenges of electricity distribution is to do so with maximum efficiency, minimum energy loss. Large, low resistance cables are used and very high voltages (up to 400,000 volts) are employed in order to reduce current and consequent energy loss through heating.

❖ Renewable and non-renewable energy sources

An energy resource is something that can provide us with usable energy.

A **renewable energy** resource is one that is replenished naturally and within a short time scale

A **non-renewable** resource is one that cannot be replaced (in the foreseeable future) once used.

Renewable:	Non-Renewable:
Hydroelectric Power	Oil and gas
Geothermal Power	Coal
Tidal Power	Nuclear Power (but virtually unlimited)
Solar Power	
Wind Power	
Wave Power	
Biomass	

Discussion

A hundred years ago there was little though about non-renewable energy sources being limited. More recently there have been concerns of them running out: particularly oil. This has been one reason for the huge price increases of petrol and diesel in the last 30 years of the last century (especially from around 1970 to 1980).

The problem is that (i) massive and expensive infra-structure (especially in first world countries) has already been developed (ii) the energy density of renewable sources is generally very low, so space, convenience, costs and profits become real challenges.

In the last 20 years, from the start of this century, concerns have shifted from the issue of energy availability (non-renewable sources running out) to concerns of global pollution – and especially global warming. The burning of fossil fuels is thought to be a major contributor to this potentially very serious problem.

The next generation will undoubtedly be one where new methods of energy sourcing will be a major focus for society and scientists alike.

8.2   Thermal energy transfer

❖ Conduction, convection and thermal radiation

A note on thermal energy

If energy is added to matter it can either get hotter or it can change state (from solid to liquid or from liquid to gas). If it gets hotter, this means that the average kinetic energy (could be rotational and/or vibrational and/or translational kinetic energy) of the particles has increased. If it changes state (S→L or L→G) it means that the average (electrical) potential energy of the particles has increased. If either or both of these forms of energy has increased we say that the internal energy of the matter has increased.

Often thermal energy, heat energy and internal energy are interchanged and confused with each other.

To clarify:

If energy is added to a substance by exposure to a hotter surrounding, heating or thermal energy transfer has occurred.

The added energy will result in an increase in internal energy of the substance.

Thermal energy transfer can happen in three different ways:

1. **Conduction**: thermal energy (vibrations) is passed on by molecules colliding with adjacent molecules – adjacent molecules therefore move more, increasing their kinetic energy, and so on

2. **Convection**: energy is moved simply by molecules with internal energy moving from one place to another

3. **Radiation**: energy is transferred from a "hot" body by infra-red (heat) radiation. This radiation can then be absorbed by another body, whose internal energy would then increase. The internal energy of the object that has emitted the radiation will decrease.

Some characteristics of thermal energy transfer

- The only type of thermal energy transfer in solids is conduction
- The main type of thermal energy transfer in liquids and gases is convection
- Radiation is most effective when there are no particles in the way – i.e. in a vacuum
- Conduction and convection require matter
- Heat transfer by convection is usually in the upwards direction, since hotter particles move more, take up more space and make that part of the fluid (liquid or gas) less dense
- All objects radiate heat – the hotter, the greater the amount of radiation
- Conduction can and does take place in fluids, although generally only to a minor extent since the particles are not in close proximity to each other, as in solids
- Metals are good conductors of heat, since they contain free electrons that assist the passage of heat through the substance
- Non-metals are classed as thermal insulators
- Good conductors that are hot feel hot to touch because they quickly transfer heat to the contact point, whilst hot insulators don't feel so hot – the contact point cools on contact and the thermal energy is not quickly replaced. (the same applies to cold objects).

Example T 8.8

Respond with true or false, with a reason, for the following:

  (a) Conduction only occurs in solids
  (b) Convection does not occur in solids
  (c) Radiation only occurs most effectively in gases
  (d) Radioactivity is a form of radiation, and so is a valid form of thermal energy transfer.

❖ Black body radiation

A "black body" absorbs all radiation that falls on it and reflects none; hence it is black (reflects no light) when it is cold. However, when a black body is hot it emits radiation. If it is at the same temperature as the surroundings it will emit exactly as much radiation as it absorbs and at every wavelength. So, (hot) black bodies always emit radiation at all wavelengths.

An important property of a black body is that the radiation it emits is characteristic of the body itself: i.e. its temperature. (A star is a good approximation of a black body. The Earth and other terrestrial, low temperature solid objects are quite poor approximations, but approximations nonetheless).

The relative proportions of radiation emitted depend on the temperature of the body. The following di-agram shows the emission spectra of black bodies at different temperatures:

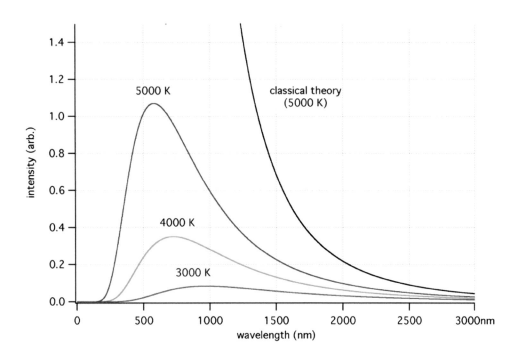

As the temperature increases, the peak intensity moves to higher intensity and shorter wavelength.

The theory of black body radiation explains and can be used to predict the colour of very hot objects. A heated metal, for example, first appears red hot, then white hot (at very high temperatures) this col-our corresponds to the peak intensity on the above diagram. Most objects at "everyday Earth" temperatures emit radiation mostly in the infrared region of the spectrum – so the peak would be in the infrared region in above diagram.

Wien's Displacement law

This is an equation that enables us to predict the temperature of a body based on the most intense wavelength of radiation emitted, or vice-versa.

$$\lambda_{max}(metres) = \frac{2.90 \times 10^{-3}}{T(kelvin)} \qquad \text{given in data booklet}$$

Example T 8.9

The most intense wavelength of radiation emitted from a star is 320nm. Calculate the approximate temperature of the star. See if this seems to fit with the pattern shown on the black body spectra (graphs) shown previously (and, for more practice, try confirming the wavelengths of the three other bodies using the temperatures provided).

❖ Albedo and emissivity

Albedo

The ability of a planet to reflect radiation back is called albedo. The Earth's albedo varies significantly depending on season (colours) and surface: snow (being white and shiny), for example has a high albedo, whereas oceans have low albedos.

Albedo – definition: the proportion of power (or energy) reflected compared to the total power (or energy) received.

$$albedo = \frac{total\ scattered\ power}{total\ incident\ power} \qquad (\text{in data book})$$

The albedo of snowy surfaces, for example, is about 0.85 – indicating that this type of surface reflects 85% of the sun's radiation back. The global annual mean albedo of the Earth is 0.3 (so approximately 70% of the radiation reaching the sun is absorbed by the Earth.

Intensity

Intensity is a way of measuring the concentration of energy (radiation and sound being two main examples) falling on a surface.

It is simply the joules per second (power) falling on an area perpendicular to the radiation, per square metre of that area.

$$Intensity = \frac{power}{area}$$

However, we must be careful to realise that the intensity of radiation at a given place may not be the same as the intensity of radiation received by a surface.

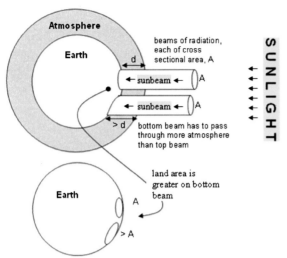

The following diagram illustrates how this concept causes uneven heating at the Earth's surface.

The area over which the radiation is spread is greater as you move towards the "edges" of the Earth, so received intensity is reduced.

(The Earth's atmosphere is another factor contributing to uneven heat distribution addressed in the diagram)

Example T 8.10

Consider a beam of light coming from the sun towards the Earth.

The beam width is exactly the diameter of the Earth, so all of this light is received by a disk with Earth's diameter.

However, the light is spread over the surface of the Earth and, because the Earth is not a flat disk, the area over which the radiation is spread is greater.

Given that the solar constant (intensity of light from sun) is $1400Wm^{-2}$ and that the radius of the Earth is 6400km:

(a) Calculate the total power received by the Earth
(b) Calculate the average intensity of radiation received by the surface of the Earth facing the sun, assuming no cloud cover
(c) Calculate the average intensity of radiation received by the Earth over a 24 hour period (assuming no cloud cover).

Note: you will need to know the formulae for area of a circle and a sphere to solve the above problems:

Circle area = πr^2

Surface area of sphere = $4\pi r^2$

Example T 8.11

Given that the average albedo of the Earth is 30%, calculate the power of radiation actually absorbed by the Earth.

Emissivity

The emissivity is a number (from 0 to 1) measuring of how well a surface emits radiation. Good emitters have emissivities close to 1 (A perfect emitter, a black body, has an emissivity equal to 1).

Note: for non-transparent bodies emissivity + albedo = 1

<u>Stefan-Boltzmann law</u>

This law links the total power emitted (radiated) by a body to its temperature, in the following equation:

$P = e\sigma AT^4$ (equation provided in IB data booklet)

Where: e = the emissivity of the surface

σ = Stefan-Boltzmann constant = $5.67 \times 10^{-8} Wm^{-2}K^{-4}$

A = surface area of the emitter

T = absolute (Kelvin) temperature of the emitter

Example T 8.12

Find the approximate radiation power of the Sun and the Earth, given the following data:

Radius of Sun:	$7.0 \times 10^8 m$
Radius of Earth:	$6.4 \times 10^6 m$
Surface temperature of Sun:	$5800K$
Surface temperature of the Earth:	25ºC

(Surface area = $4\pi r^2$, assume $e(Earth) = 0.7$ and $e(sun) = 0.95$)

❖ The solar constant

(This has already been referred to in example T 8.10).

The solar constant is defined to be the average intensity of radiation received from the sun before it has reached the Earth's atmosphere, when the Earth is at the average distance from the sun.

Notes

The Earth moves in a slightly elliptical orbit around the sun, hence the need for stating average distance. The variation in distance from sun has little effect on intensity received, since the distance is so great and the variation so small in proportion.

The literature value of the solar constant is $1367Wm^{-2}$. When calculating power received by the Earth the value will be lower due to the albedo of clouds and atmosphere effects.

❖ The greenhouse effect

The greenhouse effect is the warming effect that the atmosphere has on the earth.

To understand the greenhouse effect, we first need to understand that the Earth is always absorbing energy from the sun and it is also always emitting radiation. All bodies possessing thermal energy emit radiation. The type of radiation emitted depends on the temperature of the body. The Earth emits mainly infrared radiation.

The greenhouse warming effect occurs because some gases in the atmosphere are able to absorb infrared radiation emitted from the Earth. As the gases increase in temperature, they then begin to emit radiation. However, they emit radiation in all directions, so some of the energy is sent back to Earth. Hence warming occurs.

Greenhouse gases are gases that easily absorb infrared radiation. Examples include carbon dioxide, water vapour, methane and nitrous oxide. These gases all have bonds that oscillate with the same range of frequencies as part of the infra-red range of frequencies. They are therefore able to absorb energy by a process known as resonance (the driving frequency, infrared radiation) is the same as the natural frequency as the oscillator being driven (the greenhouse gases). These gases have both man-made and natural origins.

Stepwise summary

- The sun, being a very hot body, emits a high proportion of short wavelength light (see "black body radiation"). Light is predominantly ultra-violet
- Much of this radiation passes easily through the Earth's atmosphere, with little interaction
- Some of the radiation is absorbed by the Earth (the amount depends on albedo)
- Radiation is reemitted by the Earth but, since the Earth is a much lower temperature than the sun, it will be at a much longer wavelength (predominantly infra-red)
- When infra-red radiation reaches the Earth's atmosphere its wavelength (and frequency) now happens to be a similar frequency to the natural frequency of the greenhouse gases so the radiation is absorbed by the gases
- The greenhouse gases re-emit the absorbed radiation (at similar frequencies) in all directions, so a good proportion will be emitted back towards the Earth
- This causes a greater amount of radiation to be received at the Earth. Global warming is a possible consequence.

Energy balance in the Earth surface-atmosphere system

We now see that the interactions between radiation and the Earth's surface and atmosphere result in a complex situation.

Added to this is the fact that the atmosphere is a changing environment: there are multiple chemical reactions occurring and new gases (diffusing upwards from Earth) are continually added to the mix. Gases from the Earth take around 10 years to reach the upper atmosphere so the consequences of human activities continue for many years, even if the activities are stopped. For example, in the late 1980's many countries reduced the amount of CFCs (chlorofluorocarbons, from refrigerators and aerosol cans, among other things) released since they were identified as harmful to the atmosphere. However, the atmosphere would still have been receiving these gases for 10 more years or so.

The only way to try to predict future temperature patterns on Earth is to use computer models, where all the various parameters (affects) can be adjusted until the model appears to work based on previously recorded patterns.

One big problem in trying to make such predictions is the lack of past data. The Earth has been around for a very long time and the last 100 years or so is only a tiny fraction of this. Previous patterns would provide us with a better insight into how the Earth reacts to temperature variations and how much variation occurred before significant human (pollution) activity occurred.

Topic 9: Wave Phenomena

Summary Checklist

9.1	Simple Harmonic Motion
	The defining equation of shm Energy changes
9.2	**Single-slit diffraction**
	The nature of single slit diffraction
9.3	**Interference**
	Young's double slit experiment Modulation of two-slit interference pattern by one-slit diffraction effect Multiple slit and diffraction grating interference patterns Thin film interference
9.4	**Resolution**
	The size of a diffracting aperture The resolution of simple monochromatic two-source systems
9.5	**Doppler effect**
	The doppler effect for sound waves and light waves

Equations Provided (in IB databook) & Explanations

$$\omega = \frac{2\pi}{T}$$	The **angular frequency** of an object in simple harmonic motion (SHM) is equal to the ratio of 2π and the **period of oscillation** of the object
$$a = -\omega^2 x$$	The **acceleration** of an object in SHM is equal to negative the product of the **square of the angular frequency** and the **displacement** of the object (from equilibrium)
$$x = x_0 \sin(\omega t); \quad x = x_0\cos(\omega t)$$	The **displacement** of an object in SHM after time t is equal to the maximum displacement (**amplitude**) multiplied by the **sine or cosine of the product of the angular frequency and the time**. The first equation applies to the initial motion at zero displacement and maximum positive velocity and the second, to initial motion at maximum positive displacement and zero velocity (going negative)
$$v = \omega x_0 \cos(\omega t); v = -\omega x_0\sin(\omega t)$$	The **velocity** of an object in SHM after time t is equal to the **product of angular frequency and amplitude** multiplied by the **cosine or sine of the product of the angular frequency and the time**. The first equation applies to the initial motion at zero displacement and maximum positive velocity and the second, to initial motion at maximum positive displacement and zero velocity (going negative).

$v = \pm\omega\sqrt{x_0^2 - x^2}$	The **velocity** of an object in SHM at any given **displacement**, x, is equal to the **product of the angular frequency** of the object and **the square root of the difference between the squares of the amplitude and the displacement** (the direction cannot be determined only from displacement and angular frequency, hence $\pm$).
$E_K = \frac{1}{2}m\omega^2(x_0^2 - x^2)$	The **kinetic energy** of an object in SHM at any given **displacement**, x, is equal to half the **product of the mass of the object, the square of its angular frequency** and **the difference between the squares of the amplitude and the displacement** of the oscillation of the object.
$E_T = \frac{1}{2}m\omega^2 x_0^2$	The **total energy** of an object in SHM is equal to half the **product of the mass of the object, the square of its angular frequency** and **the amplitude** of oscillation of the object.
Pendulum: $T = 2\pi\sqrt{\frac{l}{g}}$	The time period of a swinging pendulum is equal to 2π multiplied by the square root of the ratio of the length of the pendulum to the gravity-field (9.81N/kg).
Mass-spring: $T = 2\pi\sqrt{\frac{m}{k}}$	The time period of an object on a spring is equal to 2π multiplied by the square root of the ratio of the mass of the object to the spring (stiffness) constant.
$\theta = \frac{\lambda}{b}$	When light is passed through a single slit, the **radian angle** between the centre-line (drawn from the centre of the single slit to the screen) and the first minimum is equal to the ratio of the **wavelength** of light passed through the slit and the **slit width.**
$n\lambda = d\sin\theta$	For light with wavelength λ, passing through a diffraction grating with slit separation, d, the angles, θ, from the grating to the central maximum and the zeroth ($n = 0$), 1st ($n = 1$), 2^{nd}($n = 2$) etc. bright fringe (maximum) are given by this formula.
Constructive interference: $2dn = \left(m + \frac{1}{2}\right)\lambda$	When light passes through a thin film (with refractive index n, thickness d) constructive interference will result if the product of the refractive index and the film thickness is equal to an odd number of half wavelengths, $\left(m + \frac{1}{2}\right)\lambda$, $m = 0, \pm1, \pm2, etc.$ This condition also assumes that the refractive index of the film is greater than that of the material on which it coats.
Destructive interference: $2dn = m\lambda$	When light passes through a thin film (with refractive index n, thickness d) destructive will result if the product of the refractive index and the film thickness is equal to a whole number of wavelengths, $m\lambda$, $m = 0, \pm1, \pm2, etc.$ This condition also assumes that the refractive index of the film is greater than that of the material on which it coats.

$$\theta = 1.22\frac{\lambda}{b}$$	When light is passed through a single circular aperture, the **radian angle** between the axis-line (drawn from the centre of the aperture to the screen) and the first minimum is equal to 1.22 multiplied by the ratio of the **wavelength** of light passed through the slit and the **aperture diameter.**
$$R = \frac{\lambda}{\Delta\lambda} = mN$$	The **resolving power** (resolvance) of a diffraction grating to resolve two maxima, corresponding to two different wavelengths of light, is equal to the **ratio of the average of the two wavelengths to the difference between the two wavelengths**, and this is also equal to the **product** of the **order** at which the lines are observed and the **total number of slits** on the grating.
Moving source: $$f' = f\left(\frac{v}{v \pm u_s}\right)$$	When a sound source is moving away from/towards an observer the **frequency** heard by the observer is equal to the **product of the frequency** of the sound **emitted** by the source and the **ratio of the speed of sound** to the **sum/difference of the speed of sound and the speed at which the source** is moving.
Moving observer: $$f' = f\left(\frac{v \pm u_0}{v}\right)$$	When an observer is moving towards/away from a source of sound the **frequency** heard by the observer is equal to the **product of the frequency** of the sound **emitted** by the source and the **ratio of the sum/difference of the speed of sound and the speed of the observer** to the **speed of sound.**
$$\frac{\Delta f}{f} = \frac{\Delta\lambda}{\lambda} \approx \frac{v}{c}$$	When there is relative motion between a light source and an observer the **difference in frequency** between that observed and that emitted divided by the **frequency emitted** is equal to the ratio of the **difference in wavelength** observed and emitted to the **wavelength emitted**, which is approximately equal to the ratio of the **relative speed of the observer** towards or away from the source to the **speed of light**.

9.1   Simple Harmonic Motion

❖ The defining equation of SHM

SHM is defined as motion where the acceleration of the particle is proportional to but in the opposite direction to the displacement of the particle.

i.e. $a \propto -x$ where: $a = acceleration$, $x = displacement$

The defining equation for simple harmonic motion is thus as follows:

$$a = -\omega^2 x \qquad \text{where: } \omega \text{ is the angular frequency of the oscillating particles}$$

Example T 9.1

A student sets up a motion sensor to measure the displacement and acceleration of an object which oscillates back and forth. He wants to determine whether the motion is simple harmonic.

(a) Explain how the student should analyse the data to test whether or not the motion is SHM and to find the value of any relevant constants.

Three of his processed data are as follows:

x/cm	a/ms^{-2}
-5.0	5.50
-2.5	2.70
3.0	-3.30

(b) Using these data show that the motion is likely to be SHM
(c) Determine the angular frequency of the motion

Other SHM "motion" equations

SHM varies sinusoidally with time.

The displacement, velocity and acceleration of a particle describing SHM can all be plotted as a sine or cosine function. The trick is selecting the correct equation and graphs corresponding to what is actually happening. The confusing thing is that the appropriate graphs/equations will depend on where the timing starts.

On this course, we will only start the timing either at the equilibrium position (moving "forwards" or "backwards" or at one of the maximum displacement positions (with "forwards" or "backwards") displacement.

This means we have 4 possible basic graphs to choose for any of the motions. The next example illustrates this.

❖ Key points

+ Sine graphs start at the origin (when $t = 0, x, v \ or \ a = 0$) and increase initially
+ Cosine graphs start at maximum positive (when $t = 0, x, v \ or \ a = \max +$)
- Sine graphs are same as + sine graphs but reflected across t axis
- Cosine graphs are the same as − cosine graphs but reflected across t axis

Displacement equations start with $x = x_0$ ....
Velocity equations start with $v = v_0$ ....   or $v = \omega x_0$ ..... $(v_0 = \omega x_0)$
Acceleration equations start with $a = a_0$ ..... or $a = -\omega^2 x_0$ .... $(a = -\omega^2 x,\ a_0 = -\omega^2 x_0)$

Remember:

- Velocity can be determined from a displacement/time graph by taking slope
- Acceleration can be determined from a velocity/time graph by taking slope.

Acceleration and displacement are always graphs on opposite sides (reflected) of x axis for SHM

The 4 graphs show how either displacement, velocity or acceleration vary (y axis) with time (x axis). They will be referred to in the examples 9.2 to 9.7.

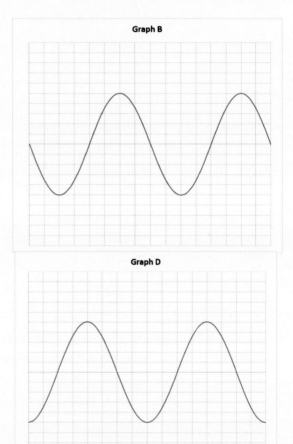

Example T 9.2

(a) Which graph shows how displacement varies assuming the motion starts from:
    (i)   Maximum negative displacement?
    (ii)   Zero displacement, moving backwards (in negative direction)?

(b) Which graph shows how velocity varies assuming that motion starts from:
    (i)   Maximum negative displacement?
    (ii)   Zero displacement, moving in the forwards direction.

Example T 9.3

Match each of the following equations with the relevant graph (assuming they are all displacement graphs):

(a) $x = x_0\sin(\omega t)$
(b) $x = x_0\cos(\omega t)$
(c) $x = -x_0\sin(\omega t)$
(d) $x = -x_0\cos(\omega t)$.

Example T 9.4

Match each of the following equations with the relevant graph (assuming they are all velocity graphs):

(a) $v = -v_0\cos(\omega t)$
(b) $v = -v_0\sin(\omega t)$
(c) $v = -\omega x_0\sin(\omega t)$
(d) $v = \omega x_0\sin(\omega t)$.

Example T 9.5

Match each of the following equations with the relevant graph (assuming they are all acceleration graphs):

(a) $a = a_0\cos(\omega t)$
(b) $a = -\omega^2 x_0\sin(\omega t)$
(c) $a = \omega^2 x_0\cos(\omega t)$

You may also see the equations written (i) without the brackets around the trig function argument (ii) with ω replaced by $\frac{2\pi}{T}$

Example T 9.6

Match each of the following equations with the relevant graph (this time assuming they are _velocity_ graphs):

(a) $v = \frac{2\pi}{T}x_0\cos\frac{2\pi}{T}t$

(b) $x = -x_0\sin\omega t$

(c) $a = a_0\cos\frac{2\pi t}{T}$

Example T 9.7

(a) Given that Graph A shows how displacement varies with time, which graphs shows how (i) velocity (ii) acceleration varies with time for the same particle motion?
(b) Given that Graph B shows how velocity varies with time, which graph shows how (i) displacement (ii) acceleration varies with time for the same particle motion?
(c) Given that Graph A shows how acceleration varies with time, which graph shows how (i) displacement (ii) velocity varies for the same particle motion?

Using the SHM motion equations

A pendulum and a mass on a spring approximate simple harmonic motion. The equations for the period of these systems are given in the data booklet (see table at start of chapter).

We can use the equations discussed above for finding displacement, velocity or acceleration at a given time. We can also use the equations for velocity, kinetic energy and total energy of the object describing SHM at a given displacement, using the final three SHM equations.

Example T 9.8

A pendulum bob with a mass of 145g is attached to a string so that its swinging length is 1.85m. It is initially drawn backwards, and it swings forwards from this initial position for a distance of 36.0cm. It continues to oscillate in this manner with minimal damping (resistance effects).

Notes: take $g = 9.81ms^{-2}$, *displacement is measured from equilibrium position*

Determine the following:

(a) The period
(b) The angular frequency
(c) The amplitude
(d) The maximum kinetic energy
(e) The total energy
(f) The velocity when the displacement is $+12cm$
(g) The kinetic energy when the displacement is $-9.0cm$
(h) The displacement, velocity and acceleration after exactly 12.5s has elapsed.

❖ Energy changes

SHM will always involve cyclic energy changes: from kinetic energy to some form of potential energy, back to kinetic energy and so on. If the motion is damped (by some resistive force(s), then a transfer of energy out of the system, as internal energy, will also result.

For a swinging pendulum bob the energy transfer cycle will be from gravitational potential energy to kinetic to gravitational potential energy, back to kinetic and so on.

For an object bouncing up and down on a spring, the energy transfer will be from elastic energy (at lowest position) to kinetic + gravitational potential energy (at equilibrium position) to gravitational potential energy (at highest position), back to KE + GPE etc.

Kinetic energy can be found using the equation given and potential energy can be found by subtracting kinetic energy from total energy (equation also given).

Example T 9.9

Referring to the pendulum example in T 9.8:

(a) Describe the energy transfers taking place within the system (assuming no resistive forces)
(b) Calculate the potential energy of the system after exactly 12.5s has elapsed.

9.2   Single Slit Diffraction

❖ The nature of single slit diffraction

[Refer back to chapter 4 (Waves) for a qualitative discussion of diffraction and interference]

To explain single slit diffraction, we consider that when a straight wavefront reaches the slit it behaves as an infinite number of point sources along the slit. Each point source then emits wavelets that combine to determine how the wave progresses.

We then show that for every point on the upper half of the slit, there is a point symmetrically below, on the lower half of the slit such that the wavelets meet at the screen, along the centre-line shown, in phase with each other – so that a crest meets a crest and a trough meets a trough: constructive interference results and the screen is brightest at the centre (intensity curve/graph is at a maximum). This is shown on the diagram at point p_2.

As we move outwards from the centre we find that these successive wavelets begin to become increasingly out of phase with each other and the interference becomes less constructive, and the intensity curve (graph) is therefore lower.

We show that at a certain point (shown as p_2 on the diagram) for every wavelet coming from the upper half of the slit there will be one a half slit width further down the slit that cancels, since each pair of lines will be 180° out of phase with each other.

The logic in the previous paragraph is extended to form a mathematical derivation of the "single slit equation" (see after diagram).

Diagram showing how light diffracts to form an interference pattern after it passes through a single slit:

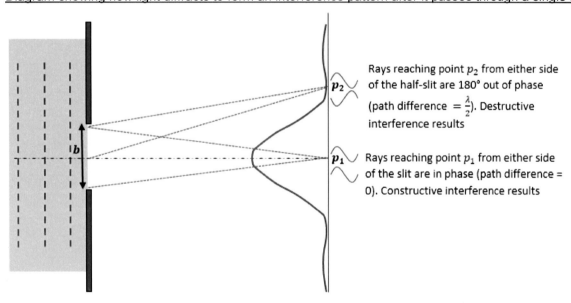

Rays reaching point p_2 from either side of the half-slit are 180° out of phase (path difference $= \frac{\lambda}{2}$). Destructive interference results

Rays reaching point p_1 from either side of the slit are in phase (path difference = 0). Constructive interference results

Single Slit Diffraction equation:

Consider again the single slit set-up. The diagram below shows the pattern as observed on the screen, along with the intensity graph.

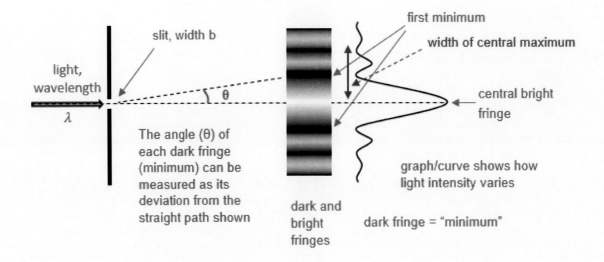

Note that the dark regions of the screen correspond to minima shown on the graph.

The width of the central maximum, with minima at its edges, is marked with a red double-headed arrow.

The angular width of the central maximum is thus 2θ, where θ is defined as the angle from the central axis to the position of the first minimum.

Equation: $\theta = \dfrac{\lambda}{b}$, where θ *must* be in radians

---

Example T 9.10

Light with a wavelength of 500nm is shone through a slit of width 0.04mm so that the diffraction pattern falls on a screen 2.5m away.

  (a) Calculate the position of the first minimum.
  (b) Find the approximate width of the central bright fringe.

Further Notes

The pair of secondary maxima (either side of the central maximum) are of the order of 4.5% that of the central maximum. Further maxima diminish in intensity close to zero.

Increasing slit width or decreasing wavelength have the effect of squashing the diffraction pattern, with narrower bright and dark fringes. Different coloured light (with different wavelengths) will therefore create diffraction patterns of varying width.

White light contains a mixture of wavelengths; red being the longest and violet, the shortest. White light therefore creates overlapping patterns of all the wavelengths. The centre of the central bright fringe will be white but either side of the centre the colours start to split: red spreading the widest and violet; the narrowest.

9.3   Interference

❖ Young's double-slit experiment

The experimental set-up and equation for the Young's double slit experiment has been discussed at some length in chapter 4 (Waves). The HL section focusses on detailed analysis of the interference/intensity patterns produced.

If light is directed towards a double slit, the two slits act as point sources and each diffracts towards a screen. The interaction between the two light sources forms a pattern on the screen, as follows:

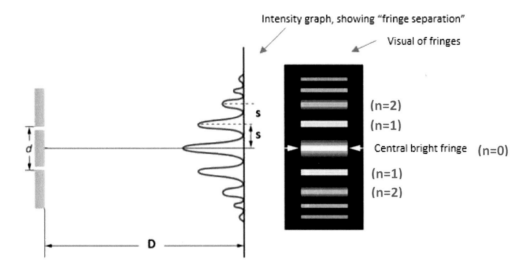

Notes

- The central maximum (bright fringe) is referred to as $n = 0$ (order $=0$). As we move away from the centre we define the fringes either side of the maximum as $n = \pm 1, \pm 2, etc$ (1st, 2nd order etc.)
- We can apply the diffraction grating equation: $n\lambda = d\sin\theta$ to the Young's double slits experiment, where the angles give position of the relevant maxima.
- The above diagram gives the pattern for slits that themselves have non-zero widths. Each single slit then also has an interference pattern as discussed in the previous section. This results in diminished intensity either side of the central maximum can be explained by considering the overlap of these two (single and double slit) interference patterns.

Example T 9.11

(a) Calculate the angle (in degrees) from centre-line to the first minimum when light with wavelength $600nm$ passes through a single slit of width $5\mu m$.

(b) Calculate the angular position of the first, second and third order maxima when light of wavelength $600nm$ passes through double slits separated by $50\mu m$.

❖ Modulation of two-slit interference pattern by one-slit diffraction effect

The solutions to the last problem do not give the intensities of both situations.

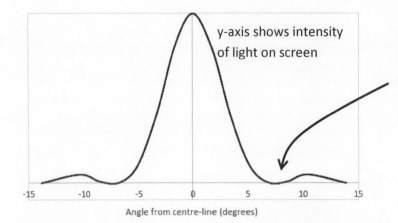

y-axis shows intensity of light on screen

Angle from centre-line (degrees)

The angle from centre-line to first minimum, per previous example, is 6.9°

The pattern, as previously discussed, for the single slit (width $5\mu m$) is as follows:

The pattern for a double slit (separation $50\mu m$) where each slit has negligible width (so no single-slit interference pattern occurs) is as follows:

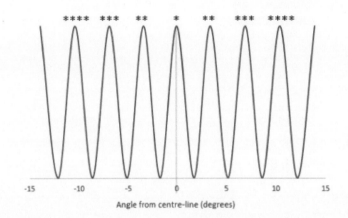

Angle from centre-line (degrees)

Per previous example, maxima occur at:

$n = 0: \ \theta = 0°$ *

$n = \pm1: \ \theta = \pm3.4°$ **

$n = \pm2: \ \theta = \pm6.9°$ ***

$n = \pm3: \ \theta = \pm10.4°$ ****

When these two patterns overlap we get the interference pattern for two single slits, width $5\mu m$, separated by $50\mu m$ (i.e. a "double slit") is as follows:

Angle from centre-line (degrees)

The double-slit interference pattern is enveloped in the single slit pattern.

The purple intensity pattern is the result (observed intensity)

Example T 9.12

Explain how the above diffraction pattern will change if:

(a) The separation between the two slits is increased
(b) The width of each slit is increased.

This is explained/illustrated as follows:

❖ Multiple slit diffraction grating interference patterns

Multiple slit interference patterns, effected using diffraction gratings, are an extension of the above. Each time an additional slit is added, one extra overlapping pattern is added.

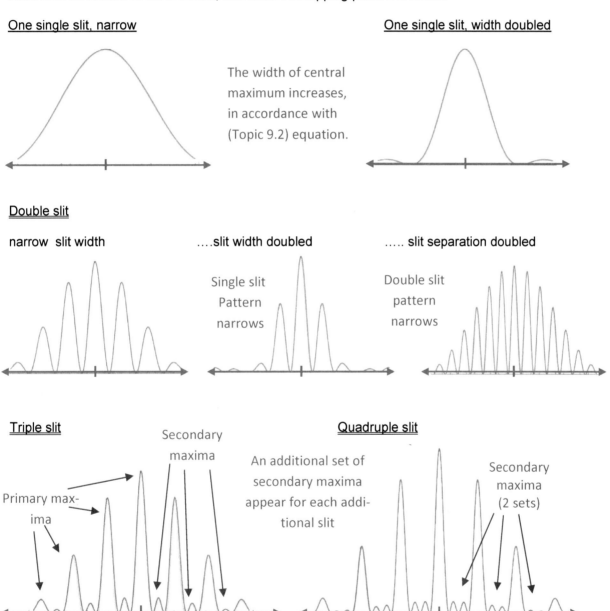

The final change (not shown here) is that the greater the number of slits, the greater the intensity of all the lines.

❖ Summary

As slits width is increased, broad outline interference pattern narrows.

As slits separation is increased, inner interference pattern narrows.

As number of slits is increased:
(i) Number of sets of secondary maxima increase
(ii) Width of primary maxima decreases
(iii) Intensity of primary maxima increases
(secondary maxima begin to diminish/disappear).

Example T 9.13

The following multiple-slit interference patterns, (A) and (B) show how intensity on a screen varies as angular distribution from central maximum varies, as follows:

Both patterns have been produced from the same number of slits:

   (a) Determine how many slits there are
   (b) Describe and explain any differences between the slit arrangement in A and in B
   (c) Explain what difference(s) would be observed if the number of slits is increased.

The diffraction grating formula

The formula, $n\lambda = d\sin\theta$, not only allows us to determine angular position of the maxima, but also how many maxima will be observed (if n becomes too large this leads to $\sin\theta > 1$, which is not possible). Diffraction gratings can have hundreds of slits (also referred to as rulings or lines), and the number of lines per millimeter is often quoted, rather than the slit separation. This, then, must be calculated for use in the above formula.

Example T 9.14

Monochromatic (single wavelength) light with wavelength 580nm falls on a diffraction grating with 540 lines per millimetre inscribed.

   (a) Determine the angle between the two first order maxima
   (b) Determine the number of maxima that can be observed.

❖ Thin film interference

This is the effect observed when light is shone onto a thin film of transparent material: beautiful coloured patterns are observed on the surface of such films. Examples include bubbles produced by washing liquid, oil spilled on water and the surface of a compact disk or DVD in light. The effect is caused by the interference of light reflected off the top surface of the film and that transmitted through the film then reflected off the lower surface. It is a consequence of the fact that whenever a wave meets a new medium it will partially reflect and partially transmit (and refract).

The following diagram explains the phenomenon:

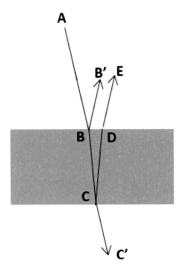

- A section of the thin film is shown in blue. A light-ray is directed at the film along the line AB, meeting the film at point B.
- At point B, some of the light reflects (BB') and some is transmitted, refracting along the line BC.
- At point C, the ray reaches a new boundary at the lower part of the thin film. Again, some light will refract (along CC') and some will reflect (along CD).
- At point D the ray again meets a boundary, where some light will reflect (not shown) and some will refract (along DE)
- The rays BB' and DE will interfere. The type of interference (constructive or destructive) will depend on the film thickness, the wavelength of the light and the film and surrounding material refractive indices.

Thus, if white light is shone onto the film, different colours will be enhanced (for example, if red wavelengths are reinforced (by constructive interference), then it will be brighter. If green wavelengths are diminished (by destructive interference), then red and blue will be relatively brighter in that region.

Mathematical treatment: the equations for thin film interference.

First, some key points:

When light meets a new medium which has a greater refractive index it will undergo a 180° phase change (so a "crest" becomes a "trough" and vice-versa).

When light meets a new medium, there will be a change in wavelength and the ratio of wavelengths will be the reciprocal of the ratio of refractive indices of the two media, i.e.

$$\frac{\lambda_1}{\lambda_2} = \frac{n_2}{n_1}$$

This is in accordance with Snell's law (as discussed in Chapter 4).

If we assume that the light starts off in air ($n \approx 1$) with a wavelength λ and that the thin film has refractive index n, we get $\lambda = n\lambda_2$, so the wavelength in the medium will be $\frac{\lambda}{n}$

Referring again to the diagram and defining the film thickness to be d, we have:

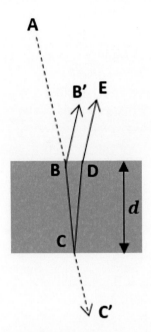

We are interested in how the light that emerges from the film (BB' and DE) will interfere.

We will get destructive interference if light coming from point B and from point D at the surface are 180° out of phase (e.g. crest + trough or trough + crest).

We will get constructive interference if light coming from these two points is in phase (e.g. crest + crest, trough + trough).

To determine which of these it is, we need to consider two things:

    (i)   Wavelength of the light and the path difference
    (ii)   Whether any phase changes take place at each boundary, as a result of reflection at the respective boundary.

The <u>path difference</u> between the ray reflected directly at B and the ray that transmits and refracts along BC then reflects at C, following the path CD to emerge is simply the length BCD: this is the extra distance travelled by the ray that has transmitted then reflected back.

We assume that the light is shone onto the surface at approximately 90° to the surface.

We can therefore say that the path difference between the two "sources" (from B and from D) is twice the thickness of the thin film, i.e. $2d$. If no phase changes occur as the light reflects off each surface we would only need consider this path difference. In this case we get constructive interference if the path difference is equal to a whole number of wavelengths.

i.e. if $2d = m\lambda_2$, where $m = 0,1,2,3, ...$ and where λ_2 is the wavelength of light in the film

But, as stated earlier, $\lambda_2 = \frac{\lambda}{n}$ so $2d = m\frac{\lambda}{n} \Rightarrow 2dn = m\lambda$

For destructive interference we need crest to meet trough, so the waves must be out of phase with each other by a half (or 1.5, 2.5 etc.) wavelength.

So we get the conditions interference (<u>assuming no phase changes</u>) as:

$2dn = m\lambda$ => constructive interference

$2dn = \left(m + \frac{1}{2}\right)\lambda$ => destructive interference

However, since we have supposed that air is the initial medium, there must be a "hard reflection" off the first boundary, resulting in a 180° phase change of the ray that reflects directly at the first boundary (BB').

This means that, assuming there is no phase change of the transmitted beam when it reflects at C, then in order to maintain this half-wavelength shift we need the path difference to be a whole number of wavelengths.

Hence, <u>for one phase change</u> the conditions are as follows:

$2dn = m\lambda$ => destructive interference

$2dn = \left(m + \frac{1}{2}\right)\lambda$ => constructive interference

We can extend this argument to the situation where there are <u>phase changes at both surfaces</u>, to get:

$2dn = m\lambda$ => constructive interference

$2dn = \left(m + \frac{1}{2}\right)\lambda$ => destructive interference

Whether or not we get a phase change at each boundary depends on whether the refractive index increases or decreases.

<u>Summary:</u>

Number of phase changes	Condition for constructive interference	Condition for destructive interference
1	$2dn = \left(m + \frac{1}{2}\right)\lambda$	$2dn = m\lambda$
2	$2dn = m\lambda$	$2dn = \left(m + \frac{1}{2}\right)\lambda$

Note that theoretically it is possible to have no phase changes at the first boundary. This leads to the possibility of a total of zero phase changes (with same conditions as 2 phase changes) or a single phase change at the second boundary. However, since we deal with air as our incident material these are very unlikely IB scenarios.

We are generally looking at either a single phase change at the first boundary or phase changes at both boundaries.

Example T 9.15

Light is shone from air into a thin film, with refractive index X and thickness D. The material immediately below the film has refractive index Y.

Complete the table below to determine the nature of the interference for each situation:

Refractive indices	Number of phase changes	Film thickness	$\therefore$ Value of 2dn	Type of interference
X>Y	1	$\dfrac{1}{4}\dfrac{\lambda}{X}$	0.5λ	constructive
X>Y		$\dfrac{1}{2}\dfrac{\lambda}{X}$		
X>Y		$\dfrac{3}{4}\dfrac{\lambda}{X}$		
X>Y		$\dfrac{\lambda}{X}$		
X>Y		$\dfrac{5}{4}\dfrac{\lambda}{X}$		
X<Y		$\dfrac{1}{4}\dfrac{\lambda}{X}$		
X<Y		$\dfrac{1}{2}\dfrac{\lambda}{X}$		
X<Y		$\dfrac{3}{4}\dfrac{\lambda}{X}$		
X<Y		$\dfrac{\lambda}{X}$		
X<Y		$\dfrac{5}{4}\dfrac{\lambda}{X}$		

Example T 9.16

The surface of an object with refractive index 2.9 is coated with a transparent material with a refractive index of 1.8. Calculate the minimum thickness of the surface required to minimize the reflection of monochromatic light of frequency $6.25 \times 10^{14} Hz$ from the surface.

Example T 9.17

A child blows a bubble which consists of a layer of soap solution with approximate 240nm and with a refractive index of 1.35.

(a) Given that the human eye can perceive electromagnetic radiation in the wavelength range from 390 to 700nm, determine the wavelengths of visible light:

    (i)   Corresponding to the colour that has been eliminated from the reflected light
    (ii) Corresponding to the colour that has been enhanced in the reflected light.
(b) Explain why we observe a multitude of colours when we see a soap bubble.

9.4 Resolution

Resolution is the ability of a device (example: human eye/brain) to observe two distinct objects as two distinct images. A high resolving power means the device has the ability to separate two images when the corresponding objects are very close together.

❖ The resolution of simple monochromatic two-source systems

Note: monochromatic means only one wavelength/single colour.

Try drawing two small dots, very close together on a piece of paper.

As you move the paper away from your eyes the dots will, at a certain point, appear as a single dot. If you see both dots you have successfully resolved the two dots. The ability to resolve decreases as the distance from the dots increases.

The reason you see the two dots as a single dot is that when light from each dot enter your eye the light diffracts as it passes through your pupil. This causes a diffraction pattern, for each dot, consisting of concentric circles (disks) as shown below. As the distance between your eye and the dots increase, the images (and diffraction patterns) begin to move together. When there is too much overlap the images are perceived as a single image (dot).

The diffraction pattern that will result when the human eye (or other circular aperture) views two dots.

Note that in this case (with the two patterns separated) the image will appear as two dots.

❖ The size of a diffracting aperture

When images of two points are formed by the light passing through an aperture (hole), for example a slit, a camera lens, a radio-telescope dish, or a human pupil, the slit width or hole diameter is a key factor that determines whether or not the images are resolved.

The Rayleigh criterion allows us to know if two points are resolvable (distinguishable as two separate points.

It states that **two points will be resolvable if the central maximum of the diffraction pattern formed of one point coincides with the first minimum of the other** (and this is the closest that the two diffractions can get to each other before they appear to be one point.

Thus, the following diagrams show diffraction patterns to illustrate resolved, just resolved and unresolved image:

(a) Resolved

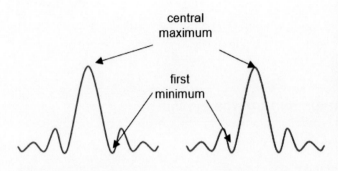

There is effectively no overlap between the two diffraction patterns.

Blue and red patterns are shown here to aid the argument that follows. The two diffractions can move together until they reach the limit prescribed by the Rayleigh Criterion.

Thus:

(b) Just resolved

The central maximum from the red pattern has over-lapped to the point that it overlaps the first minimum of the blue pattern

If the two patterns overlap any further they will be appear as a single image.

Thus:

(c) Unresolved

The blue and red diffraction patterns now go beyond the level of overlap as prescribed by the Rayleigh Criterion: they lines will thus appear as a single line.

Applying the Rayleigh Criterion to Circular apertures (e.g. human vision).

For human vision, the aperture through which the light passes is the pupil of the eye. This circular aperture causes diffraction and the diffraction pattern falls on the retina of the eye as an image.

We have seen that the position for the first minimum for a single slit is given by the formula:

$$\theta = \frac{\lambda}{b}$$

It has been shown that for a circular aperture a similar formula can be applied to determine the minimum distance apart that two objects need to be to be resolvable (still seen as two objects). It is:

$$\theta = 1.22\frac{\lambda}{b}$$

Where b is the diameter of the aperture (e.g. pupil) and θ is the angle, as shown in the diagram below:

Maximum resolution power (minimum angle) given by $\theta = 1.22\frac{\lambda}{b}$ where b is pupil diameter (or other lens aperture, such as microscope

Example T 9.18

Two black dots with centres exactly 2mm apart, are drawn on a piece of white paper. How far back from the eyes can the paper be moved until the two dots are seen as one? (assume that the wavelength of light is 550 nm and that the pupil diameter is 2.5mm).

- Note that the angle, θ, must be in radians

Note also that to solve the distance, you can either use $s = r\theta$ where r is distance from eyes to objects, s is distance between objects or you can use your own geometric solution based on the above triangle – the angles at the right end on above diagram can be assumed to be 90°.

Practical Importance of resolution

Microscope and telescopes must be able to resolve separate images (example: cell walls). To change the resolving power one can only change the aperture size or the wavelength of light used. To increase resolving power one could use shorter wavelengths but one is limited since too short becomes not visible. Electron microscopes can be used – high energy, low wavelength electrons can be detected by sensors thus making them visible.

Very large apertures can also be used. Hence good quality telescope lenses typically have very diameters, as do radio telescopes (can be over 50m!).

Reading a CD or DVD involves shining light off pits on the disk. Sensors detect the light received, after reflection, and the information is then used to create sound, music etc. To be able to distinguish information from one pit to another, the pits must be resolvable. To increase the amount of information on a disk, the pits need to be small and close together. However, if they are too close they become unresolvable. Applying the Rayleigh criterion we see that we can increase the resolution power (and therefore be able to minimize pit size) by using light of very short wavelength. Short wavelength laser beams are thus used.

Resolvance of diffraction gratings.

Diffraction gratings are used to split mixed light (e.g. white light) into its various constituent wavelengths. As we saw earlier, when monochromatic light passes through a diffraction grating it splits into bright and dark fringes (maxima and minima). The equation: $n\lambda = dsin\theta$ shows us that if λ increases then so does the separation angle. So for example red light will form a more spread out diffraction pattern than blue light since the former has a longer wavelength.

The ability of a diffraction grating to split two distinct wavelengths of light into two lines on a spectrum is the ability for the grating to resolve. Different diffraction gratings are rated according to their resolving power (also termed "Resolvance") R, where:

$$R = \frac{\lambda}{\Delta\lambda} = mn$$

where: λ is the average wavelength of the two wavelengths being (just) resolved,

               $\Delta\lambda$ the difference between the two wavelengths

               m, the order at which the lines are observed

               N, the total number of slits on the grating being illuminated.

Example T 9.19

A beam of mixed light is incident on a diffraction grating with 540 lines/mm such that it illuminates a circle of diameter 0.82cm

(a) Calculate the resolvance of the grating for this beam (i) for the first order (ii) for the second order

(b) Determine whether or not two wavelengths present; $502.132nm$ and $502.214nm$ will be resolved by the grating (i) in the first order (ii) in the second order

(c) Why is it pointless to refer to resolution of two wavelengths for the zeroth order?

(d) By referring to the diffraction pattern produced by a grating, explain the results of (b) above.

9.5   Doppler effect

❖ The Doppler effect for sound and light waves

Sound

When an ambulance speeds past a stationary observer, the note heard by the observer changes pitch. When approaching, the pitch is higher than usual and when moving away, the pitch is lower. This is an example of the Doppler Effect: when there is relative motion between a source of sound and an observer, the observed frequency is different from the emitted frequency. Hence a similar effect to that described above would be observed if an observer sped towards a stationary ambulance – the pitch would be greater as the observer approaches, and lower when departing.

To explain this, consider the wavefronts emitted from a sound source, marked ✲ and consider what the observers, marked 😐 and 😊, will hear (Note that sound waves travel much faster than observers!)

Situation 1 – Observers and source stationary:

Wavefronts are all emitted from same point and thus form concentric circles with equally spaced circumferences.

Both observers hear the sound at the same frequency as it is emitted.

Situation 2: Source moving towards *and away from*

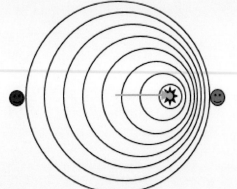

Source moves to right so centre of each circular wavefront keeps moving to right

The effect is for wavefronts to bunch-up on the right and to spread apart on the left

Hence 😊 hears a higher than usual frequency and hears 😐 a lower than usual frequency

Situation 3: Source stationary, both observers moving to right

(towards ☼ and ☻ away from ☼)

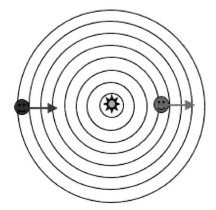

Observer ☻ moves towards the wavefronts so observes them more frequently

Observer ☺ moves away from the wavefronts (the ones on his right have already passed him) so observes them less frequently

Therefore the approaching observer hears sound of a higher frequency and the departing observer hears sound of a lower frequency.

The Doppler effect is also observed with light (ie electromagnetic waves) – this is why stars moving away from an observer show a "red shift" and stars moving towards an observer show a "blue shift" (red light is the lowest frequency in the visible range and blue/violet, the highest).

Doppler Effect Equations for Sound

We have 4 equations: two for a moving source and two for a moving observer, as follows:

$$f' = f\left(\frac{v}{v \pm u_s}\right) \quad moving\ source$$

$$(+\ for\ source\ moving\ away\ from\ observer, -for\ towards)$$

$$f' = f\left(\frac{v \pm u_o}{v}\right) \quad moving\ observer$$

$$(+\ for\ observer\ moving\ towards\ source, -for\ away)$$

Where:

$f' = frequency\ of\ sound\ heard\ by\ observer$

$f = frequency\ of\ sound\ emitted\ by\ source$

$v = speed\ of\ sound\ (in\ air)$

$u_s = speed\ of\ source$

$u_o = speed\ of\ observer$

When using these equations, always check that your observed frequency has changed as expected.

Example T 9.20

A car sounds its horn as it travels at a speed of $30ms^{-1}$ past Asaf and towards Buha, two people standing at the edge of a straight road. Describe, with calculations, the difference in the sound as observed by Asaf and by Buha. (The frequency of the sound emitted is 510Hz, and the speed of sound in air is 340ms⁻¹).

Doppler Equation for Electromagnetic Waves

$$\frac{\Delta f}{f} = \frac{\Delta\lambda}{\lambda} \approx \frac{v}{c}$$ where $\Delta f = change\ in\ frequency\ (frequency\ shift)$

$f = frequency\ of\ electromagnetic\ wave\ (light)emitted$

$\Delta\lambda = change\ in\ wavelength\ (wavelength\ shift)$

$\lambda = wavelength\ of\ electromagnetic\ wave\ (light)\ emitted$
$if\ the\ source\ and\ observer\ were\ stationary$

$v = relative\ velocity\ between\ source\ and\ observer$

$c = speed\ of\ light$

The equation is an approximation that can only be used when v is much less than c

---

Example T 9.21

An element in a star is known to emit radiation of wavelength 610nm. Light received at the Earth from the element in this star is analyzed as having a wavelength of 645nm. How fast is the star moving relative to the Earth and in what direction?

Examples of use of Doppler effect:

Blood flow rate: ultra-sound signals are directed into the body. The ultrasound machine can both emit and receive/detect the ultrasound signal. The machine can also measure the time delay and hence the depth of reflecting particle and can measure the frequency of the reflected signal. If the reflected signal has a higher frequency, then the reflecting particles must be moving towards the machine, and vice-versa for a lower frequency. The machine can thus calculate the speed of blood flow.

Police speed cameras also work on this principle but use microwaves or infrared radiation rather than ultrasound.

Topic 10: Fields

<u>Summary Checklist</u>

10.1	**Describing fields**
	Gravitational fields Electrostatic fields Electric potential and gravitational potential Field lines Equipotential surfaces
10.2	**Fields at work**
	Potential and potential energy Potential gradient Potential difference Escape speed Orbital motion, orbital speed and orbital energy Forces and inverse-square law behaviour

<u>Equations Provided (in IB databook) & Explanations</u>

$W = q\Delta V_e$	The **work done** (energy transferred) on a charged object by (or against) an electric field is equal to the product of the **charge** of the object and the **electric potential difference** through which the object moves.
$W = m\Delta V_g$	The **work done** (energy transferred) on an object by (or against) a gravitational field is equal to the product of the **mass** of the object and the **gravitational potential difference** through which the object moves.
$V_g = -\dfrac{GM}{r}$	The **gravitational potential** at a position in the vicinity of a point object (planet) is equal to the product of the **universal constant of gravitation** and the **mass** of the object (planet) divided by the **distance** from the object (this quantity is always negative in sign, with a maximum value of zero).
$V_e = \dfrac{kq}{r}$	The **electric potential** at a position in the vicinity of a point charged point object is equal to the product of Coulomb's constant and the **charge** of the object divided by the **distance** from the object (the sign of the charge gives the sign of the quantity).

Note: the "objects" referred to above (and on the next page) are assumed to be "point objects", although in reality they can be any shaped object and the distance is taken from the centre of the object. This deviation from ideality only becomes a problem if the shape of the object is quite non-spherical and distances are relatively small.

$$g = -\frac{\Delta V_g}{\Delta r}$$	The **gravitational field strength** at any given place is equal to the negative **rate of change of gravitational potential with distance (potential gradient)** in the direction of the field lines at that point. This is approximated as the **change in potential** between two points along a field line divided by the **distance** between the points.
$$E = -\frac{\Delta V_g}{\Delta r}$$	The **electric field strength** at any given place is equal to the negative **rate of change of electric potential with distance (potential gradient)** in the direction of the field lines at that point. This is approximated as the **change in potential** between two points along a field line divided by the **distance** between the points.
$$E_p = mV_g = -\frac{GMm}{r}$$	The **gravitational potential energy** of an object in the vicinity of a planet is equal to the product of its own **mass** and the **gravitational potential** at its position and also equal in magnitude to the product of the **universal constant of gravitation**, its **own mass** and the **mass** of the planet divided by the **distance** from the planet. The quantity is always negative, having a maximum value of zero.
$$E_p = qV_e = \frac{kq_1q_2}{r}$$	The **electric potential energy** of a charged object in the vicinity of another charged object is equal to the product of its own **charge** and the **electric potential** at its position and also equal to the product of **Coulomb's constant**, its own **charge** and the **charge** of the second object divided by the **distance** from the second object. The sign of the quantity is generated by correctly multiplying the signs of the two charges.
$$F_G = G\frac{m_1m_2}{r^2}$$	The **gravitational force** on either of two objects is equal to the product of the **universal constant of gravitation** and **the two masses** divided by the **square of the distance** between the two objects. These forces are always attractive.
$$F_E = k\frac{q_1q_2}{r^2}$$	The **electric force** on either of two charged objects is equal to the product of **Coulomb's constant** and **the two charges** divided by the **square of the distance** between the two objects. These forces may be attractive or repulsive depending on the signs of the two charges.
$$v_{esc} = \sqrt{\frac{2GM}{r}}$$	The **speed** necessary to give an object sufficient speed to escape (entirely) from or near to a planet is equal to the square root of the ratio of twice the product of the **universal constant of gravitation** and the **mass** of the planet to the distance to (the centre of) the planet. This assumes there are no resistive forces (air resistance).
$$v_{orbit} = \sqrt{\frac{GM}{r}}$$	The **speed** of an object in orbit around a planet required to maintain a stable orbit is equal to the square root of the ratio of the product of the **universal constant of gravitation** and the **mass** of the planet to the **distance** to the (centre of) the planet.

10.1   Describing Fields

A <u>field</u> is a region in space (a place) where an "object" experiences a <u>force</u> due to its presence in the field. The interaction between the object and the field causes the force on the object.

❖ Gravitational fields

A gravitational field is a place where an object with mass experiences a force

A gravitational field is produced by an object with mass.

❖ Electrostatic fields

An electrostatic field is a place where an object with charge experiences a force

A electrostatic field is produced by an object with charge.

❖ Field lines

Gravitational fields are described by field lines, which are the lines followed by objects with mass that are released from rest. Gravitational field lines point in the same direction as the gravitational force on an object in the field.

Electrostatic fields are also described by field lines, which are the lines followed by positively charged objects that are released from rest. Electrostatic field lines point in the same direction as the electrostatic force on a positively charged object in the field.

(Note: positively charged objects are chosen arbitrarily: negatively charged objects also obviously interact with a given field, with the force acting in the direction opposite to the direction of the field line).

Example T 10.1

The diagram below shows field lines in an electrostatic field. Describe the motion of an electron:

(a) Placed in the field at point X

(b) Ejected into the field, horizontally from the left, at Y.

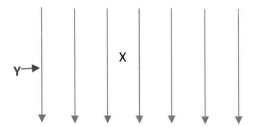

❖ Electric potential and gravitational potential

Potential is a quantity that describes the energy associated with a position in a field (electrostatic or gravitational). The gravitational potential of a position in a gravitational field increases as the distance from the mass (planet) causing the field increases.

Objects in regions of high gravitational potential will also have high gravitational potential energy and are able to fall to regions of lower potential, thus losing gravitational potential energy and gaining kinetic energy. Positively charged objects in regions of high electrostatic potential will also have high electric potential energy and are able to move to regions of lower potential, thus losing (electric) potential energy and gaining kinetic energy.

The calculation of the numerical quantity: potential will be discussed and explained in section 10.2

Example T 10.2

True or false? Discuss.

(a) Gravitational potential measures a property that an object with mass has:

(b) If a region in a field has a high gravitational potential, it means an object (with mass) will have a high gravitational potential energy

(c) If an electron has a high electric potential energy, it must be in a region of an electrostatic field that has a high electric potential

(d) If an object (mass or charge) in a field (electrostatic or gravitational) has a high potential energy it means that the field is able to do lots of work on the object to increase its kinetic energy by a large amount.

❖ Equipotential surfaces

For objects with mass

A gravitational equipotential ("equipotential surface") is a surface that describes a region where an object has equal gravitational potential energy at all points on the surface. Since gravitational potential energy is dependent on height, we logically find that equipotentials are spherical shells around planets.

The diagram below shows Earth with a set of equipotentials (red circles, that are actually 3D shells) and green field lines Five equipotentials are shown (the inner one, difficult to see, is at the surface of the earth). Potential has the symbol V (or V_g to show we are talking about gravitational rather than electric potential).

The calculation of potentials is dealt with in the second section of this chapter.

The diagram below is used to explain the qualitative nature of field lines and equipotentials for a typical planet – Earth – in this case.

Notes

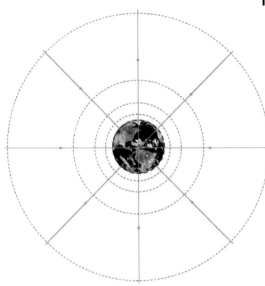

- Equipotential are always spherical 3D shells
- They are always perpendicular to field lines
- They always increase their spacing as you move further from the planet
- Like field lines, their spacing is an indication of field strength: the closer the spacing, the stronger the field
- Unlike field lines, they have no direction (hence, no arrows)
- Unlike equipotentials, field lines do not have the same field strength along each line.

Example T 10.3

True or false? Discuss

(a) Equipotentials for planets or point/spherical charged objects are lines forming concentric circles
(b) Equipotentials are surfaces where a point object would have the same potential energy everywhere on the surface
(c) Equipotentials surfaces are always at 90° to the surface of a planet or charged sphere
(d) If the spacing of equipotentials increases, this means that field strength has also increased in magnitude
(e) For spherical or point planets or charged objects, equipotential surfaces are always parallel to each other
(f) The direction of a given equipotential is dependent on the direction of the field line that it is perpendicular to
(g) The field strength at all points on a given equipotential is the same everywhere
(h) A field line shows a line with equal field strength along the line.

10.2   Fields at Work

Potential and potential energy

The potential energy of an object (with mass or charge, or both) is defined as the work done in bringing the object from infinity to the point where it is.

Notes

- Since objects with mass are always attracted to where they are, work is actually required to get them away – to infinity, so objects with mass always have negative gravitational potential energies.
- The electric potential energy of an object with (net) charge will depend on whether the field it is in is attractive or repulsive (attractive $\Rightarrow$ −, repulsive $\Rightarrow$ +)

Example T 10.4

True or false? Discuss

(a) The electric potential energy of a charge is the work done in moving it to infinity
(b) The maximum value of the gravitational potential energy of an object is zero
(c) The electric potential energy of a negative charge is negative, and of a positive charge, positive

The (gravitational) potential energy, E_p, of an object with mass due to its position in the field of a planet (or some other massive object) is given by:

$$E_p = -\frac{GMm}{r}$$

where: G is the constant of gravitation ($6.67 \times 10^{-11} Nm^2kg^{-2}$, *given in data booklet*)
M is the mass of the planet/other object with (considered to be a "point mass")
m is the mass of the object whose potential energy is to be calculated
r is the distance between (centres of) the planet and the object

Example T 10.5

(a) Calculate the approximate gravitational potential energy of a 56kg person standing on (i) the surface of the Earth (ii) standing on the surface of the moon given that the radius of the moon is about 1600km, the radius of the Earth; about 6400km, the mass of the moon; $7.3 \times 10^{22} kg$, and the mass of the Earth; $6.0 \times 10^{24} kg$
(b) Comment about what these values tell us:

The (electric) potential energy, E_p, of a charged object due to its position in the field of another point or spherical charged object is given by:

$$E_p = -\frac{kq_1q_2}{r}$$

where: k is the Coulomb constant ($8.99 \times 10^9 Nm^2C^{-2}$, *given in data booklet*)
q_1 is the charge of one of the charged objects (point/sphere)
q_2 is the charge of the other charged object (point/sphere)
r is the distance between (centres of) the two charged objects.

IBHL Physics Guide 2015

Example T 10.6

(a) Calculate the approximate electric potential energy of an electron which is about $10^{-9}m$ from a carbon-12 nucleus (containing 6 protons and 6 neutrons)
(b) Explain what this value tells us
(c) Explain how your answers to (a) and (b) would differ if we were talking about a proton at this position rather than an electron.

Potential measures a place rather than an object.

The <u>gravitational potential</u> (of a place) is defined to be the gravitational potential energy of an object <u>per unit mass</u> (i.e. per kilogram) at the position in question.

The <u>electric potential</u> (of a place) is defined to be the electric potential energy of a small positively charged object <u>per unit charge</u> (i.e. per coulomb) at the position in question.
Referring back to the definition of potential energy, this means that gravitational potential (of a place/position) is the work done per unit mass in bringing a small mass from infinity to that point and the electric potential is the work done per unit charge in bringing a small positive charge from infinity to that point.

Example T 10.7

Use the above definitions to determine whether the following quantities are positive or negative:
(a) the gravitational potential near to a point mass
(b) the electric potential near to a point positive charge
(c) the electric potential near to an electron.

Note: the electric potential inside a hollow, charged, conducting sphere is uniform everywhere inside the sphere and always the same as the potential at the surface of the sphere. The field strength inside such a sphere is always zero.

❖ Potential gradient

Potential gradient measures the rate at which potential changes: it is the change in potential difference per metre, measured perpendicularly to the equipotential surfaces (i.e. measured along a radius line with the planet/ point charge at the centre).

Potential gradient is written as: $\dfrac{\Delta V}{\Delta x}$

❖ Potential difference

Potential difference is the change in potential from one point to another.

Work is done whenever an object with mass moves through a gravitational field and this involves a change in gravitational potential or when an object with charge moves an electric field and this involves a change in electric potential.

In equation form:

$$W = m\Delta V_g$$

$$W = q\Delta V_e$$

Example T 10.8

An object with a mass of 65kg moves from a place which has a gravitational potential of $-45MJ/kg$ to another place which has a potential of $-37MJ/kg$. The distance moved by the object is 12,300km although the shortest distance (radius line distance) between the two equipotential surfaces is 1,800km.

(a) Calculate the potential difference between the two points
(b) Calculate the potential gradient between the two equipotentials containing the two points
(c) Calculate the work done in moving the object from one point to the other.

Further notes

- No work is done in moving an object along an equipotential surface
- No *net* work is done in moving an object from one point to another if the two points lie on the same equipotential surface (i.e. if both points have the same potential)

Example T 10.9

An electron moves from point A, one side of a helium nucleus (containing 2 protons, 2 neutrons) to point B, diametrically opposite point A (on the other side of the nucleus). It then moves to point C, which is closer to the nucleus and on the same side as point A.
Given that points A, B and C have potentials of $-1.8V$, $-2.6V$, $+1.2V$ respectively:

(a) Calculate the net work done on the electron in moving:
   (i) From A to B
   (ii) From B to C
   (iii) From A to C.
(b) Comment on the energy changes occurring during these movements.

Example T 10.10

A circuit is set up where a 6.0V battery is connected to a filament bulb:
(a) Calculate the work done by an electron as it moves through the bulb filament
(b) Calculate the work done by a number of electrons required to give a charge of 1C in passing through the bulb.

The connection between field strength and potential gradient

We know (and can show with the equation in topic 6) that the gravitational field strength in the region of the Earth's surface is 9.81N/kg. Consider an object with a mass of exactly 1kg.

If we raise it by 1m we can use the equation: $\Delta E_p = mg\Delta h$ to see that its GPE has increased by 9.81J

So, near to Earth's surface we find that the potential energy of objects increase by 9.81J/kg for every 1m increase in height. Hence, we say the potential gradient near to Earth's surface is 9.81J/kg. We can show that at any place on any planet, the field strength has the same magnitude as the potential gradient.

This is also the same for electric potential gradient and electric potential.

Hence:

$$g = -\frac{\Delta V_g}{\Delta r}$$

$$E = -\frac{\Delta V_g}{\Delta r}$$

The negative sign shows that direction of the field is opposite to the direction of increasing potential (So, for example, potential increases as you move away from the Earth's surface, but field strength decreases).

Example T 10.11

Consider a 2.0kg object near to the surface of the Earth (radius and mass given earlier):

(a) Calculate the increase in potential energy of the object when it is raised from where it is to a point 5m higher (using $\Delta E_p = mg\Delta h$ with $g = 9.81Nkg^{-1}$)

(b) What is the increase in potential from the point where the object started to the point where it finished (use $V_g = \frac{E_g}{m}$)?

(c) Calculate a value for the potential gradient between these two points?

The object is then raised further, to a potential which is another 8500J/kg higher:

(d) Calculate the additional GPE gained by the object

(e) Calculate the additional height gained by the object and state any assumptions made.

We could draw (or imagine) a set of equipotentials near to the Earth's surface. If we constructed them so that they were exactly 9.81J per kilogram apart, we would have spherical shells exactly 1 metre apart and parallel to each other.

We could also choose a set of equipotentials near to the Earth's surface that are 98.1J (per kilogram) apart. So, to increase the potential energy of 1kg by 98.1J, we would need to increase the height by 100m. This set of equipotentials would therefore be a set of parallel concentric shells that are 100m apart (so, the first would be a shell with a radius equal to Earth's radius; the second would be Earth's radius + 100m, and so on).

However, if we move a long way from the Earth, the field strength starts to weaken. We can no longer use the equation $\Delta E_p = mg\Delta h$ (at least not with the same g value) to calculate the increase in potential energy associated with the increase in height.

If we consider much greater heights, we find that a set of equipotentials increasing by a constant value, say 9.81MJ per kilogram are no longer equally spaced (over smaller distances they are not either, but they are to a very close approximation).

If we used $\Delta E_p = mg\Delta h$ to calculate the height increase associated with a potential energy increase of 9.81MJ for 1kg, we would find that the height increase would be 1000,000m (since $1kg \times 9.81N/kg \times 1000,000m = 9.81MJ$).

However, the 1kg object would actually need to be raised more than 1000,000m since as it moves away from the Earth, field strength weakens and it takes less energy to further increase the height by a set amount.

We therefore find that any given set of equipotentials (increasing in potential by a fixed amount) will actually be further spaced the further they are from the planet.

Example T 10.12

(a) Use the potential equation to find:

   (i) The potential at a point 5000km above the surface of the Earth (radius 6400km)
   (ii) The potential at a point 5001km above the surface of the Earth (radius 6400km)
   (iii) Using (i) and (ii) (store accurate values in calculator memory), find the approximate potential gradient at this position using $\frac{\Delta V_g}{\Delta r}$

(b) How could the accuracy of this approximation be improved?

(c) Use the field strength equation (in T6) to find the field strength 5000km above the surface of the Earth

(d) Discuss the two answers in (a) (iii) and (c).

Example T 10.13

A basic parallel plate capacitor is constructed from two parallel plates separated by 4.5mm and connected to positive and negative electrodes, as follows:

(a) What is the emf of the supply (assuming negligible internal resistance)?
(b) What is the magnitude of the potential gradient between the two plates?
(c) By considering the field strength between the plates, determine the force on an electron when placed between the plates
(d) Assuming that the electron is placed midway between the two plates and allowed to be deflected to the positive plate,
(i) calculate its acceleration
(ii) use the equations of motion (see T2) to determine its speed immediately before it strikes the positive plate
(iii) using the electron rest mass (from data booklet), calculate its kinetic energy at this instant
(iv) using the equation, $W = q\Delta V_e$, calculate the work done on the electron by the field
(v) explain why the last two answers are the same.

Note: for parallel plate capacitors such as the one shown above, the field strength between the plates is uniform and the equipotentials are parallel and equidistance from each other. Consider, again, the equipotentials for Earth. This time the actual values are shown (calculations for this come later)

This set of equipotentials has been chosen so that we start at the surface of the Earth, then reduce the potential by one fifth to get the next equipotential and so on. Distances from the centre of the Earth are shown in terms of Earth radii (R):

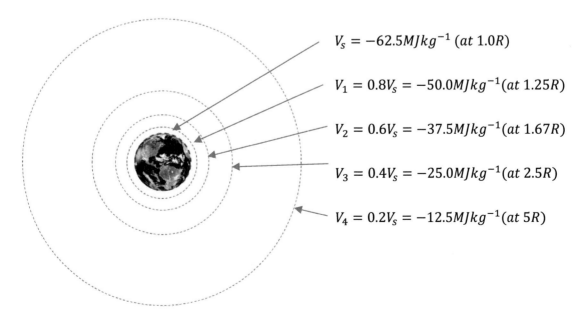

$V_s = -62.5 MJkg^{-1} \ (at \ 1.0R)$

$V_1 = 0.8V_s = -50.0 MJkg^{-1}(at \ 1.25R)$

$V_2 = 0.6V_s = -37.5 MJkg^{-1}(at \ 1.67R)$

$V_3 = 0.4V_s = -25.0 MJkg^{-1}(at \ 2.5R)$

$V_4 = 0.2V_s = -12.5 MJkg^{-1}(at \ 5R)$

Notes

- Gravitational potential is always negative, as are equipotentials, and they increase towards zero as height increases
- The height above the planet has to be infinite in order to reach zero potential (representing escape from the planet)
- Moving from one of the above equipotential surfaces to the next one requires the same energy. So we can move greater and greater distances with a given amount of energy as height increases.
- The work done in moving an object from one point to another is independent of the path taken: whichever path is taken, work done is equal to mass of object multiplied by change in potential from one point to the other ($\Delta E_p = W = m\Delta V_g$).
- So, in the above diagram it takes the same amount of energy to escape completely from Earth, from a starting point of 5 Earth radii away as it does to move from 2.5R to 5R.
- It takes no energy (work) to orbit a planet (the path followed would be an equipotential).

Example T 10.14

Use the above diagram to calculate the gain in kinetic energy of a 240kg space pod as it falls from a height of 1.5 radii above the surface of the Earth to 0.25 radius above the surface.

❖ Escape speed

Escape speed is the speed that an object requires in order to give it sufficient kinetic energy to completely escape from the surface of the planet where it is situated, assuming that the only force holding the object back is the gravitational attraction to the planet (i.e. no air resistance). Escape implies "to infinity".

Example T 10.15

By equating surface kinetic energy to the increase in gravitational energy (from surface value to infinity), derive the equation for escape speed:

$$v_{esc} = \sqrt{\frac{2GM}{r}}$$

Example T 10.16

Find the theoretical escape speed of an object:

(i)   On the moon
(ii)   On Earth

Radius of Earth = $6380\ km$

Radius of Moon = $1740\ km$

Mass of Earth = $6.0 \times 10^{24}\ kg$

❖ Orbital motion, orbital speed and orbital energy

An orbit is the path followed by an object around another object, or around a point. For example the moon is said to orbit the Earth.

We only consider circular orbits.

Objects moving in circles at constant speed are continually accelerating, because they are continually changing direction and therefore velocity. It can be shown that this acceleration is always directed towards the centre of the circle. This acceleration is called centripetal acceleration. There is therefore a resultant force required to keep a mass moving in a circle. This force is called centripetal force. This force can come from a variety of sources. For example, it can be the tension in a piece of string (with a mass on the end, twirling in a circle).

In the case of planets or satellites (such as moons – natural satellites) centripetal force is provided by the gravitational attraction between the planet and star (for planets orbiting stars), or between planets and satellites (for satellites orbiting planets).

Kepler's third law

This law describes the relationship between the time taken for a satellite to orbit another body and its average (mean) distance from the body. As the distance (orbit radius) increases it is not surprising that the orbit time also increases but the exact relationship is not immediately obvious.

The law states that the square of the time of revolution of a satellite (ie its period time, T) is proportional to the cube of the mean distance (r) from it.

$$\text{ie: } r^3 \propto T^2 \text{ or } \frac{r^3}{T^2} = \text{a constant}$$

Example T 10.17

If planet A has an average orbit radius twice that of B, by what factor is its orbit time period greater than that of planet B?

Example T 10.18

Given that Earth has an orbit time period about the sun of 1 year (3.16×10^7 seconds) and that Uranus has an orbit time period of 84.0 years, and that the mean distance from the Earth to the sun is 1.49×10^{11} metres, calculate an expected mean orbit radius for Uranus, and state this as a ratio to that for Earth.

Kepler's third law – derivation

An orbiting satellite can be assumed to be moving in an approximate circle. It therefore requires a force, called centripetal force, to maintain its path. The force is provided by the gravitational attraction between the satellite and the planet that it is orbiting. So centripetal force required = gravitational force provided. (If gravitational force is larger than centripetal force required, satellite would spiral into the planet, if is it smaller, satellite would spiral outwards into space).

gravitational force = centripetal force

$$\Rightarrow \frac{GMm}{r^2} = \frac{mv^2}{r} \Rightarrow v^2 = \frac{GM}{r}$$

(where m is mass of satellite; M is mass of planet, r is distance between centres)

Algebraically:

but, since speed is constant, $v = \dfrac{\text{distance}}{\text{time}} = \dfrac{2\pi r}{T}$

(if we take distance as one complete orbit, radius r, T = time period)

$$\left(\frac{2\pi r}{T}\right)^2 = \frac{GM}{r} \Rightarrow \frac{4\pi^2 r^2}{T^2} = \frac{GM}{r} \Rightarrow \frac{r^3}{T^2} = \frac{GM}{4\pi^2} \approx 1.01 \times 10^{13} \text{ (a constant)}$$

Therefore $\dfrac{r^3}{T^2}$ = constant

An interesting consequence of Kepler's third Law is the fact that geostationary satellites have to all be the same distance above the Earth. Since $r^3 \propto T^2$, it follows that at a certain distance from the Earth, a satellite will have a certain time period (orbit time). A geostationary satellite has to follow a point on the Earth, so it has to have a time period the same as the time taken for a single rotation of the Earth about its axis – ie. 1 day. Therefore we can easily calculate such a satellite's distance above the Earth.

Example T 10.19

Calculate the orbit height of an Earth geostationary satellite.

Satellite Energy

A satellite will have gravitational potential energy due to its position in a gravitational field, and kinetic energy due to its movement. Once it is in place, orbiting the planet, its total energy will remain constant – there is no resistance, since it will be out of the planet's atmosphere. It is therefore easy to deduce that if the orbit is not perfectly circular, then as it moves closer to the planet, its potential energy will decrease and therefore its kinetic energy will increase. As a satellite moves closer to a planet its speed therefore increases.

Satellite Energies – derivation
$E_k = \frac{1}{2}mv^2$, where m is mass of satellite and v, speed

but $\dfrac{mv^2}{r} = \dfrac{GMm}{r^2}$ (equating centripetal and gravitational forces, as earlier)

where M is mass of planet being orbited

$$\Rightarrow mv^2 = \frac{rGMm}{r^2} = \frac{GMm}{r} \Rightarrow \tfrac{1}{2}mv^2 = \tfrac{1}{2}\frac{GMm}{r} = \frac{GMm}{2r}$$

So, $E_k = \dfrac{GMm}{2r}$ (kinetic energy)

We already have that $E_p = -\dfrac{GMm}{r}$ so, $E_T = \dfrac{GMm}{2r} + -\dfrac{GMm}{r} = -\dfrac{GMm}{2r}$

Summary : $E_k = \dfrac{GMm}{2r}$, $E_p = -\dfrac{GMm}{r}$, $E_{Total} = -\dfrac{GMm}{2r}$

The following graph shows how kinetic energy, (gravitational) potential energy and total energy for a satellite vary as its distance (number of planet radii) from a planet increases.

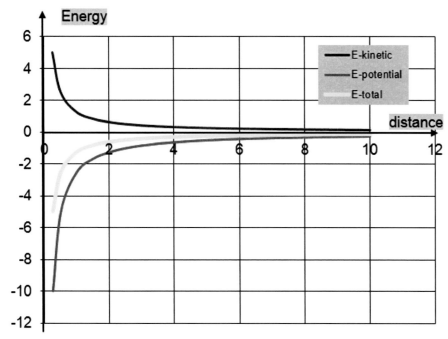

Notes

- Potential energy is always negative – its maximum value is zero when it escapes the planet's field.

- Total energy is always negative – this is because kinetic energy is never great enough to overcome (negative) potential energy – if it were, the satellite would escape the planet, and fly off into space with zero potential (out of the field) and positive kinetic energy (moving). The graph refers only to satellites in orbit, so total energy must be negative.

Example T 10.20

Calculate the kinetic energy, potential energy and total energy of a 650kg geostationary satellite. (Hint – use the distance from centre of Earth as calculated in Example T 10.19.

❖ Forces and inverse square law behaviour

As discussed in topic 6, the force between two masses is proportional to the product of the two masses and inversely proportional to the square of the distance between the two masses (taken to be point masses – all mass is assumed to act at the centre).

Charges are analogous: the force between two charges is proportional to the product of the two charges and inversely proportional to the square of the distance between the two charges (taken to be point charges – all charge is assumed to act at the centre)

Hence:

$$F = G\frac{m_1 m_2}{r^2}$$ where:

G is the universal constant of gravitation

m_1, m_2 are the values for the two masses

r is the distance between centres of the masses

(Newton's law of gravitation)

and

$$F = k\frac{q_1 q_2}{r^2}$$ where:

k is the coulomb constant

q_1, q_2 are the values for the two charges

r is the distance between centres of the charges

(Coulomb's law)

So the theory and mathematical treatment for the force between charges is almost identical to that for the force between masses (the only difference is that, for charges, the force can be attractive or repulsive but for masses the force is always attractive).

Example T 10.21

Find the forces involved and draw force diagrams for the following interactions:

(a) Two masses, 500kg and 1000kg, 5cm apart

(b) A proton and a helium 2+ ion, 1.2×10^{-12} m apart.

Topic 11: Electromagnetic Induction

Summary Checklist

11.1	Electromagnetic induction
	Electromotive force (emf) Magnetic flux and magnetic flux linkage Faraday's law of induction Lenz's law
11.2	**Power generation and transmission**
	Alternating current (ac) generators Average power and root mean square (rms) values of current and voltage Transformers Diode bridges Half-wave and full-wave rectification
11.3	**Capacitance**
	Capacitance Dielectric materials Capacitors in series and parallel Resistor-capacitor (RC) series circuits Time constant

Equations Provided (in IB databook) & Explanations

$\phi = BA\cos\theta$	The **flux** through a coil is equal to the product of its **area**, the **magnetic field strength** it is exposed to and the **angle** between the axis of the coil and the direction.
$\varepsilon = -N\dfrac{\Delta\phi}{\Delta t}$	The **emf** induced in a coil is equal in magnitude to the product of the **number of turns** in the coil and the **rate of change of flux** in the coil (or, emf magnitude is equal to the rate of change of flux linkage in the coil). (The negative sign shows that the direction of the induced emf opposes the change causing it).
$\varepsilon = Bvl$	The **emf** induced in a conducting rod moving through a magnetic field, perpendicular to the field is equal to the product of the **magnetic field strength**, the **speed** of the conductor and the **length** exposed to the field.
$\varepsilon = BvlN$	The emf induced in a square coil with one side entering a magnetic field, perpendicular to the field is equal to the product of the **magnetic field strength**, the **speed** of the conductor the **length** exposed to the field and **the number of turns** in the coil.
$I_{rms} = \dfrac{I_0}{\sqrt{2}}$	**Root mean square (alternating) current** through a device (with a.c. supply) is equal to the **peak current** divided by square root of 2.
$V_{rms} = \dfrac{V_0}{\sqrt{2}}$	The **root mean square voltage** across a device is equal to the **peak voltage** divided by square root of 2.

$$R = \frac{V_0}{I_0} = \frac{V_{rms}}{I_{rms}}$$	The **resistance** of a device connected to an a.c. supply is equal to the ratio of the **peak voltage** across the device to the **peak current** through the device. It is also equal to the ratio of the **root mean square voltage** to the **root mean square current**.
$$P_{max} = I_0 V_0$$	The **maximum power** of a device connected to an a.c. supply is equal to the product of the **peak current** through the device and **peak voltage** across the device.
$$\bar{P} = \frac{1}{2} I_0 V_0$$	The **average power** delivery of a device (over time) connected to an a.c. supply is equal to one half the product of the **peak current** through the device and the **peak voltage** across the device.
$$\frac{\varepsilon_p}{\varepsilon_s} = \frac{N_p}{N_s} = \frac{I_s}{I_p}$$	The ratio of **emf in the primary coil** of a transformer to the **emf induced in the secondary coil** is equal to the ratio of the **number of turns in the primary coil** to that in the **secondary coil** and is also equal to the ratio of **current induced in the secondary coil** to the **current in the primary coil** (can be peak or rms current, voltage).
$$C = \frac{q}{V}$$	The **capacitance** of a parallel plate capacitor is equal to the ratio of **charge** stored in the capacitor to the **potential difference** (voltage) applied across its plates.
$$C_{parallel} = C_1 + C_2 + \cdots$$	The combined **capacitance** of several capacitors in parallel to each other is equal to the **sum of their individual capacitances**
$$\frac{1}{C_{series}} = \frac{1}{C_1} + \frac{1}{C_2} + \cdots$$	The **reciprocal of the combined capacitance** of several capacitors in parallel to each other is equal to **the sum of the reciprocals of their individual capacitances**
$$C = \varepsilon \frac{A}{d}$$	The **capacitance** of a parallel plate capacitor is equal to the product of the **dielectric** of the material between the plates and the ratio of the **area** in common to the two plates to the **distance** between the plates.
$$E = \frac{1}{2} C V^2$$	The (electrical) **energy stored** in a charged capacitor is equal to one half the product of the **capacitance** of the capacitor and the square of the **voltage** applied across its plates.
$$\tau = RC$$	The **time constant** of a capacitor connected in series with a resistor is equal to the product of the **resistance** of the resistor and the **capacitance** of the capacitor.
$$q = q_0 e^{-\frac{t}{\tau}}$$	The **charge stored** in a capacitor connected to a resistive circuit after a given connection time is equal to the product of the **initial charge** in the capacitor and **Euler's number** (e) raised to the negative ratio of **connection time** and **time constant** of the capacitor.
$$I = I_0 e^{-\frac{t}{\tau}}$$	The **current through** a capacitor connected to a resistive circuit after a given connection time is equal to the product of the **initial current** in the capacitor and **Euler's number** (e) raised to the negative ratio of **connection time** and **time constant** of the capacitor.
$$V = V_0 e^{-\frac{t}{\tau}}$$	The **voltage** across a capacitor connected to a resistive circuit after a given connection time is equal to the product of the **initial voltage** across the capacitor and **Euler's number** (e) raised to the negative ratio of **connection time** and **time constant** of the capacitor.

11.1 Electromagnetic Induction

❖ Electromotive force (emf)

An emf is a potential difference resulting from a source of electrical power. For example, the internal voltage, or potential difference supplied by a battery is referred to as its emf.

In this topic, the potential difference resulting from a conductor moving through a magnetic field is referred to as emf. Emf or current is said to be induced in a conductor if there is relative motion between the conductor and a magnetic field.

This can happen in one of several ways:

- If the wire/coil moves
- If the magnet or electromagnet moves
- If the electromagnet is switched on or off or is alternating.

Note that emf (voltage) is only induced if field lines are "cut" by the wire/coil and that the rate of cutting determines the size of the emf induced.

Definition: Induced emf is the amount of mechanical energy converted into electrical energy per unit charge.

The unit of emf is the volt.

❖ Magnetic flux and magnetic flux linkage

Magnetic flux: a measure of the *amount* of field lines passing through an area, at right angles to that area can be increased by increasing the area or the concentration (flux density) of field lines and is maximum when field lines are at right angles to area (component at right angles to the area decreases as field lines deviate from this angle).

Think of magnetic flux as the number of field lines and think of magnetic flux density as field strength

To understand the definition of magnetic flux density, remember that field strength is defined as the force per unit current length on a wire placed perpendicularly to the magnetic field. So it is essentially defined in terms of force.

Definition: Magnetic Flux (Φ) (formula given in Data Book):

$$B = magnetic\ field\ strength - Tesla\ (T)$$
$$\Phi = BA\cos\theta, \quad where\ A = area - square\ metres$$
$$\theta = angle\ between\ flux\ and\ line\ normal\ to\ area$$

Unit: The weber (Wb) $1\,Wb = 1\,Tm^2$

Example T 11.1

A coil of wire measuring 7.5cm by 11.5cm is placed between the poles of a magnet as follows:

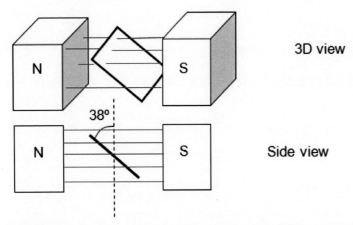

3D view

Side view

Find the magnetic flux passing through the coil, if the magnetic field between the poles of the magnet is 75mT

<u>Magnetic Flux Linkage</u>: is a measure of the number of turns of wire "linked" to (passing through) magnetic flux. Can be increased by increasing magnetic flux or number of turns of wire.

<u>Definition</u>: *Flux linkage = flux × number of turns = $\Phi \times N$*

Example T 11.2

If, in the previous example, the coil has 120 turns, find the flux linkage of the magnetic field through the coil.

Note: Flux linkage has the same units as flux

❖ Faraday's law of induction

Consider a wire moving through a uniform magnetic field, as follows:

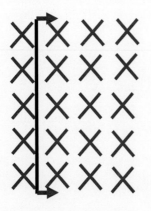

- The wire contains electrons free to move (free electrons).
- The movement of the wire from left to right means that the electrons within the wire also move from left to right.
- From previous work (chapter 5) we saw that charges moving within a magnetic field experience a force.
- The movement of the electrons, with the wire, from left to right, can be thought of as an electric current, from right to left (conventional)
- Using Fleming's Left Hand Rule (FLHR), we can predict a force on each electron down the wire (from top to bottom)
- This force on the electrons is the induced emf and a current will be induced in the wire, if allowed, from bottom to top (conventional current)

So, whenever a wire moves through a magnetic field, an emf is induced in the wire. The direction of the induced current can be determined using the method described above, but it is easier using Fleming's Right Hand Rule (FRHR).

❖ Fleming's right hand rule

The thumb and fingers of the *Right Hand* are arranged as follows:

ThuMb = Motion

Right Hand

First finger

= Field

SeCond finger = (Induced) Current

Notes

- If conductor moves through a magnetic field parallel to the field lines, no emf is induced; there must be a component of the field perpendicular to the movement of the conductor
- As a conductor moves through a magnetic field, field lines (flux) are said to be cut
- The size of the induced emf is dependent on the rate at which field lines are cut

---

Example T 11.3

An emf is induced across the wings of an aircraft as it takes off and continues on its flight-path. Give two reasons why the induced emf may be greater during the aircraft's flight-path than during take-off.

Faraday's law

"The induced emf (ε) in a circuit is equal to the rate of change of flux linkage through the circuit".

In symbols:

$$\varepsilon = -\frac{\Delta(N\Phi)}{\Delta t} = -N\frac{\Delta\Phi}{\Delta t} \ (given \ in \ data \ book)$$

Gradient of $N\Phi$ versus t graph.

Gradient of Φ versus t graph.

Notes

- The minus sign indicates that the emf is always induced so as to oppose the change causing it – see Lenz's law.
- Flux linkage changes if a wire or a coil moves through a magnetic field (area cut multiplied by turns) or if a coil spins or moves in a magnetic field.

Derivation: emf induced in a straight conductor moving through a uniform magnetic field

Faraday's law can be applied to a straight conductor moving through a uniform magnetic field at right angles to the field, as follows:

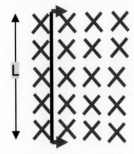

Let:

Strength of field = B

Area swept out per second = A

Length of wire in contact with field = L,

Wire move through field at speed v

$$\frac{\Delta \Phi}{\Delta t} = \frac{\Delta(BA)}{\Delta t} \ Since \ \Phi = BA\cos 90 = BA$$

$$B\frac{\Delta A}{\Delta t} \ (since \ B \ is \ constant)$$

$$= B\frac{L \times d}{\Delta t} \ (where \ d = distance \ moved)$$

$$= BL\frac{\Delta d}{\Delta t} \ (since \ L \ is \ constant)$$

$$= BLv \ \left(\frac{\Delta d}{\Delta t} = speed\right)$$

For a wire moving through a magnetic field, at speed v, at right angles to the field, strength B, the induced emf, ε, is given by:

$$\varepsilon = BLv$$

Example T 11.4

A horizontal steel rod of length 235mm is dropped horizontally through a magnetic field of strength 45mT and direction horizontal and at right angles to the rod. Find the size of the induced emf after (a) 0.1 second (b) 0.5 seconds, assuming g=10ms^{-2} and that the rod remains in the field as it drops, and remains horizontal.

Example T 11.5

A 35 turn rectangular coil, measuring 5.0cm by 8.5cm is moved through a uniform 35mT magnetic field at a speed of 10 cms^{-1}, as shown in the diagram below:

(a) Describe the motion of the electrons and the current in the coil as the coil:

(i) Begins to enter the magnetic field

(ii) Moves totally within the magnetic field

(iii) Begins to move out of the magnetic field, on the right hand side.

(b) Calculate the maximum current in the coil, assuming that the resistance of the coil is 0.01Ω and explain where the coil is in order to attain this maximum current

(c) Sketch a graph showing how the current on the bottom edge of the coil varies with distance moved by the coil, as it moves forward 30cm, as shown in the diagram.

❖ Lenz's law

"The direction of the induced current (or emf) is always so as to oppose the change causing it".

Lenz's law is an application of the principle of conservation of energy. If Lenz's law did not apply, energy could be made from nothing. Consider, for example, moving a bar magnet into a cylindrical coil, with the North end entering first, as follows:

- The magnet is pushed into the coil
- This movement is the change causing the induced current.
- The direction of the induced current will be so as to oppose this motion
- A north pole will therefore be induced on the right hand end of the coil (to repel the magnet)
- This corresponds to an anti-clockwise current (see diagram below magnet) as viewed from this end of the coil
- The current in the coil is therefore as indicated on the diagram.

Note that if a S pole was induced on the coil-end, the magnet would be attracted into the coil, so it would move faster into the coil, a greater induced current would result, and electrical energy would be created out of nothing. As it is, in order to induce current, a force has to be applied to overcome repulsion and work done against this force equals electrical energy induced in the coil. Energy is conserved.

Using similar arguments, as the coil is pulled out, an attractive S pole will be induced on the right hand end of the coil, and current will flow in the opposite direction. In many instances Lenz's law or FRHR can be used to predict the direction of the induced current. However, the Lenz's Law method is often simpler and easier to use.

Example T 11.6

A long straight wire is in the same plane as a rectangular loop of metallic wire. The straight wire carries a current, I as shown, and is moved towards the rectangular loop. Describe what happens to the loop of wire.

11.2   Power Generation and Transmission

❖ Alternating current (ac) generators

Electricity is generated by using a primary source of energy to turn turbines which in turn rotates coils of wire in magnetic fields. This form of electricity generation results in an alternating emf, that varies sinusoidally. Hence our domestic electricity is not dc (direct current) but alternating, with a frequency of 50 Hz (50 cycles per second) in the United Kingdom and many other countries.

To understand this, consider a simple ac generator:

The ac generator is very much like a motor, except that instead of current being fed into the coil and the coil interacting with the magnetic field and turning, the coil is made to turn through a magnetic field and this results in current being induced in the coil.

Consider the coil in its current position:

- If it is made to rotate clockwise (as viewed from in front of the page)
- The left hand side of the coil moves upwards
- Using FRHR, current is induced in the wire on this side into the page
- The right hand side of the coil moves downwards
- Using FRHR, current is induced in the wire on this side out of the page, towards the observer.
- The current through the bulb will be moving from right to left (←).

However, as the coil continues to rotate, the direction of the current changes. As it is moving at 90° from its current position, there will in fact be zero current induced in the coil. At this position, the wires (at top and bottom of coil, in this position) are not cutting field lines, but moving along them.

Consider the following end-on diagrams of the side of the coil moving through the magnetic flux:

The sides of the coil are represented by the marks (●). These wires are the ones that move through the magnetic field and where emf is induced. The size of the induced emf depends on the rate at which the flux is cut.

initial position	after 90°	after 180°	after 270°
flux cut rapidly	flux not being cut	flux cut rapidly	flux not being cut

As viewed from the front (generator diagram), current is always induced into the page. However, every 180°, the wires swap over the brush that they feed into. This results in a reversal of direction of current every 180°.

To show this, we can look at the relevant parts of the generator as it turns through 180°:

A current-time graph thus reveals the sinuisoidal emf (and current) that results in the coil: Time corresponds to angle of coil, since the coil rotates at a constant speed.

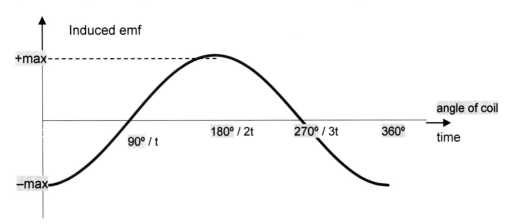

Note that the maximum flux change (rate of cutting flux) is when the coil is parallel to the field (and the flux linkage is zero at this point) – this may seem confusing, but refer to the four diagrams above and count how many field lines are cut in the top 45° sector of the coil's rotation path (≈ 0) and compare this with the number cut in a 45° sector at either the left or right of the centre of the circle ($\approx 3\ or\ 4$).

Note also that if the rotation frequency of the coil is doubled, the peaks on the above graph occur twice as often and the maximum (peak) emf is twice as high – so the graph will have twice the amplitude.

❖ Average power and root mean square (rms) values of current and voltage

a.c. and d.c electricity

Direct current (d.c.) is current that always flows in the same direction. Electrical supplies that produce d.c. current usually produce current that is not only in a constant direction, but also of a constant size.

For example, $3A\ d.c \Rightarrow$ current is a constant value of $3A$.

So what does $3A\ a.c$ mean?

To run many electrical appliances, either a.c. or d.c. electricity may be used. For example, a 60 watt light bulb appears to be identical in brightness whether run on a.c. or d.c. (as long as the correct voltage is used in both instances).

The problem is that the voltage of an a.c. supply varies from negative to zero to positive. One could quote the maximum positive voltage, as the voltage of an a.c. supply. If we do this, then compare running a bulb with 50V d.c. with 50V a.c. Clearly the 50V d.c. supply would supply a higher amount of energy to the bulb, since it remains at 50V, whilst the a.c. supply varies, producing a lower average rate of energy-supply, and resulting in a dimmer bulb.

We measure a.c. voltage and current by considering the average power delivery of such a supply.

Consider a supply that produces an alternating voltage, with maximum (peak) value, 2V. Suppose that this results in a current of peak value 1A. The current produced by a sinuisoidal a.c. voltage is also sinuisoidal, as long as the conductor is ohmic (in which case, $V \propto I$)

This is represented on the graph shown – the red line represents current and the green line; voltage.

The average current, if one wished to find it, is clearly zero, and the average voltage is zero. However, since *power = current × voltage* and *negative × negative = positive* , power is always positive. When the current and voltage as shown in the graph are multiplied together, the result is the blue line, representing power.

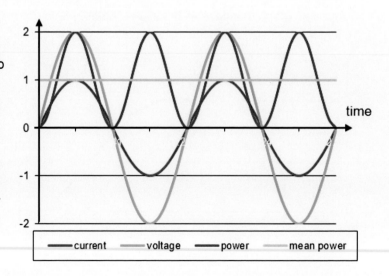

One can see intuitively from the graph that the average power is half peak (maximum) power, 1 watt, in this case. Maximum power is 2 watts, and minimum power is 0 watts, so power also varies. With mains appliances, voltage and current change direction so rapidly that the maximum and zero power are not observed – one does not see the bulb dim and brighten (in fact, the bulb would not have time to cool down). The average power is observed.

So average power of an a.c. supply is equal to half peak power. This leads us to the concept of root-mean-square current and voltage:

I'll start by defining the problem: imagine an a.c. circuit , of resistance R, that has a peak supply voltage equal to V_0 which results in a peak a.c. current of I_0 . We want to find the equivalent d.c. voltage and equivalent d.c. current that will deliver the same power as the a.c. circuit.

$power = current \times voltage$

$peak\ power(P_0) = peak\ current \times peak\ voltage = I_0 V_0$

$average\ power = \frac{1}{2}\ peak\ power = \frac{1}{2}(I_0 V_0)$

$But\ V = I \times R \Rightarrow V_0 = I_0 R \Rightarrow I_0 = \dfrac{V_0}{R}$

$\therefore average\ power = \frac{1}{2}(I_0(I_0 R)) = \frac{1}{2}I_0{}^2 R = \frac{1}{2}\left(\dfrac{V_0}{R}\right)V_0 = \frac{1}{2}\dfrac{V_0{}^2}{R}$

So we have four possible expressions for average power:

$average\ power = \frac{1}{2}P_0$

$average\ power = \frac{1}{2}(I_0 V_0)$

$average\ power = \frac{1}{2}I_0{}^2 R$

$average\ power = \frac{1}{2}\dfrac{V_0{}^2}{R}$

Now to find the d.c. voltage and current. Suppose the voltage required to produce the same power as the average power calculated above is V and the current, I

$Power = V \times I,\ but\ V = I \times R \ \therefore Power = (I \times R) \times I = I^2 R$

$or,\ I = \dfrac{V}{R} \ \therefore Power = V \times \dfrac{V}{R} = \dfrac{V^2}{R}$

Equating d.c. power to a.c. power, we get:

$$I^2 \cancel{R} = \tfrac{1}{2}I_0{}^2 \cancel{R} \Rightarrow I^2 = \tfrac{1}{2}I_0{}^2 \Rightarrow I = \sqrt{\tfrac{1}{2}I_0{}^2} = \dfrac{I_0}{\sqrt{2}}$$

$$and,\ \dfrac{V^2}{\cancel{R}} = \tfrac{1}{2}\dfrac{V_0{}^2}{\cancel{R}} \Rightarrow V^2 = \tfrac{1}{2}V_0{}^2 \Rightarrow V = \sqrt{\tfrac{1}{2}V_0{}^2} = \dfrac{V_0}{\sqrt{2}}$$

We call the d.c. voltage and current required to give the same power as the average (mean) power produced by peak voltage and current of $V_0\ and\ I_0$ the rms (root mean square) voltage and current, and give them the symbols, $V_{rms}\ and\ I_{rms}$

Hence: $I_{rms} = \dfrac{I_0}{\sqrt{2}}\ and\ V_{rms} = \dfrac{V_0}{\sqrt{2}}$

Example T 11.7

A bulb is usually powered with an a.c. supply with a peak emf of 12V. What d.c. voltage would be required to power the bulb with equal brightness?

Example T 11.8

In the U.K. mains electricity is alternating at 50Hz, and has rms voltage of 240V. What is the maximum voltage produced by a U.K mains supply?

Example T 11.9

An electric heater designed for use for the U.K. mains supply, (a.c, 240V,rms), is rated as 2000W.

(a) What is the rms current through the heating element when connected to the mains?

(b) What is the maximum current when connect to the mains?

(c) What is the resistance of the heating element?

(d) If the heater is run on an a.c. supply with a peak voltage of 240V, how will this affect the power of the heater?

❖ Transformers

Transformers make use of electromagnetic induction, but also allow voltage to be increased or decreased without significant loss of power. Transformers basically consist of 2 coils of wire. The first coil, called the primary coil, is powered by an a.c. electrical supply. Electro-motive-force (voltage) is induced in the other (secondary) coil. This induced voltage and current is caused by expanding or collapsing field lines caused by the changing current in the primary coil (supply is alternating). The field is therefore continually cut by wires in the secondary coil.

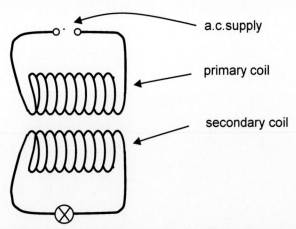

The voltage induced in the secondary coil depends on the turns in the primary and secondary coil and on the voltage across the primary coil so by altering the turns ratio for the two coils, the voltage in the secondary can be changed from that provided by the supply (in the primary coil).

Equation:

$$\frac{V_p}{V_s} = \frac{N_p}{N_s}, \text{ where,}$$

V_p = voltage in primary coil, V_s = voltage in secondary coil

N_p = turns in primary coil, N_s = turns in secondary coil

Transformers which increase the supply voltage are called **step up transformers** and those which reduce it are called **step down transformers**.

Example T 11.10

A transformer has been designed to convert voltage from 240V to 12V. If the secondary coil has 125 turns, how many turns should the primary coil have? (assume transformer is 100% efficient).

Obviously, if voltage is increased, there must be a decrease in current, (so that power is same in both coils) otherwise energy would be created.

If transformers are completely efficient in transferring energy from one coil to the other then,

Power used in primary coil   = power produced in secondary

$$\Rightarrow V_p I_p = V_s I_s$$

$$\Rightarrow \frac{V_p}{V_s} = \frac{I_s}{I_p}, \; and \; \frac{N_p}{N_s} = \frac{I_s}{I_p}$$

Ideal Transformer – construction

Transformers are never 100% efficient, but they are designed to be as close as possible to "ideal" (100% efficient). They are constructed, as follows:

Metallic core, to provide magnetic link and designed not to easily overheat.

Shape of core is important – should be continuous loop for good magnetic link.

Core is laminated (made of layers) to reduce eddy currents.

Coils are made of low resistance wire, to reduce power loss by heating.

Note: Eddy current are currents induced in the core which try to oppose and reduce the current induced in the wire. Laminating the core makes it difficult to conduct electricity without changing significantly the magnetic linkage properties of the core.

Power Transmission

Transformers are hugely useful in the National Grid system of electricity distribution, since the transfer of electricity is more efficient at high voltage and low current than at high current and low voltage (high current leads to a high level of energy loss by heating – as a consequence of resistance in the transporting wires).

Transformers are thus used to increase voltages at power stations for transport over the grid. They are employed again to decrease voltages to the appropriate level at the users end of the network. The power lost as heat in the wires is given by:

Power Loss = $I^2 R$ where I is the current and R is the total resistance of the wires

used.

Example T 11.11

A factory requires electrical energy at a rate of 20MW. If the resistance of the electricity cable used to transport electricity to the factory is $4.8\,\Omega$, calculate the power losses in the cable if the supply voltage is: (a) 100kV (b) 10kV.

The example demonstrates that increasing the current in the cable by a factor of 10 causes a 100-fold increase in power loss. Therefore using high voltage and low current electricity transmission (particularly over long distances) is far better than using low voltage and high current.

Risks and Concerns

Being in the presence of power lines or electrical appliances can cause the induction of tiny currents in the human body. However, it seems unlikely that low frequency magnetic fields such as these cause any harm to the human body.

❖ Diode bridges & half-wave and full-wave rectification

Diodes are devices which only allow current through in one direction (the "forwards" direction). They can be used to convert a.c. electricity into d.c.

Symbol for diode: as shown, allows current to flow from left to right

Consider the following 3 circuits, each of which can be connected to an oscilloscope (like an ammeter but can measure how current varies with time. The symbol for the oscilloscope is shown on the right hand side of the circuit, magnified for illustration purposes:

Unrectifiied a.c circuit

The oscilloscope shows that the current changes direction rapidly. The red (dashed) line shows the "zero line" so the current continually changes from negative to positive and so on.

Half-wave rectification

The diode stops any reverse current so the result is half-wave rectified d.c. in the circuit. Any current is effectively removed. Although the current is not steady (constant) it is classed as d.c.

Note this current is identical at all parts of the circuit (even the a.c. supply now has d.c.)

Full-wave rectification

The bridge of diodes now collects both positive and negative current and diverts it into the load circuit so that it all flows in the same direction. The negative parts of the current are effectively reversed. In the circuit shown, current will flow clockwise in the blue part of the circuit – from right to left through the load. The blue part of the circuit has d.c whilst the black, supply part, has a.c.

Adding a capacitor in parallel to the load will "smooth" the current through the load, since it discharges through the load as the current drops. The next section explains this.

Example T 11.12

The four arrangements below (A,B,C,D) show diodes connected to form squares. Which of them could be used as part of a full-wave rectification circuit and which two connections (1,2,3,4) should be connected to the a.c. supply and which two should be connected to the output (load)?

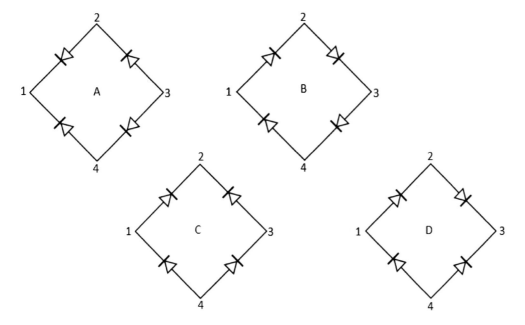

11.3   Capacitance

❖ Capacitance

A capacitor is a device which can be charged, using a d.c. supply, stored, then discharged.

Consider two plates made from metal and suspended so that they are not connected to each other or to the Earth. We'll refer to the left plate as A and the right as B, as follows:

This arrangement of two simple plates of disconnected metal forms a very simple parallel plate capacitor, just as it is!

It is called a capacitor because it has the ability to store charge: anything that stores charge has a capacitance, and the greater the capacitance the more charge it can store.

To charge the plates we need only connect each side to the terminals of a battery

Under normal circumstances, connecting the two plates to a battery would not result in anything happening – it would be an incomplete circuit. This is true: capacitors in circuits do effectively break the circuit. However, they still have the ability to store charge.

Suppose we connect A to the negative terminal of a cell and B to the positive terminal, as follows:

Usually we would say that, as the circuit is incomplete, no current will flow in the circuit.

However, what actually happens is a very small current flows for a very short time. As long as the plates are not too far apart, there will still be an electric field transmitted through the wires in the circuit and through the space.

Free electrons in the wire will therefore experience a force and move away from the negative terminal of the cell and towards the positive terminal. Electrons will therefore accumulate at A and there will be an excess of protons at B (since the electrons will be drawn towards the positive terminal of the cell. The blue arrows show the direction that the electrons move.

The capacitor is now charged. For example, if A has $-2C$ of charge, B will have $+2C$ of charge and we say the charge stored by the capacitor is $2C$.

If it is disconnected from the battery and reconnected to its own circuit, the capacitor will discharge, as follows:

If the switch is closed electrons move in an anticlockwise direction, away from A around the circuit, and towards B.

The amount of charge that can be stored (then released) in this way will be greater if the applied voltage is greater or if the spacing between the plates is smaller. It also depends on an electrical (dielectric) property of the material between the plates, known as the permittivity of the material (dealt with in next section).

Capacitance is thus defined as the charge stored per unit potential difference applied, per the following equation:

$$C = \frac{q}{V}$$

C is capacitance, measured in farads (F)
q is charge stored, measured in coulombs (C)
V is potential difference applied, in volts (V)

Example T 11.13

(a) How much charge is stored in a $6.0\mu F$ capacitor when $200V$ is applied?
(b) How many electrons have moved to the negative side of the capacitor when it is charged in this way?
(c) What must be the capacitance of a capacitor is it is to store twice the charge as the one in (a) when only 100V is applied?

❖ Dielectric materials

A dielectric material (or simply dielectric) is a material that resists an electric field. The electrical property that leads to this resistance is called permittivity.

The minimum possible resistance of the transmission of an electric field is that offered by a vacuum.

Thus: ε_0 – permittivity of free space, $\varepsilon_0 = 8.85 \times 10^{-12} C^2 N^{-1} m^{-2}$
ε – permittivity of a material, value depends on material
ε_r – relative permittivity (compared to that of a vacuum), For a vacuum, $\varepsilon_r = 1$.
$\varepsilon = \varepsilon_0 \times \varepsilon_r$
κ – dielectric constant (another word for relative permittivity), For a vacuum, $\kappa = 1$
For all materials, the dielectric constant/relative permittivity is greater than 1
For a conductor, there is no resistance to an electric field so $\varepsilon_r (= \kappa) = \infty$.

To understand how a dielectric resists an electric field, consider again a set of parallel plates with a potential difference applied across them (and, thus, with an electric field in the space):

With just a vacuum, the field is created by the charge separation between the two plates.

However, if a material is placed between the plates it will rearrange (the amount of rearrangement depending on the chemical composition and bonding within the material). Since all matter is made from protons and electrons (as well as neutrons), the rearrangement will be such that the positive will align towards the negative plate and the negative, towards the positive plate, as the following diagrams show:

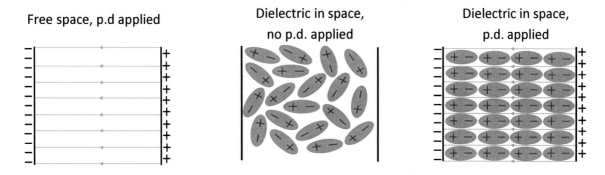

Free space, p.d applied   Dielectric in space,   Dielectric in space,
                                  no p.d. applied   p.d. applied

The green arrows show the electric field resulting from the charge separation/difference.

The dielectric effectively reduces the charge on each plate, since negative parts of the atoms/molecules are now in the proximity of the positively charged plate and the positive parts, in the proximity of the negatively charged plate. In order to maintain the field strength, a greater charge is required (which gives the capacitor a greater ability to store charge).

Consider the following two scenarios:

Scenario 1:

A capacitor with only free space between its plates is charged by applying a certain voltage. The voltage is then disconnected, so that the capacitor remains charged, but a dielectric is now inserted between the plates.

The charge at each plate is now reduced because, as described above, the charges within the dielectric cause partial neutralization so the potential difference across the plates will decrease.

There will therefore now be a greater charge stored per unit potential difference, so the capacitance has increased $\left(C = \frac{q}{V}, V \downarrow \Rightarrow C \uparrow \right)$.

Scenario 2:

A capacitor with only free space between its plates is charged by applying a certain voltage. The voltage is maintained and a dielectric is now inserted between the plates. To maintain the full potential difference across the plates, more current (and charge) must flow to increase the charge, making up for the neutralized charge caused by the dielectric. More charge is thus stored for the same applied p.d.

Once again, the capacitance has therefore increased $\left(C = \frac{q}{V}, q \uparrow \Rightarrow C \uparrow \right)$

If the area of the two plates is increased there will be more room for charge to accumulate, so capacitance will increase

If the distance between the two plates is decreased the field strength will increase and so the amount of charge on each plate, and therefore the capacitance, will increase.
In summary:

$$C = \varepsilon \frac{A}{d}$$

C – capacitance

ε – permittivity of dielectric

A – (common) area of plates

d – distance between plates

V – applied potential difference

Example T 11.14

A student makes a parallel plate capacitor by cutting two rectangles of aluminium foil, each 30cm wide and 45cm long. She separates the two sheets using a sheet of PVC (plastic) that she estimates has a thickness of 0.2mm. She lays the two sheets across each other as follows, ensuring that the PVC prevents any parts of the two aluminium sheets from touching one another.

She then connects the two sheets to a d.c power supply using two crocodile clips (shown in red) and also uses these connections to secure a charge sensor to the capacitor. She researches the value of the dielectric constant of PVC and finds it is 3.18

(a) Explain how she can determine the permittivity of PVC

(b) If she sets the power supply to 40V (the maximum it will go to), what value should the charge sensor give?

(c) Explain two reasons why it is important that the two sheets of aluminium are kept separate from each other at all points.

❖ Capacitors in series and parallel

Like resistors, capacitors may be combined to vary the overall capacitance of the circuit.

The equations that result (for series and parallel combinations) are the exact opposite of those used for resistance combinations.

Series

There are two important things to remember for capacitors in series:

(i) Adding resistors in series reduces the capacitance – think of several capacitors in series as a single capacitor: every time one is added, the distance increases.
(ii) Whatever the capacitances, the charge stored in each capacitor will be the same – for the same reason that current is the same at all points in a series circuit.

So, if we have many capacitors in series with each other and suppose a small pulse of current flows when all these are connected to a potential difference resulting in a number of electrons amounting to a charge of $-q$, moving to the right along the wire shown. Suppose also that the capacitors have capacitances C_1, C_2, etc and let the combined capacitance (if we treated the whole set as a single unit) be C_T.

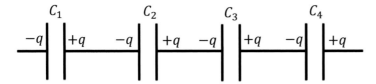

The total charge stored in the above combination is only q (not $4q$, as one might think). This is because it has only taken a magnitude of charge, q, to charge the unit above. If it is discharged, it will similarly only release charge of magnitude q. Electrons with a total charge $-q$ will move around the discharge circuit and through each of the above capacitors to the left. This will result in the charge at either side of each capacitor being 0.

In addition, since the supply voltage is split 4 ways when we have 4 capacitors in series, each capacitor will only be charged ¼ as much as it would have been were it connected to the same supply on its own.

Equation for combined capacitors in series

$$\frac{1}{C_T} = \frac{1}{C_1} + \frac{1}{C_2} + \cdots$$

Parallel

When multiple capacitors are placed in parallel to each other a single unit will be created which has a total capacitance equal to the sum of the individual ones. This is because adding capacitors in series is like increasing the plate area of a single capacitor

Hence, for capacitors in parallel:

$$C_T = C_1 + C_2 + \cdots.$$

Example T 11.15

Calculate the charge stored in (i) a 120pF capacitor (ii) a 240pF capacitor when each is connected to 18V.

Example T 11.16

(a) Calculate the combined capacitance of the two capacitors

(b) Calculate the total charge stored by the combination of the two capacitors

(c) Calculate q_1, q_2, q_3 and q_4, the charges on the plates of the two capacitors

(d) Calculate V_1 and V_2

A 120pF and a 240pF capacitor are connected in series with an 18V supply, as the diagram shows:

Example T 11.17

A 120pF and a 240pF capacitor are connected in parallel with an 18V supply, as the diagram shows:

(a) Calculate the combined capacitance of the two capacitors

(b) Calculate the total charge stored by the combination of the two capacitors

(c) Calculate V_1 and V_2

(d) Calculate q_1, q_2, q_3 and q_4, the charges on the plates of the two capacitors

❖ Resistor-capacitor (RC) series circuits & Time constant

We now consider the way that a capacitor charges and discharges through a resistor. The following circuit shows the set-up:

A capacitor does not instantaneously become charged or discharged.

Referring to the above diagrams:

Step 1: When switch S1 is closed, electrons move in a clockwise direction accumulating on the right hand plate building up negative charge and moving away from the left hand plate, building up positive charge. As charge builds up, a reverse voltage builds up across the capacitor (pushing electrons in opposite way to battery). This means that current gradually increases, so the rate of charge build up and potential difference across the capacitor plates also decreases. The flow of charge stops once the potential difference across the capacitor plates are equal to the emf of the battery (they oppose each other). At this point we have reached maximum capacitor charge and voltage and zero current.

Step 2: Opening switch S1 now separates the resistor/capacitor from the battery so that the lower circuit can be employed (by closing switch S2)

Step 3: When switch S2 is closed there is now no opposition to electron flow, so they move (initially at maximum rate) in a clockwise direction thus reducing the accumulation of negative charge (electrons) on the right hand plate and balancing the positive charge on the left hand plate. As charge decreases in this way voltage across the capacitor also decreases. This means that current gradually decreases, so the rate at which charge stored in and potential difference across the capacitor plates also decreases. The flow of charge stops once the potential difference across the capacitor plates diminish to zero – so we now have zero charge, voltage and current.

The rate at which the capacitor charges and discharges is dependent upon its capacitance and the resistance through which current flows. We can say, it depends upon the time constant, τ, where:

$$\tau = RC$$

However, it can be shown that the charging and discharging processes are both exponential (so in theory it takes an infinite time to fully charge or discharge a capacitor).

The time constant arbitrarily tells us the time taken for an uncharged capacitor to charge to approximately 63% of its maximum, or the time taken for a fully charged capacitor to discharge by approximately 37%.

❖ Equations

$\tau = RC$ Time constant for charge/discharge of capacitor through a resistor

$q = q_0 e^{-\frac{t}{\tau}}$ \qquad Charge stored in capacitor after discharge time t & initial charge q_0

$I = I_0 e^{-\frac{t}{\tau}}$ \qquad Discharge current from capacitor after time t, initial current I_0

$V = V_0 e^{-\frac{t}{\tau}}$ \qquad Voltage across capacitor after discharge time t & initial voltage V_0

$E = \frac{1}{2}CV^2$ \qquad The energy stored in a fully charged capacitor .

We are not given nor will be expected to use equations relating to charging a capacitor only discharge is required. However, we are expected to be able to qualitatively/graphically describe both the charge and discharge of a capacitor.

Example T 11.18

The following circuit shows a battery with an emf of 12V (negligible internal resistance) connected to a $4.7\mu F$ capacitor in series with an $82k\Omega$ resistor, as shown below.

(a) Explain how the capacitor can be charged and discharged and how the current through the resistor changes throughout the process

The capacitor is now fully charged using the circuit, and both switches left in the open position.

(b) How much charge is stored in the capacitor?

(c) How much energy is stored in the capacitor?

Switch S2 is now closed

(d) What is the initial current in the circuit

(e) What is the circuit current, voltage across the capacitor and charge stored in the capacitor after (i) 0.5s (ii) 1.0s.

Example T 11.19

An RC circuit like the one above is constructed and the capacitor charged, then immediately discharged. The same 12V supply is used, but a different capacitor and resistor. The following graph shows how the charge on the capacitor changes with time:

Use the graph and information provided (& any relevant equations) to find approximate values for:

(a) The time constant of the RC circuit, and hence the resistance of the resistor.

(b) The potential difference across the capacitor one time constant after commencement of discharge

(c) The initial capacitor current.

Charge/Discharge graphs comparison

R/Ω	C/mF	V/V
10	10	10

p.d. graph is same shape as charge graph since q=CV,
current changes direction on discharge

R/Ω	C/mF	V/V
10	10	20

doubling p.d. doubles charge and current (q=CV, I=V/R)
discharge rates don't stay the same ($\tau = RC$, not dependent on V)

R/Ω	C/mF	V/V
10	20	10

doubling capacitance doubles charge (q=CV)
and doubles discharge times ($\tau = RC$)

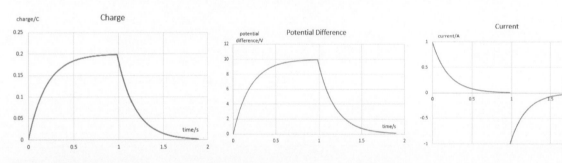

R/Ω	C/mF	V/V
20	10	10

doubling resistance halves current (I=V/R)
and doubles discharge times ($\tau = RC$)

Topic 12: Quantum and Nuclear Physics

Summary Checklist

12.1	The interaction of matter with radiation
	Photons The photoelectric effect Matter waves Pair production and pair annihilation Quantization of angular momentum in the Bohr model for hydrogen The wave function The uncertainty principle for energy and time and position and momentum Tunneling, potential barrier and factors affecting tunneling probability
12.2	Nuclear physics
	Rutherford scattering and nuclear radius Nuclear energy levels The neutrino The law of radioactive decay and the decay constant

Equations Provided (in IB databook) & Explanations

Equation	Explanation
$E = hf$	The **energy** of a wave-particle (photon) is equal to the product of **Planck's constant** and the **frequency** of the wave.
$E_{max} = hf - \phi$	The **maximum kinetic energy** of the photoelectrons emitted when radiation is shone on a material (surface) is equal to the difference between the **photon energy** (as previous) of the radiation and the **work function** of the material.
$E = -\dfrac{13.6}{n^2} eV$	The **atomic energy** of a hydrogen atom, in electron volts, is the negative ratio of 13.6 to the **square of the energy level** (shell) number (1,2,3,…).
$mvr = \dfrac{nh}{2\pi}$	The **angular momentum**, that is, the product of **mass**, **tangential speed** and **radius** of an atom has quanta equal to the ratio of the product of **quantum level number** and Planck's constant to 2π.
$P(r) = \|\psi\|^2 \Delta V$	The **probability** of finding an electron at a particular position (r) is equal to the product of square of the **wave-function amplitude** and the small **volume** occupying the position under consideration.
$\Delta x \Delta p \geq \dfrac{h}{4\pi}$	The product of the fractional uncertainty in **position** and the fractional uncertainty in **momentum** of a particle is at least as great as the ratio of Planck's constant to 4π.
$\Delta E \Delta t \geq \dfrac{h}{4\pi}$	The product of the fractional uncertainty in **energy** and the fractional uncertainty in **time** of an interaction is at least as great as the ratio of Planck's constant to 4π
$R = R_0 A^{1/3}$	The **radius** of a nucleus is equal to the product of the **Fermi radius** and the **nucleon number** of the nucleus raised to the power one third.

$$N = N_0 e^{-\lambda t}$$	The **number of radioactive nuclei** present in a sample is equal to the product of the **initial number of radioactive nuclei** and Euler's number raised to the power negative product of the **decay constant** (for this particular radioisotope) and the **time** elapsed.
$$A = \lambda N_0 e^{-\lambda t}$$	The **activity** of a radioisotope sample is equal to the product of the **decay constant**, the **initial number of radioactive nuclei** and Euler's number raised to the power negative product of the **decay constant** (for this particular radioisotope) and the **time** elapsed.
$$sin\theta \approx \frac{\lambda}{D}$$	When a beam of electrons or neutrons is directed towards stationary nuclei, the **sine of the angle** between the direction of the path of the beam and the first minimum formed is equal to the ratio of the **de Broglie wavelength** and the **diameter of the nuclei**.

12.1   The Interaction of Matter with Radiation

This topic discusses the fact that light can be considered as particles (each with a quantum of energy called a photon) and also as waves, where the energy is continuous and unbroken).

In more general terms, the so called "wave particle duality" considers that what we normally consider as waves (like light, X rays etc.) can behave like particles and what we usually consider as particles (like electrons) can behave like waves.

❖ Photons and the photoelectric effect

The photoelectric effect is one experimental effect that gives evidence for the particle behaviour of light.

The Photoelectric Effect

light shone onto metal surface

each electron ejected absorbs all the photon's energy, before being ejected

electrons ejected have maximum kinetic energy $= E_{k_{max}}$

energy of each photon $= hf$

difference between kinetic energy of electron and photon energy is the work needed to remove electrons from surface, ϕ

metal surface

This is the effect whereby if light is shone onto a metal surface, electrons (called photoelectrons) are emitted.

- Electrons are only emitted if the light is above a certain frequency, called the threshold frequency (ultra-violet light is needed for some metals)
- The value of this threshold frequency depends on the metal being used and, assuming the frequency of the light is above threshold frequency:

  - The number of photoelectrons emitted depends on the intensity of the light
  - The photoelectrons emitted have a range of kinetic energies, up to a certain maximum value (and this maximum kinetic energy depends on the metal used and the frequency of light).

This is explained by the fact that free electrons each require a certain amount of energy to escape from the surface of the metal. The minimum energy required to release an electron from a certain metal is called the work function (ϕ) of the metal

Further, it is necessary to consider that the light hitting the metal behaves as particles (photons), rather than continuous waves.

If light behaved as a wave then, even at low frequency the light would eventually provide enough energy to release an electron. This is not the case. Electrons are either emitted or they are not, and if they are emitted the emission is always instantaneous. So the energy comes from a particle of light. When a "light particle", (called a photon) hits an electron, it gives up all of its energy to the electron. The energy of each photon depends on the frequency of the light.

Each photon has energy given by the equation: $E = hf$

E is energy, in joules, h is Planck's constant, $6.63 \times 10^{-34} Js$ and f is the frequency of the light

If the work function of the metal is greater than the photon energy (ie. if light frequency is too low), then no photoelectrons will be emitted.

$$hf < \phi \Rightarrow no\ emission$$

The minimum frequency required to just release photons from the metal is called the threshold frequency - f_0, and the photon energy at this frequency is therefore equal to the work function of the metal.

$$hf_0 = \phi$$

If the frequency is above threshold frequency, then electrons (with kinetic energy) are emitted:

$$f > f_0 \Rightarrow hf > hf_0 \Rightarrow hf > \phi \Rightarrow emission\ results$$

Since an electron absorbs all of a photon's energy then if photon energy is greater than energy required to release electron (work function), electron will not only be released, but will have kinetic energy. The kinetic energy will be equal to the amount of energy provided by the photon, over and above the energy required to release it. This is the maximum kinetic energy of the electron since it may have required a little more energy than the work function, (work function is minimum energy required) to escape.

$$E_{k_{max}} = hf - \phi \Rightarrow hf = \phi + E_{k_{max}}$$

(This equation was derived by Einstein who explained the photoelectric effect, as above)

Example T 12.1

Light is shone onto a potassium surface and the frequency is gradually increased until, when the frequency is just above $5.38 \times 10^{14} Hz$, photoelectrons are emitted from the surface. The frequency is then increased to $5.95 \times 10^{14} Hz$.

(a) Calculate the work function of potassium, in electron volts.

(b) Calculate the maximum speed of the photoelectrons when the higher frequency light is applied.

❖ **Stopping Potential**

Energy of each photon = hf

Metal now connected to a power supply, and potential (voltage) gradually increased until photoelectrons just stop being emitted – voltage required = stopping potential, V_s

$$hf = hf_0 + eV_s$$

If the metal surface is given a positive charge it will attract back the electrons, making it more difficult for them to escape.

The energy required to "move" an electron through a potential difference of V volts, or put another way, the energy required to increase the potential of an electron by V volts, is given by the equation $W = qV$. Since we are talking about electrons, $q = e$ and therefore, $W = eV$.

So, in order to remove an electron from a metal surface with a (positive) potential, V, the energy of the photon has to be sufficient to overcome the work function of the metal and to increase the potential of the electron, for it to escape the attraction of the metal.

Conversely, if a frequency above threshold frequency is used, so that, under normal circumstances, electrons would escape with additional kinetic energy and the potential of the metal is gradually raised until photoelectric emission just stops, then this potential is called stopping potential – symbol V_s.

Summary:

Energy available by photons	$= hf$ (photon energy)
minimum energy required to release	
Electrons (no potential)	$= \phi$ (work function) $= hf_0$
Where minimum frequency of light	$= f_0$ (threshold frequency)
Additional energy available for E_k	$= hf - \phi = hf - hf_0$

If stopping potential, V_s applied to metal, $eV = hf - hf_0 \Rightarrow hf = hf_0 + eV_s$ and electrons can no longer escape (kinetic energy is reduced to zero).

❖ Equations

$E = hf$ ⁣ ⁣ to find photon energy of incident radiation (light)

$hf = \phi + E_{k\,max}$ ⁣ ⁣ to find kinetic energy of photoelectrons

$hf = hf_0 + eV_s$ ⁣ ⁣ to find stopping potential ($E_{k_{max}} = 0$)

This last equation tells us that stopping potential depends on the threshold frequency (which depends on the metal surface) and on the frequency of the incident radiation.

Example T 12.2

(a) Referring to T12(1), calculate the stopping potential for the potassium surface when the high frequency light is used.

(b) calculate the stopping potential when ultra-violet light, of wavelength 375nm is used as the incident radiation.

❖ Graphical

If, for a certain metal, the stopping potential is measured for various frequencies of incident radiation, the following graph is obtained:

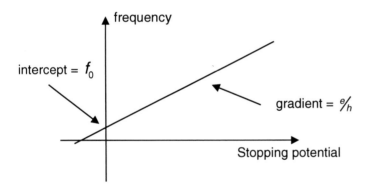

We get a straight line graph, because the relationship between stopping potential and frequency is linear – as shown by the equation:

$$hf = hf_0 + eV_s$$
$$\Rightarrow f = \frac{hf_0 + eV_s}{h} = f_0 + \tfrac{e}{h}V_s$$
$$\therefore f = \tfrac{e}{h}V_s + f_0$$

Comparing this with the formula of a general straight line, $y = mx + c$, we see that the gradient of the line is equal to $\tfrac{e}{h}$ and the y-axis intercept, f_0

❖ Matter waves

Wave-particle duality

We have seen that waves behave as particles (e.g. photoelectric effect). It has also been shown that what we usually consider to be particles show wave-like behaviour. The waves observed from classical particles (e.g. electrons) are referred to as matter waves.

de Broglie's Hypothesis

de Broglie suggested that all (moving) particles have a wave like nature. He linked the wavelength (so called de Broglie wavelength) with the momentum of the particle in the following equation:

$$\lambda = \frac{h}{p} \Rightarrow p = \frac{h}{\lambda} \text{, where, } \begin{array}{l} p = momentum \ of \ particle \\ h = Planck's \ constant \\ \lambda = (de \ Broglie) \ wavelength \ of \ particle \end{array}$$

(This equation is not provided in the current data booklet!).

❖ Validation

de Broglie's theory was tested by directing electrons at a thin metal foil. It was shown that the electrons were diffracted to form a pattern of rings on a screen – the same pattern as that produced by X-rays. This experiment was carried out by physicists Davisson and Germer in the early 1900s, who directed a beam of electrons towards a nickel crystal and measured the deflection angles of the scattered electrons.

The angles predicted using the diffraction equation: $n\lambda = d\sin\theta$ (topic 9) and calculating the de Broglie wavelength of the electrons were in close agreement with those found experimentally.

Electrons are usually considered as particles and diffraction is wave behaviour. Therefore de Broglie was proven right: particles do behave as waves.

Example T 12.3

Find the de Broglie wavelength of a beam of electrons moving at $2.5 \times 10^5 ms^{-1}$

Example T 12.4

Find the speed of electrons necessary for an electron beam to behave like x-rays, of frequency $3.4 \times 10^{18} Hz$

Example T 12.5

An electron beam is accelerated through a potential difference of 52V in an electron gun, and directed towards a nickel crystal. On the diffraction pattern produced by the scattered electrons, the first order maximum is found to be at 51° from the central maximum. Calculate the atomic spacing of the nickel crystal.

❖ Pair production and pair annihilation

Particle physics tells us that every particle has an antiparticle. Particles and their antiparticles always have equal mass and opposite charge. For example, the electron (e^-) and positron (e^+) form a particle-antiparticle pair.

When two particles come together they annihilate to form pure energy (in the form of two identical gamma-ray photons, moving in opposite directions). Conversely, a single gamma ray photon can change into a particle-antiparticle pair (a nucleus must also be in the vicinity of the photon for pair creation to occur, otherwise both energy and momentum would not be conserved)

The rest-masses of the pair (i.e. what particular particle-antiparticles we have) determines the frequency of the photon created, with annihilation and, conversely, the photon frequency determines the possible particle-antiparticles created.

For example, a proton-antiproton pair will annihilate to form a gamma ray photon with much higher frequency than an electron-positron pair (the latter pair have much lower rest masses).

Further, kinetic energies of the pair is also related to photon frequency.

This is all rationalized in terms of Einstein's mass-energy equivalence relation: $E = mc^2$

Thus, for pair creation:

Total energy equivalent of the particles & antiparticle and their combined kinetic energies will be equal to the total photon energy of the two gamma-ray photons.

And for annihilation:

Photon energy will be equal to sum of kinetic energies and energy equivalence of masses created.

To find energy equivalence of mass, use $E = mc^2$.

To find photon energies, use $E = hf$.

To find kinetic energies, use $E = \frac{1}{2}mv^2$.

Example T 12.6

Find the minimum frequency that a gamma-ray photon must be to form an electron-positron pair. Explain why the frequency must be at least this size.

Example T 12.7

Calculate the maximum wavelength of the two photons produced when a proton annihilates with its antiparticle. Comment on reasons for any deviations from your answer.

Example T 12.8

An electron moving at $2.2 \times 10^8 ms^{-1}$ strikes a stationary positron. Calculate the frequency of the two gamma-ray photons produced.

❖ Quantization of angular momentum in the Bohr model for hydrogen

In the early 20th century, physicist Neils Bohr tried to explain the absorption and emission spectra (see topic 7). The key idea was that the energy of the atom must only take certain values, and these values could be explained by considering atomic electron orbit radii, momentum and energy. Bohr this made the following postulates:

1. Orbits: The electron revolves around the proton in stable circular orbits

2. nh/(2π): The orbits/energy levels allowed are determined by the formula: angular momentum = nh/(2π):

3. Energy: Radiation of energy only occurs when an electron jumps from one shell (orbit, state) to another, not whilst in a shell

4. E=hf: The energy radiated or absorbed can be calculated from the frequency of radiation emitted or absorbed using the equation E=hf.

The Bohr Model could successfully be used to explain/predict:

Some of the wavelengths in the spectrum of atomic hydrogen.

The Bohr Model did not explain:

The fine structure of the spectrum of atomic hydrogen

The relative intensity of lines in the spectrum of atomic hydrogen.

For this topic, we consider in more detail the second postulate, that the angular momentum of the electrons is quantized. The theory links up, algebraically, with quantization of atomic energies and with the wave-particle duality.

Derivation of atomic radius and energy level formulae for hydrogen, from Bohr's angular momentum postulate

From Bohr's postulate:

Angular momentum of orbiting electrons $= \dfrac{nh}{2\pi}$

i.e. $mvr = \dfrac{nh}{2\pi}$

Note

The linear momentum of an object is the product of its mass and its velocity.

The angular momentum of an object moving in a circle is the product of its mass, the radius of the circle and the (tangential) speed of the object. Consider an electron moving in a circle:

The force required to hold the electron in a circle (centripetal force) is provided by the electrostatic attraction between the nucleus and the electron. Since the nucleus only contains a single proton (for a hydrogen atom), the charge is e $(1.6 \times 10^{-19} C)$.

Centripetal force $= \dfrac{mv^2}{r}$, Electrostatic force $= k\dfrac{q_1 q_2}{r^2} = k\dfrac{e^2}{r^2}$

Hence: $\dfrac{mv^2}{r} = \dfrac{ke^2}{r^2}$

To bring in Bohr's postulate, we do the following:

1. Multiply both sides by mr^3:
$$m^2v^2r^2 = ke^2mr \quad \Rightarrow \quad (mvr)^2 = ke^2mr$$

2. Substitute, using Bohr's postulate:
$$\left(\frac{nh}{2\pi}\right)^2 = ke^2mr$$

Now we make r the subject to give us the equation for quantized atomic radii (for the hydrogen atom). Thus:

$$r = \frac{n^2h^2}{4\pi^2ke^2m}, \quad where \; n = 1,2,3,4, \dots (shell \; number), m \; is \; mass \; of \; electron$$

To find a formula for atomic energy levels, we first consider the total energy of an orbiting satellite (in this case, an electron):

$$E_T = E_K + E_P$$

Now, $E_K = \frac{1}{2}mv^2$

But, as stated earlier, for an orbiting electron:
$$\frac{mv^2}{r} = \frac{ke^2}{r^2}$$

(multiplying both sides by $\frac{1}{2}r$)
$$\Rightarrow \frac{1}{2}mv^2 = \frac{ke^2}{2r}$$

So, $E_K = \frac{ke^2}{2r}$

And, according to field theory, $E_P = \frac{kq_1q_2}{r} = -\frac{ke^2}{r}$ (negative since we have an attractive field)

Hence: $E_T = \frac{ke^2}{2r} - \frac{ke^2}{r} = -\frac{ke^2}{2r}$

Finally, we substitute r into this equation, the quantized radii. Thus:

$$E_T = -\frac{ke^2}{2\left(\frac{n^2h^2}{4\pi^2ke^2m}\right)}$$

This simplifies to give:

$$E_T = -\frac{2\pi^2k^2e^4m}{n^2h^2} = -\frac{2\pi^2k^2e^4m}{n^2h^2} \cdot \frac{1}{n^2}$$

With the exception of n, all the other terms are constant, and we get: $E_T = \frac{-2.17\times10^{-18}}{n^2}$

This is the energy in joules. To convert to eV, we divide by 1.6×10^{-19}, giving $E = -\frac{13.6}{n^2}eV$

Hence, the energy of the orbiting electron in a hydrogen atom (i.e. the atomic energy of

a hydrogen atom) is given by:

$$E = -\frac{13.6}{n^2}eV$$

Example T 12.9

Use the above theory to predict the atomic radius of hydrogen:

(i) In its ground state (lowest energy state)

(ii) In its first excited state (when the electron has jumped into the n=2 level).

Example T 12.10

Calculate the wavelength of the photon that must be absorbed by atomic hydrogen in its ground state to give it sufficient energy for the electron to jump to its first excited state.

❖ The wave function

The wave function gives us an alternative model of the atom, provided by Erwin Schrodinger, some ten years after Bohr made his postulates. His (wave-function) equation takes several forms and is very complicated and advanced. We only require a basic familiarity and understanding at this level.

Schrodinger's model takes the following form:

- The atom is considered as a cloud of negative charge surrounding the nucleus
- The distribution of charge (ie electrons) is considered as a 3d standing wave ("wave-function")
- The mathematical equation, or the wave-function graph produced can be used to determine the probability of finding an electron at a particular position within an atom
- The probability of finding the electron at a particular location is proportional to the amplitude^2 of the standing wave at the given position.

This model can be used to explain the discreet energy levels in a hydrogen atom, as follows:

- The electron is considered as having a wavelength
- This electron – wave must fit certain boundary conditions (in the space it occupies)
- Only certain wavelengths are allowed (standing waves)
- The wavelength determines the energy.

Comparison: (the Schrödinger model unlike Bohr's)

> ➤ It does not have well defined orbits for the electrons

> ➤ It does not treat the electron as a localized particle: it assigns a probability wave

> ➤ It predicts the relative intensities of various spectral lines (based on probabilities).

Example T 12.11

(a) What does Schrodinger's wave-function enable us to determine?

(b) What are meant by boundary conditions in the development of the wave-function?

(c) What feature of the theoretical standing wave created within given boundary conditions gives us the probability of the electron being at a given position?

❖ The uncertainty principle for energy and time and position and momentum

Around about the same time as Schrodinger's Wave-Function, Werner Heisenberg, a German physicist, introduced the so called uncertainty principle.

"It is not possible to know simultaneously and with certainty both the momentum and the position or both the energy and the interaction time for a particle". This means, for example, that if a particle has a uniquely defined de Broglie wavelength, then its momentum is known precisely but all knowledge of its position is lost.

(If one thing is known with 100% certainty, the other is not known at all, as we decrease the certainty of one, we increase the certainty of the other).

It can be shown: $\Delta p \Delta x \geq \frac{h}{4\pi}$; $\Delta E \Delta t \geq \frac{h}{4\pi}$

Where Δp is the uncertainty in momentum, Δx; in position, ΔE; in energy and Δt; in interaction time and h is Planck's constant.

Example T 12.12

An electron is confined within a hydrogen atom. What is the approximate order of magnitude of the uncertainty in the momentum of the electron?

Example T 12.13

An electron-electron collision (electromagnetic interaction) results in the production of an intermediate (virtual) photon, with an energy of $34eV \pm 5\%$. Calculate the absolute uncertainty in the electromagnetic interaction time.

❖ Tunnelling, potential barrier and factors affecting tunnelling probability

Overview

(Quantum) tunneling is the process whereby quantum particles (such as protons & electrons) are able to overcome a (potential) barrier deemed impossible according to classical physics principles.

This occurrence can be explained by considering the particle concerned as a wave: to predict probabilities (and therefore numbers) of particles that are able to pass the barrier, the wave-function can be used.

As an analogy, consider a ball as the quantum particle and a hill as the potential barrier, as follows:

Quantum tunnelling ball & hill analogy

Suppose the ball is moving towards the hill with kinetic energy E_K.

Suppose that the ball has to increase in (gravitational) potential energy by ΔE_p to reach the top of the hill.

But suppose that $\Delta E_P > E_K$

According to classical physics (principle of conservation of energy) it is impossible for the ball to reach the other side of the hill: there is a zero probability of this happening.

The ball will simply be reflected back off the hill in the direction where it came from.

However, quantum physics explains (and predicts) that there is a chance of the ball "tunnelling" through the barrier (hill, in this case) and reaching the other side.

This analogy serves well to articulate quantum tunnelling, on a microscopic level, with very large numbers of particles involved.

The ball is analogous to the quantum particle (say a proton, or an electron).

The hill is analogous to the potential barrier (typically a potential difference, exerting a force on the quantum particle).

Now let us consider reality, with (for example) electrons and protons as quantum particles and potential differences as potential barriers.

This can be represented diagrammatically as follows:

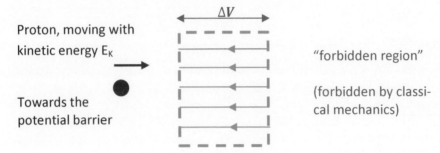

In order to move through the potential difference, ΔV, (shown with green field lines, repelling the proton), the proton must do work, $W = q\Delta V = e\Delta V$.

If $E_K > e\Delta V$ then this is possible according to classical physics (energy conservation).

If $E_K < e\Delta V$, then classical physics predicts that the proton cannot reach the other side of the potential difference: there is a zero probability of the proton passing through.

The potential difference is referred to as a potential barrier.

However, in reality if many protons are directed towards the barrier, some will get through. There is then a greater than zero probability of a proton tunnelling through the potential barrier.

The ball analogy helps us to rationalise and remember the three factors affecting the probability that a quantum particle will tunnel through the potential barrier:

- The greater the mass of the particle, the lower the probability

- The greater the "width" of the barrier the lower the probability

- The greater the energy difference between the energy of the particle and the energy required to "climb"/move through the barrier, the lower the probability.

Example T 12.14

Which of the following has the greatest probability of tunnelling:

(a) A proton and an electron with equal energies approach a potential barrier

(b) Electron a, with energy 12ev and electron b, with energy 15ev approach a potential barrier

(c) Electron a, with energy 12ev approaches a 15v potential barrier and electron b, with energy 6ev approaches a 9ev potential barrier.

(d) Two protons, a and b, have been accelerated through a potential difference of 21V. Proton A approaches a 25V potential barrier and proton B approaches a 28V potential barrier.

Further notes

- Wave-functions can be used to find probabilities of quantum particles at various positions either side of a potential barrier

- The continuity of a wave-function is an explanation of why the probability does not drop to zero at the barrier

- Due to reflections (of "unsuccessful quantum particles") and the interference of incoming matter-waves and reflected matter-waves a standing wave is set up on the "incident" side of the barrier: probability of quantum particle position on this side therefore oscillates high and low, as the amplitude of the standing wave varies along this position

- Throughout the "forbidden region" (see diagram on previous page), the wave-function has a minimum but non-zero amplitude, consistent with a non-zero probability of the quantum particle reaching this region.

12.2   Nuclear Physics

❖ Rutherford scattering and nuclear radius

One method of finding the approximate size of a nucleus is from the results of Gieger & Marsden's alpha scattering experiment – as described in Topic 7. Please review this experiment before continuing.

The information we need from this experiment is that if alpha particles are directed at a gold foil about $6.0 \times 10^{-7} m$ thick, one in 8000 are deflected by angles greater than 90°. As explained earlier, we assume that deflections of this kind can only occur when the alpha particle hits one of the gold nuclei and "bounces" back.

For this approximation we also need to know the approximate size of an atom. This can be found by accurate density measurements (details not required) and the diameter of an atom is found to be approximately $3.0 \times 10^{-10} m$.

Now let's define some variables:

Let:
D_N = diameter of a nucleus
D_A = diameter of an atom $(= 3 \times 10^{-10} m)$
A_N = cross sectional area of a nucleus
A_A = cross sectional area of an atom

We consider a single layer of the gold atoms:

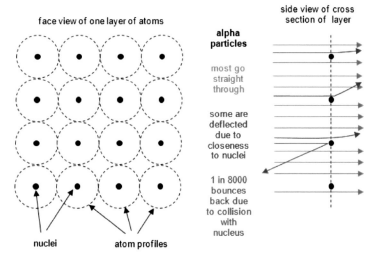

The number of layers, n, of gold atoms in the $0.6\,\mu m$ gold foil is equal to the thickness of the foil divided by the diameter of one atom.

$$n = \frac{6 \times 10^{-7}\,m}{3 \times 10^{-10}\,m} = 2000$$

Since alpha particles are only deflected by the gold nuclei (and not the rest of the atom), the proportion of alpha particles deflected by one layer of gold nuclei

$$= \frac{area\ of\ nuclei\ in\ one\ layer}{area\ of\ atoms\ in\ one\ layer} = \frac{cross\ sec\ tional\ area\ of\ a\ nucleus}{cross\ sec\ tional\ area\ of\ an\ atom}$$

(the atoms are so small that they effectively fill up all space in the layer)

$$= \frac{A_N}{A_A}$$

Hence, proportion of alpha particles deflected by 2000 layers (ie by the gold foil)

$$= 2000 \times \frac{A_N}{A_A}$$

but we know that the foil deflects 1 alpha particle in 8000

hence:
$$\frac{1}{8000} = 2000 \times \frac{A_N}{A_A}$$

$$\Rightarrow A_N = \frac{A_A}{8000 \times 2000}$$

$$\Rightarrow \pi \frac{D_N^2}{4} = \frac{\pi^{D_A^2}/_4}{8000 \times 2000} = \frac{\pi D_A^2}{4 \times 8000 \times 2000} \quad \left(\pi r^2 = \pi \frac{D^2}{4} \right)$$

$$\Rightarrow D_N^2 = \frac{D_A^2}{16000000}$$

But, $D_A = 3 \times 10^{-10}\,m \Rightarrow D_N^2 = \frac{(3 \times 10^{-10})^2}{16000000} = 5.63 \times 10^{-27}$

$$\Rightarrow D_N = \sqrt{5.63 \times 10^{-14}} = 7.5 \times 10^{-14}$$

So, using this method, we see that an approximation of the diameter of a nucleus is $7.5 \times 10^{-14}\,m$, and that an atom is about 10^4 times the size (diameter) of a nucleus.

<u>Nuclear radius approximation by closest distance of approach method</u>

The basic principle is linked to Rutherford's alpha particle scattering experiment: alpha particles are targeted towards gold nuclei. The kinetic energies of the incident alpha particles are increased until, at a certain point they no longer return. At this maximum kinetic energy it is assumed that the alpha particles are just stopped by the repulsion of the gold nucleus. We thus assume all the kinetic of a particular alpha particle has been converted into electric potential energy.

The electric potential energy of a charge q_1 distance d from a charge q_2 is given by the equation:

$$EPE = \frac{kq_1q_2}{d}$$

Hence, at closest distance r, where r is the radius of a (gold) nucleus : $\frac{1}{2}mv^2 = \frac{kq_1q_2}{r} \Rightarrow r = \frac{kq_1q_2}{E_K}$

Example T 12.15

Calculate the approximate radius of a gold nucleus (Z=79), given that the maximum initial kinetic energy of an alpha particle in order to observe its rebound is 4MeV.

Nuclear radius formula

For smaller nuclei that closest distance of approach method begins to fail, since the nuclear strong force (rather than the electrostatic force) becomes significant.

It has been shown (derivation/origin not required) that the following equation gives a reasonable approximation for nuclear diameter of a spherical nucleus:

$$R = R_0 A^{1/3}$$

where: R is the radius of the nucleus

R_0 is a constant, the Fermi radius, can be taken as the radius of a proton;

$(R_0 = 1.2 \times 10^{-15} m)$

A is the nucleon number of the nucleus (number of protons + neutrons)

Example T 12.16

(a) Estimate the nuclear radius of the Mg-24 (12n + 12p) nucleus using the closest distance of approach method, given that the maximum kinetic energy of alpha particles is 7.6MeV

(b) Use the nuclear radius formula ($R = R_0 A^{1/3}$) to find a second approximation

(c) Comment on any differences.

Note: the above equation can be used to show that all nuclei have the same density (and we also find that this gives us the density of a neutron star.

Estimation of nucleus diameter by diffraction

We can use the single slit diffraction formula (topic 9) to deduce the diameter of a nucleus.

Note, however, that instead of $\theta = \frac{\lambda}{b}$, we use $sin\theta = \frac{\lambda}{D}$
This is because the first formula uses the "small angle approximation", that is; for small angles $sin\theta \approx \theta$ since for basic single slit light diffraction the diffraction angles will be very small. However, with an incredibly small "slit" (i.e. a single nucleus), the diffraction angles become much larger, so we must use the more accurate $sin\theta$ version of the formula (θ can now be in degrees or radians).

Example T 12.17

A beam of neutrons, each with energy 78MeV, is directed at 90° towards a thin sheet of gold foil. Given that the diameter of a gold nucleus is approximately 14fm, calculate the expected deflection angle between the central maximum formed (directly in line with the beam) and the first minimum.

❖ Nuclear energy levels

Experimental evidence shows that nuclei, not only atoms, have certain energy levels. One example of such evidence is during radioactive decay processes. When a parent nucleus undergoes radioactive decay, the decay product, or daughter nucleus, is usually in an excited state. It relaxes back to its ground state by emitting a gamma-ray photon. The fact that a gamma ray photon is emitted is evidence for the fact that the nucleus can be in an excited, high energy state. Further, nuclei only emit photons of a certain frequency (and, therefore, energy) – the photon energy is observed to be characteristic of the nucleus. This is evidence for the fact that nuclei have well-defined energy levels, as do atoms (and their "electron shells"). So we nuclei, as well as atoms, have quantized energy levels.

The fact that alpha particles produced by the decay of a nucleus have discrete energies is evidence for the quantization of the nucleus. Similarly, gamma-ray spectra (resulting from nuclear emission) are discrete and not continuous is also consistent with this quantization. Beta particle emission (also from the nucleus) is not discrete: this is explained in the next section.

❖ The neutrino

The discovery of the neutrino comes about as a result of the study of radioactive decay reactions

Beta Decay

There are 3 types of beta decay: electron emission, positron emission and electron capture.
We only consider the first two.

Electron emission

Electron emission occurs when a nucleus is unstable due to the high neutron:proton ratio, and resulting instability. A neutron within the nucleus changes into a proton and an electron. The proton remains within the nucleus, but the electron is ejected, as a beta-particle. Symbol: $_{-1}^{0}e$ or $_{-1}^{0}\beta$ or β^-

---

Example T 12.18

Carbon-14 (atomic number, 6) decays to Nitrogen-14 (atomic, number, 7), with emission of another radiation. Explain this process by reference to the neutron: proton ratio of the two nuclei and write a nuclear reaction equation to illustrate it. Name the radiation emission.

Positron Emission

A positron is the anti-particle of an electron. It has the same mass and charge of an electron, except that the charge is positive and not negative. Symbol: : $_{1}^{0}e$ or $_{1}^{0}\beta$ or β^+.

Positron emission occurs when a nucleus is unstable due to the high proton: neutron ratio, and resulting instability. A proton within the nucleus changes into a neutron and a positron. The neutron remains within the nucleus, but the positron is ejected – as a positive beta-particle.

Example T 12.19

Complete the nuclear reaction equation by filling in the mass and atomic number for Neon. Explain why the decay has occurred and name the emission.

$$_{11}^{22}Na \rightarrow Ne + _{1}^{0}e$$

Notes

- There are no naturally occurring positron emitters – for example, sodium-22 is not naturally occurring – it must be created by another nuclear reaction.
- Stable neutron:proton ratios change as atomic number increases (neutron:proton ratios increase from 1:1 to a higher proportion of neutrons, as nuclei get bigger)

Neutrino / Antineutrino emission

The anti-neutrino is the anti-particle of the neutrino. They are both identical except that a neutrino has $spin = \frac{1}{2}$ and an antineutrino has $spin = -\frac{1}{2}$ (spin is an angular momentum characteristic of a particle).

They both:

- Have zero charge
- Have zero mass ($\approx \frac{1}{2000} \times mass\ of\ electron$)
- Travel at speed of light
- Do not interact with matter (pass straight through, unaffected)
- Have spin = $\pm \frac{1}{2}$ ($+\frac{1}{2}$ neutrino, $-\frac{1}{2}$ antineutrino).

Symbols: neutrino: $v\ or\ v_e$ antineutrino: $\bar{v}\ or\ \bar{v}_e$

Neutrino or antineutrino emission was shown to accompany beta-emission, since $\beta - particles$ are emitted with a range of energies. This is not be possible unless the decay also emits a third particle (in addition to the daughter nucleus and a beta-particle).

The diagrams on the next page helps to explain this:

Without third particle:

The process illustrated above is not possible because this kind of two-particle interaction, where momentum is conserved and energy of products is equal to a certain energy (according to the decay process) would mean that the beta particle would have to have a certain energy (not due to quantization of nucleus, but due to interaction energetics).

However, it is observed that beta-particles are emitted with a continuous range of values. This can only be possible if a third particle is also emitted, as follows:

Since there are an infinite number of ways to draw the three momentum vectors so that resultant momentum = zero (just like there are an infinite numbers of ways of drawing a triangle) it is now possible for the beta-particle emitted to have a range of energies – the neutrino (or antineutrino as shown here) can also have any energy (and momentum).

The full beta-particle decay processes are thus:

β^- decay   *parent* → *daughter* + *electron* (β^-) + *antineutrino* ($_0^0\bar{v}$)

β^+ decay   *parent* → *daughter* + *positron* (β^+) + *neutrino* ($_0^0 v$)

So, β^- decay always involves the emission of an antineutrino

and β^+ decay always involves the emission of a neutrino

Example T 12.20

Redo questions T 12.18 and T 12.19 showing the correct & full nuclear reaction in each case

The fact that beta decay in a given nuclear reaction involves a continuous spectrum (range) of energies is no longer inconsistent with the fact that the nucleus is quantized: if the energy of the neutrino/antineutrino is also taken into account, the sum of their energies is found to be quantized. This is consistent with alpha and gamma nuclear emission and thus with the idea that the nucleus is quantized.

❖ The law of radioactive decay and the decay constant

There are two versions of the decay law. The first states that the activity of a radioactive sample is proportional to the number of radioactive nuclei present. This is equivalent to saying that the rate of disintegration of a radioactive sample is proportional to the number of radioactive nuclei present. ie.

$$\frac{dN}{dt} \propto N$$, where, $N = number\ of\ radioactive\ nuclei\ at\ time,\ t$

$$\Rightarrow \frac{dN}{dt} = -\lambda N$$,where, $\lambda = radioactive\ decay\ constant$, $\frac{dN}{dt} = rate\ of\ decay$

The second form can be derived from the first by integration (not required for this course) and is as follows:

$$N_0 = number\ of\ radioactive\ nuclei\ present\ initially$$

$$N = N_0 e^{-\lambda t}$$, where, $N = number\ present\ at\ time,\ t$

$$\lambda = decay\ constant$$

Example T 12.21

A tree dies, and, on its death, contains 2.2×10^{19} atoms of carbon-14, which is radioactive and has a half life of 5730 years. The tree is then buried underground and remains for many years. Given that the decay constant for C−14 is $1.21 \times 10^{-4}\ years^{-1}$, calculate the number of radioactive atoms per gram remaining after (a) 2000 years (b) 5730 years

Note that the answer to part (b) does not need to involve the use of the decay law equation, since 5730 years is equal to a whole half-life – and the amount remaining after one half life is half what you had to start with.

Decay constant: definition

"A measure of the probability per unit time that a radioactive nuclide will decay in unit time"

Also note that it is the constant of proportionality between activity (see below) and number of radioactive particles

$$i.e.\ A = -\lambda N$$

Activity

Activity is the rate of decay: the number of disintegrations per second.

The unit of activity is the bequerel (Bq), where $1Bq = 1s^{-1}$

It can be shown that the activity of a given radioisotope is only dependent on the number of particles decaying (in accordance with the above equation: $A = -\lambda N$

It follows that the radioactive decay law, $N = N_0 e^{-\lambda t}$ can be re-written $A = A_0 e^{-\lambda t}$, or, replacing A_0 with λN_0, we get $A = \lambda N_0 e^{-\lambda t}$, where A_0 is the initial activity.

Relationship between decay constant and half life

$$N = N_0 e^{-\lambda t}$$

Initially (when $t = 0$) there are N_0 particles.

After one half life has elapsed, i.e. $t = T_{\frac{1}{2}}$, the number of particles will have reduced to $\frac{N_0}{2}$

Hence, $\qquad \frac{N_0}{2} = N_0 e^{-\lambda t}$

$$\Rightarrow \frac{1}{2} = e^{-\lambda T_{\frac{1}{2}}} \Rightarrow \ln\left(\frac{1}{2}\right) = -\lambda T_{\frac{1}{2}} \Rightarrow -\ln 2 = -\lambda T_{\frac{1}{2}} \Rightarrow T_{\frac{1}{2}} = \frac{\ln 2}{\lambda}$$

Example T 12.22

A sample of a radioactive isotope contains 10^{18} atoms initially and has a half life of 10 hours.

(a) Sketch a graph showing how the number of radioactive nuclei change for the first 30 hours

(b) Find the amount remaining after 10 hours

(c) Calculate the decay constant and hence find the amount remaining after 1 day.

Note that λ must be compatible with units of $T_{\frac{1}{2}}$ (convert $T_{\frac{1}{2}}$ to "same" units as λ)

Method for determining the half-life of an isotope

Short half life

Measure the activity due to the isotope (need to subtract background radiation activity) at a certain time.
Monitor the activity and determine how long it takes for the activity to reduce to 50% the initial activity (for more accurate results, repeat several times and take average)

Long half life / any half life

Monitor and measure activity due to the isotope (need to subtract background radiation activity) over a period of time.

The radioactive decay law equation, with numbers of nuclei replaced with activities can be manipulated as follows:

$A = A_0 e^{-\lambda t} \Leftrightarrow \ln A = \ln A_0 - \lambda t$
Compare: $\qquad\qquad$ y $\quad = \quad$ c + mx

Hence, a graph of $\ln A$ versus t is plotted.

The y – intercept gives A_0
Negative slope gives λ

Half-life can then be found using: $\qquad T_{\frac{1}{2}} = \frac{\ln 2}{\lambda}$

Solutions to Problems

Topic 1: Measurement and Uncertainties

Example T 1.1

Quantity	Usual Symbol	Unit	F/D	V/S
Mass	m	kg	F	S
Length	l	m	F	S
Time	t	s	F	S
Current	I	A	F	S
Temperature	T	K	F	S
Force	F	N	D	V
Displacement	s	m	F	V
Speed	v	ms^{-1}	D	S
Acceleration	a	ms^{-2}	D	V
Pressure	P	Pa	D	S
Potential difference	V	V	D	S
Resistance	R	Ω	D	S
Energy	E or Q	J	D	S
Charge	q	C	D	S
Velocity	v	ms^{-1}	D	V
Power	p	W	D	S
Frequency	f	Hz	D	S

Example T 1.2

Units of kWh   = units of power (kW) x units of time (h)
              = watts x seconds
              = joules/seconds x seconds
              = joules
(showing that the kWh is equivalent to the joule)
Units of the joule:

Using work = force x distance and force = mass x acceleration,

Units of J = N x m = (kg x m/s^2) x m = kgm^2s^{-2}

So the kWh and the joule are derived from the base units: kgm^2s^{-2}

Solutions to Problems

Example T 1.3

Conversion to S.I. units (using scientific notation)
$300 \times 10^{-9} m = 3 \times 10^{-7} m$
$0.6 \times 10^{-6} s = 6 \times 10^{-7} s$
$500 \times 10^{-3} V = 0.5 V$
$0.3 \times 10^{-2} m = 3 \times 10^{-3} m$
$101 \times 10^{3} Pa = 1.01 \times 10^{5} Pa$
$23.4 \times 10^{6} N = 2.34 \times 10^{7} N$

Example T 1.4

(a) 0.05s
(b) 0.11 ($\frac{1}{9}$)
(c) 11.1%
(d) $0.45s \pm 0.05s$
(e) $0.45s \pm 11.1\%$

Example T 1.5

(a) (i) 6.25% (6.3%, should be 2sf)
(ii) 12.5% (13%, 2sf)
(iii) $3.1m \pm 0.4m$

(b) (i) $3.14m \pm 4cm = 3.14m \pm 0.04m$
(ii) 1.3%
(iii) $9.8ms^{-2} \pm 13.8\% = 9.8ms^{-2} \pm 1.4ms^{-2}$

Note: the absolute uncertainty should never be quoted in a lab write-up or exam to more decimal places that the measured value – so the 1.4% should not be written as 1.35%

Also note that the significant figures quoted in a calculated value should not be greater than the least significant figure accuracy of the measurements used in the calculation.

Example T 1.6

(i) $50cm^3 \pm 6cm^3$

(ii)   12%

(iii)   4%

(iv) $3.68cm \pm 0.15cm$

(v) $\frac{(560-120)g}{(48-10)cm^3} = 11.6gcm^{-3}, \; mass = 11.6r^3$ (note that intercept is taken to be zero)

(vi)   Max slope = $\frac{(600-300)g}{(44-22)cm^3} = 13.6gcm^{-3}$, Min. slope = $\frac{(520-80)g}{(48-6)cm^3} = 10.5gcm^{-3}$

(vii) $Mass/g = (12.1 \pm 1.6) \times radius^3/cm^3 + (10 \pm 10)$

       (Note that here the average slope is taken to be (max+min)/2 and uncertainty in slope is taken to be (max-min)/2. The uncertainty in y-intercept is judged to be $\pm 10g$

(viii)   Percentage uncertainty in slope = 13%

       Slope = $\frac{4}{3}\pi\rho$ so $\rho = \frac{3\times slope}{4\pi} = 2.9gcm^{-3} \pm 13\% = 2.9gcm^{-3} \pm 0.4gcm^{-3}$

Example T 1.7

(a)

By scale drawing the length of the resultant vector is 9.2N (to 2 sig. figs) and its direction is 12.3° from the horizontal.

Note that you are not expected to get the exact answer, but are expected to draw a neat, accurate scale drawing and get an answer close to the correct value.

(b)

Weight = 25x9.81N =245N

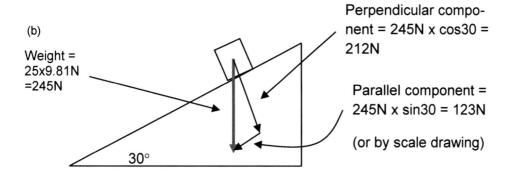

Perpendicular component = 245N x cos30 = 212N

Parallel component = 245N x sin30 = 123N

(or by scale drawing)

(c)   The resultant *speed* is the *length* of vector that is the vector sum of the two component velocities (speeds & directions) given.

By scale drawing (or using Pythagorus' theorem), length of resultant velocity vector is 3.5ms⁻¹

Resultant speed = 3.5ms⁻¹ (2 sig figs)

Topic 2: Mechanics

Example T 2.1

(a) $11ms^{-1}$

(b) $6.9ms^{-1}\ north$

(c) After 1s: speed = 11m/s, velocity = 1m/s in a direction given by the tangent to the circle at that point (the direction at which it is traveling)

(d) Yes, velocity is constantly changing since direction Is constantly changing

Example T 2.2

graph	displacement		velocity		acceleration	
	sign	change	sign	change	sign	change
A	+	C	0	C	0	C
B	+	↑	+	C	0	C
C	+	↑	+	↑	+	cannot tell – can only tell that velocity is inc
D	+	↓	–	C	0	C
E	–	↑	+	C	0	C
F	+	↑	+	C	0	C
G	+	↑	+	↑	+	C
H	+	↑	+	↑	+	↑
I	+	↑	+	↓	–	C
J	–	↓	–	↑	+	C
K	+	↑	+	↑	+	C
L	+	↑	+	↑	+	↑
M	+	↑	+	↑	+	↑
N	+	↑	+	↑	+	↓
O	–	↓	-	↓	–	↑

Example T 2.3

$acceleration = gradient$

$$= \frac{(v-u)}{t} \quad \Rightarrow a = \frac{(v-u)}{t} \Rightarrow at = v - u \Rightarrow v = u + at$$

$Equation\,1$: $\quad v = u + at$

$displacement = area\ under\ graph = \frac{1}{2}(u+v) \times t \Rightarrow s = \frac{(u+v)}{2}t$

$Equation\,2$: $\quad s = \frac{(u+v)}{2}t$

Eliminate v from Equation 1 and 2 (substitute (1) into (2)):

$$s = \frac{(u + (u + at))}{2}t = \frac{(2u + at)}{2}t = (u + \tfrac{1}{2}at)t = ut + \tfrac{1}{2}at^2$$

$\therefore$

$Equation\,3$: $\quad s = ut + \tfrac{1}{2}at^2$

Eliminate t from Equation 1 and 2:

from (1): $\quad t = \frac{(v-u)}{a}$

from (2): $\quad s = ut + \tfrac{1}{2}at^2 = u\left(\frac{(v-u)}{a}\right) + \tfrac{1}{2}a\left(\frac{(v-u)}{a}\right)^2$

$$= \frac{uv - u^2}{a} + \frac{(v^2 - 2uv + u^2)}{2a} = \frac{(2uv - 2u^2 + v^2 - 2uv + u^2)}{2a} = \frac{(v^2 - u^2)}{2a}$$

$$\Rightarrow s = \frac{(v^2 - u^2)}{2a} \Rightarrow 2as = v^2 - u^2 \Rightarrow 2as + u^2 = v^2$$

$\therefore Equation\,4$: $\quad v^2 = u^2 + 2as$

Example T 2.4

(a) 31.9m

(b) 5.1s

Example T 2.5

Range = 8.1m Speed = 13ms^{-1} (12.7ms^{-1}). Assumptions: air resistance is negligible, ground is horizontal

---

Example T 2.6

Optimum angle is 45° to the horizontal (assuming ball is projected on horizontal ground)

Example T 2.7

(a) (i) Height above ground = 28m

(ii) It hits the green building 2m from the left edge

(iii) It hits the green building at a speed of 16 ms^{-1}.

(b) The ball is projected at 7.84 ms^{-1}

Example T 2.8

Of course the iron ball would hit the ground first! However, if air resistance is ignored the only force acting is the weight of the objects and both objects would have equal accelerations, and so would hit the ground at the same time.

In reality air resistance is significant (compared to downward force – weight) in the case of low density objects so the equations of motion do not apply.

Not only is it more complicated in such cases to find the resultant force acting on objects, but air resistance increases as speed increases so acceleration is not uniform. The equations of motion therefore cannot be used to accurately determine the motion of falling objects under the influence of significant air resistance

Example T 2.9

(a) Air resistance increases, since air resistance increases as speed increases
(b) Acceleration decreases since it is decreases due to air resistance
(c) Velocity increases until acceleration drops to zero. At this point, the velocity has reached a maximum (terminal velocity) and will remain unchanged until the ball strikes the ground.

Example T 2.10

1) Woman on the floor

Note that these forces are equal (in size) and opposite (in direction).

2) Man falling through the air, ignore air resistance

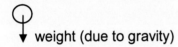

3) A mass sliding down frictionless slope

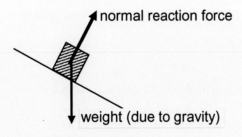

Note that the resultant of these two forces is a force parallel to the slope (acting down the slope) so the lengths should ideally correspond to this.

4) parachutist falling at terminal speed

Note that these forces are equal (in size) and opposite (in direction) since acceleration = 0

Example T 2.11

The resultant force is zero since acceleration is zero.

Example T 2.12

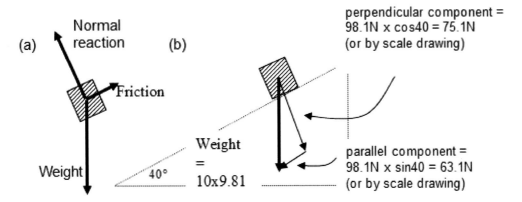

(a) Normal reaction, Friction, Weight

(b) Weight = 10x9.81, 40°

perpendicular component =
98.1N x cos40 = 75.1N
(or by scale drawing)

parallel component =
98.1N x sin40 = 63.1N
(or by scale drawing)

(c) The three forces shown on the free-body diagram must all add up (vectorially) to zero (since the mass is motionless and therefore has zero acceleration). Normal reaction cancels component of weight that is perpendicular to slope, and friction cancels component of weight parallel to slope. Therefore, frictional force = 63.1N, acting parallel to the slope, upwards

Example T 2.13

Motion	Displacement	Velocity	Acceleration	Force
Immediately after thrown	0/+	+	−	−
Half - way up	+	+	−	−
At highest point	+	0	−	−
Half - way down	+	−	−	−
just before hits ground	0/+	−	−	−

Example T 2.14

Resultant force = 63.1N
Acceleration = 6.31ms^{-2}

Example T 2.15

position A   ↓   downwards: weight

position B   ·   zero: weight = spring force

position C   ↑   upwards: spring force > weight

Example T 2.16

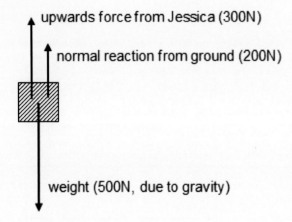

upwards force from Jessica (300N)

normal reaction from ground (200N)

weight (500N, due to gravity)

Note that since object is not accelerating, resultant force on object = 0

Pairs of equal & opposite forces:

300N applied on object, by Jessica
300N applied on Jessica, by object

200N applied on object, by ground
200N applied on ground, by object

500N applied on object, by Earth
500N applied on Earth, by object

Example T 2.17

(a) 0.37 (b) 0.25 (c) $2.5ms^{-2}$ (d) $3.4N$ $(2sf)$ (e) 20°   (f) $4.0N$

Example T 2.18

(a) $2.70N \pm 0.20N$

(b)   Must be a straight line passing through all error bars

(c) $gradient = \frac{rise}{run} = \frac{3.1N}{12.5N} =$ 0.248 $(0.25\ to\ 2sf)$ $(0.23\ to\ 0.27$ would be acceptable)

(d)   This number represents the coefficient of static friction, μ_s

(e) $F_{s(max)} = \mu_s R = (0.248)(20) =$ $4.96N$ $(5.0N\ to\ 2sf)$

Example T 2.19	(a) 0.42J	(b) $3.6ms^{-1}$

Example T 2.20	(a) $102J$ (b)$5.9ms^{-1}$	(c) $5.9ms^{-1}$

Example T 2.21	(a) $2.5cm$	(b)$0.15J$	(c)$0.49ms^{-1}$

Example T 2.22	(a) 73J (b) $1.5ms^{-1}$

Example T 2.23	(a) $19W$ (b) $27W$	(c) $35W$

Example T 2.24	(a) $9.7W$	(b) $13.7W$	(c) $17.4W$

Example T 2.25

The work done by the man in moving horizontally is zero, since he is applying a force to overcome his weight vertically. The force has zero component parallel to the displacement.

Example T 2.26	(a) 46J (b)27J

Example T 2.27	0.63 (63%)

Example T 2.28	(a) 22MJ	(b) 4.9MJ	(c) 0.23 (23%)

Example T 2.29	(a) $12ms^{-1}$	(b) $960N$	(c) $15s$

Example T 2.30	approx $5.9m$ $(\pm0.3m)$

Example T 2.31

    (a) Momentum of boy $= 122 kgms^{-1}$
          Momentum of girl $= -57 kgms^{-1}$
    (b) Total momentum $= 65 kgms^{-1}$
    (c) Total momentum after collision $0.54 ms^{-1}$

Example T 2.32

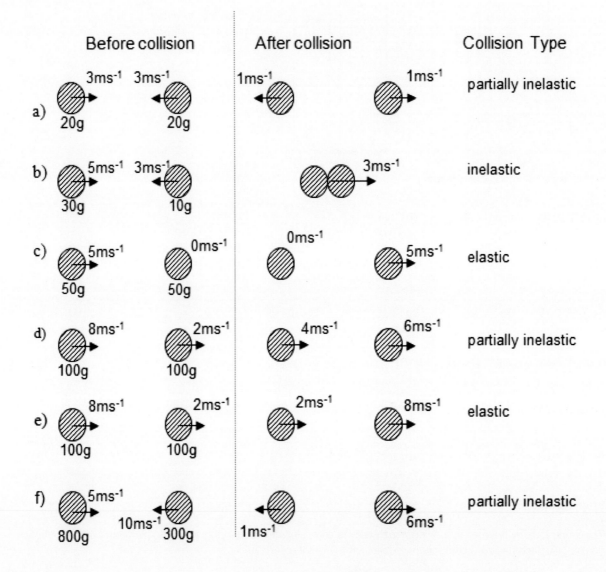

Topic 3: Thermal Physics

Example T 3.1

(a) The particles in a liquid attract each other and have only very small kinetic energy. Gravity will pull them down to the bottom of a container where they will spread out, filling the space available (the forces be-tween molecules allows them to slide past each other rather than being rigid. The particles in gases are sperated from each other and move with high speeds (since they have high kinetic energies). Their speeds are so high that the force of gravity does not affect them significantly. They therefore spread out randomly, filling the container evenly.

(b) The forces between particles in solids is relatively high. Kinetic energy is relatively low – the particles are unable to move around, just to vibrate. Potential energy is also low, since the particles are strongly attracted to each other. Liquids have higher potential energies (since the particles are separated partial-ly from each other and the attracticve forces are weakened. They also have higher kinetic energies, since they are able to move around as well as vibrate. Gases have approximately zero potential ener-gies, since the forces between them is approximately zero (particles in liquiids and solids have negative potential energies). Gases have particles with high kinetic energies (mainly translational): they are in rapid motion.

Example T 3.2

Taking air temperature to be, say $20°C \approx 300K$

$$\bar{E}_K = \frac{3}{2}k_BT = \frac{3}{2} \times 1.38 \times 10^{-23} \times 300 \approx 2 \times 300 \times 10^{-23} = 6 \times 10^{-21}J$$

Example T 3.3

(a) To compare temperatures, they must all be converted into absolute temperatures.
Thus: A has temperature $273 + 85 = 358K$
B has temperature $273 + 125 = 398K$
C has temperature $250K$
So, the substance in container B has the highest temperature, and in container C; the lowest. This also means that the average kinetic energy of any given particle in container B is higher than that in A, which is in turn higher than that in C.

However, since there is 1000 times more particles in A than in B, the internal energy (i.e. total internal energy) of particles in A is much higher than that in B, which is a little higher than that in C (less particles and lower temperature).

(b) Thermal energy will flow from the hot body to the coller body until thermal equilibrium is reached (when both bodies are the same temperature. So, thermal energy will flow from container B to container A.

Example T 3.4

$$c = \frac{Q}{m\Delta T} = \frac{27000}{3 \times 12} = 750Jkg^{-1}°C^{-1}$$

Example T 3.5

$$c = \frac{Q}{m\Delta T} = \frac{10500}{0.5 \times 5} = 4200Jkg^{-1}°C^{-1}$$

Example T 3.6

$$Q = mc\Delta T = 7.5 \times 2100 \times 13 = 2.0 \times 10^5J$$

Example T 3.7

$$Q = ml \Rightarrow l = \frac{Q}{m} = \frac{1.7 \times 10^6}{5} = 3.4 \times 10^5Jkg^{-1}$$

Example T 3.8 $Q = ml = 0.5 \times 2.26 \times 10^6 = 1.13 \times 10^6 J$

Example T 3.9

(a)

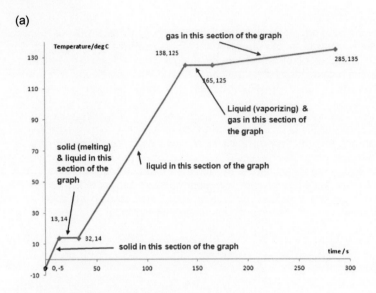

(b) (i) Melting point: $14°C$, Boiling point: $125°C$

(ii) $c_{solid} = \dfrac{Q}{m\Delta T} = \dfrac{P \times t}{m\Delta T} = \dfrac{100 \times 13}{0.15 \times (14 - -5)} = 46 Jkg^{-1}K^{-1}$

$c_{liquid} = \dfrac{Q}{m\Delta T} = \dfrac{P \times t}{m\Delta T} = \dfrac{100 \times (138 - 32)}{0.15 \times (125 - 14)} = 640 Jkg^{-1}K^{-1}$

$c_{gas} = \dfrac{Q}{m\Delta T} = \dfrac{P \times t}{m\Delta T} = \dfrac{100 \times (285 - 165)}{0.15 \times (135 - 125)} = 8000 Jkg^{-1}K^{-1}$

(iii) $Q = ml \Rightarrow l = \dfrac{Q}{m}$, $l_{fusion} = \dfrac{100 \times (32-13)}{0.15} = 13000 Jkg^{-1}$, $l_{vap} = \dfrac{100 \times (165-138)}{0.15} = 18000 Jkg^{-1}$

Example T 3.10

Average force exerted by n particles, over time $= \dfrac{nx}{t}$

Pressure $= \dfrac{F}{A} = \dfrac{nx}{tA}$

Example T 3.11

(a) $PV = nRT \Rightarrow n = \dfrac{PV}{RT} = \dfrac{220000 \times 0.015}{8.31 \times (273+28)} = 1.3 \ moles$

Example T 3.12

(a) $Particles = moles \times N_A = 1.3 \times 6.02 \times 10^{23} = 7.9 \times 10^{23}$
(b) The answer would be the same: all gases occupy the same volume (under same conditions) per mole

---

Example T 3.13

$PV = nRT \Rightarrow n = \dfrac{PV}{RT} = \dfrac{101000 \times (.25 \times .50 \times .50)}{8.31 \times (273+25)} = 2.5 \ moles$

$\therefore mass = 2.5 \times 28g = 71g$

Topic 4: Waves

Example T 4.1

"Sound waves consist of particles that **oscillate**, typically with a **frequency** of several hundred hertz – and so the time **period** would then be of the order of a hundredth of a second. Since they require particles to transfer energy, sound waves require a **medium** to travel through such as air, water or a solid (like the ground). As the sound wave passes through a material, the particles in a material are **displaced** from their usual position. This **displacement** changes from one direction to another and the **amplitude** is dependent on the power of the sound source and will affect the intensity and loudness of the sound. If we look at a line of particles in a sound wave, all along the direction that the wave is travelling in, we find that each subsequent particle is slightly out of **phase** with the next until, after a certain distance, we find a particle in **phase** with the first and the cycle is repeated"

Example T 4.2

(a) 5cm
(b) Period is time for 20cm "there and back" 0.5s
(c) 2Hz
(d) We must show that $a \propto -x$. We could use a motion sensor to determine the acceleration of the bob at different points, and we could plot acceleration versus displacement. We should get a straight line through the origin (with negative slope $= -\omega^2$)

Example T 4.3

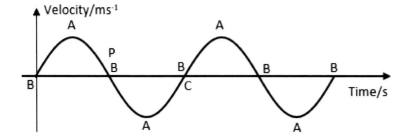

(a) Find the area between graph and x axis and the times during which displacement is to be found
(b) Find the gradient (slope) of the tangent of the curve at that point in time
(c) (i) displacement fluctuates periodically from positive to negative, so the particles moves about a fixed point. (ii) we would need to use the graph to show that the displacement from equilibrium (calculated from area) is proportional to but in the opposite direction of the acceleration (calculated from slope)
(d) This area represents twice the amplitude of the particle (since it shows the total displacement from maximum negative displacement to maximum positive displacement).

Example T 4.4

The energy starts as gravitational potential energy and converts to kinetic energy, back to GPE and so on. At any point the total energy is constant and equal to GPE + KE.

Example T 4.5

(a) $f = \frac{v}{\lambda} = \frac{3.00 \times 10^8}{3.8 \times 10^{-13}} = 7.9 \times 10^{20} Hz$ (b) $v = f\lambda = 333 ms^{-1}$

(c) $T = 0.8s, f = \frac{1}{T} = 1.25Hz, \therefore v = 3.1 ms^{-1}$

Example T 4.6

(Using $v = f\lambda$). Audible sound frequency varies from 22kHz to 16.5Hz (about 20Hz to 20kHz), whilst waves in the ems vary from $3 \times 10^7 Hz$ to $3 \times 10^{23} Hz$ (about $10^7 Hz$ to $10^{23} Hz$)

Example T 4.7

(a) The distance required is half the wavelength = 0.019m (1.9cm)

(b) (i) Vibrate the source at a greater frequency (ii) increase the amplitude (maximum displacement) of the vibrating object.

Example T 4.8

(a) (drawn in red) (b) $\lambda = \frac{5\sin 60°}{3} = 1.4cm$ (c) $0.72ms^{-1} = 72cms^{-1}$

Example T 4.9

(a) $0.018Wm^{-2}$ The main assumption is that the sound is emitted equally in all directions, so that the inverse square law applies.

(b) It would be more if the sound is directed towards the observation point than in other directions; less if directed away (speakers do direct sound mostly in a "forwards cone" so this would apply).

(c) $I \propto A^2, so\ A \propto \sqrt{I}\ (P \propto I)$ I increases by a factor of 2, so A will increase by $\sqrt{2} \approx 1.4$
$1.4 \times 5 = 7$, so new wave will have amplitude of 7 units, as shown (in blue)

Example T 4.10

Example T 4.11

$I = I_0 cos^2\theta = I_0 \times 0.75$ so intensity has reduced by 25%

Example T 4.12

$tan\theta_B = n \Rightarrow \theta_B = 56°, this\ gives\ incident\ anngle\ (to\ normal)\ so\ required\ angle\ is\ 34°$

Example T 4.13

$\frac{n_1}{n_2} = \frac{c_1}{c_2},\ \ \ \ gives\ n_{substance} = 1.4\ (1.36)$

Example T 4.14

Light is shone into a glass block (prism) at an angle of 47° to the normal (i.e. angle of incidence = 47°). It emerges at 29° to the normal.

    (a) 1.5 (1.51)   [n_{air} = 1, Snell's law with speed ratio, speed of light from data book]
    (b) $2.0 \times 10^8 ms^{-1}$ [using Snell's laws with velocity ratio]
    (c) 900nm (905) [using Snell's laws with wavelength ratio]
    (d) $3.3 \times 10^{14} Hz$ [using v=fλ]
    (e) $3.3 \times 10^{14} Hz$ [using v=fλ or frequency always stays the same for refraction].

Example T 4.15

$$\frac{3.00 \times 10^8}{2.07 \times 10^8} = \frac{sin60°}{sin\theta_{glass}} \Rightarrow \theta_g = 37°$$

Example T 4.16

Glass: 46°; Diamond: 21°

This means that for light to escape from diamond, it must strike the surface at an angle of 69° or greater (to the surface), otherwise it will totally internally reflect, which will cause the glistening effect.

Example T 4.17

Lower frequency means longer wavelength, which diffract to a greater extent, allowing waves to "bend" around objects and through spaces.

Example T 4.18

    (a) 1.1mm
    (b) Red light has a longer wavelength than yellow light, so the fringe spacing, s, will be greater. The interference pattern will therefore be more spread out/spaced.

Example T 4.19

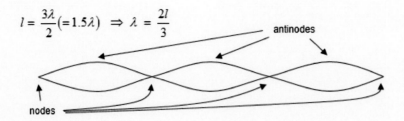

$$l = \frac{3\lambda}{2} (=1.5\lambda) \Rightarrow \lambda = \frac{2l}{3}$$

Example T 4.20

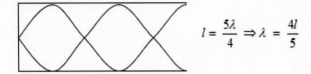

$$l = \frac{5\lambda}{4} \Rightarrow \lambda = \frac{4l}{5}$$

Example T 4.21

$$l = \frac{4\lambda}{2} \Rightarrow \lambda = \frac{l}{2}$$

Topic 5: Electricity and Magnetism

Example T 5.1   (a) $-e$ (b) $+e$ (c) $+2e$ (d) $-2e$

Example T 5.2

(a) $-1.6 \times 10^{-19}C$ (b) $+1.6 \times 10^{-19}C$ (c) $+3.2 \times 10^{-19}C$ (d) $-3.2 \times 10^{-19}C$

Example T 5.3 6.25×10^{18}

Example T 5.4

(a) Around a negatively charged sphere   (b) around a proton   c) Between two parallel plates

Example T 5.5

(a) $250NC^{-1}$ to the left   (b) $4800NC^{-1}$ downwards (c) $1200NC^{-1}$ downwards

Example T 5.6

(a) $2.3 \times 10^{-10}N$, repulsive (b) $2.3 \times 10^{-10}N$, repulsive (c) $8.0 \times 10^{-5}N$, attractive

Example T 5.7

$8.85 \times 10^{-12}(C^2N^{-1}m^{-2})$

The constant relates to the permittivity of the material (a property relating to the electrical shielding) between the two charges.

Example T 5.8

(a) Taking the diameter of a helium nucleus as $\approx 10^{-15}m$ and the distance between (centres of) two protons s half this figure, we get $F = 920N$ (repulsive) a huge figure.

(b) The obvious force is to hold these protons together is gravitational attraction, but we would find that this force is far too weak to overcome this electrostatic repulsion. The missing attractive force is the so called nuclear strong force, which is a very short range force between nuclear particles.

Example T 5.9

(a) $4.6 \times 10^{14}NC^{-1}$, outwards

(b) $1.1 \times 10^9NC^{-1}$ towards the centre of the sphere

(c) (i) $75000Vm^{-1}$ $(or\ 75000NC^{-1})$, (ii) same, since the field between parallel plates is uniform

Example T 5.10 6.25×10^{18}

Example T 5.11   (a) $0.108C$ (b) $0.0086A = 8.6mA$

Example T 5.12

(a) 2.4×10^{-5} m/s for copper; 3.4×10^{-5} m/s for aluminium (so about 40% greater for aluminium)

(b) To have an equal current in an aluminium wire compared to a copper wire a greater speed of electron flow is needed: copper is a better conductor than aluminium.

Example T 5.13

a.c electricity rapidly and continually changes direction, whilst d.c electricity always flows in the same direction

Example T 5.14

5C of electrons enter a bulb with an electric potential energy of 60J and by the time they have passed through the bulb filament, their total potential energy has dropped to 15J

(a) $45J$

(b) electrical potential energy → internal energy + light energy (radiation)

(c) $9V$

Example T 5.15 $12\ electronvolts\ (12eV) or\ 1.92 \times 10^{-18}J$

Example T 5.16 $5.0V$

Example T 5.17   Energy

Example T 5.18

(a) (i) 100keV (ii) $1.6 \times 10^{-14}J$; Speed is $1.9 \times 10^{8}ms^{-1}$

(b) 200keV; much slower – although it has twice the KE, it is many thousands of times the mass of an electron so will be going much slower

(c) $4.7 \times 10^{5}ms^{-1}$

Example T 5.19

Example T 5.20

$V_1 = 3V$; $V_2 = 1V$; $A_1 = 4A$; $A_2 = 3A$

Example T 5.21

(a) 16Ω

(b) 0.38A (0.375A)

(c) If the voltage is increased, the current will increase but the bulb filament is likely to get hotter and this will increase the resistance of the bulb (so the resistance will not remain exactly constant)

Example T 5.22

	5Ω	10Ω (a)	10Ω (b)	Total circuit
Voltage	5V	5V	15V	20V
Current	1.0A	0.5A	1.5A	1.5A
Resistance	5Ω	10Ω	10Ω	13.33Ω
Charge passed in 1s	1.0C	0.5C	1.5C	1.5C
Power	5W	2.5W	22.5W	30W

Example T 5.23

$$R = \frac{\rho L}{A} = 1.09m\Omega \quad (A = 2\pi r)$$

Example T 5.24

a) $V = IR \Rightarrow I = V/R = 12/30 = 0.4A$

b) $P = VI = 12 \times 0.4 = 4.8W$

Example T 5.25

(a) Answer: 4.5 hours (charge stored = 3240C, energy delivered = 4860J)

(b) Since the voltage would gradually drop over time, this would imply that the power delivery would also drop over time, meaning that the cell would last longer (but the bulb would become dimmer as time progressed)

Example T 5.26

(i) 2.67A (charge stored = 1440C; I=q/t)   (ii) 5040J (taking approx. voltage = 3.5V)

Example T 5.27

The voltage drop is often called "lost voltage" and is due to the internal resistance of the supply. The emf of the supply is 8 volts. 0.32V is "lost" across the internal resistance (inside the source), leaving 7.68V available for the extrenal resistor. The resistance of the internal resistance is 0.5 Ω   ($R = V/I = 0.32/0.64 = 0.5\Omega$)

Example T 5.28

(a) $0.1A$ (b) $1V$ (c) $11V$

(d) We have assumed that the voltmeter has an infinite resistance (it is an ideal voltmeter), so that it does not affect the circuit that it is in.

(e) 8.7V (treat as though the voltmeter were another resistor and find the voltage across it)

(f) A non-ideal ammeter has non-zero resistance, so would take up some of the circuit potential difference and would increase the circuit resistance, reducing circuit current. Hence: (i) lower potential difference across external resistor (ii) lower current through external resistor

Example T 5.29

(a) The direction of the force is out of the page   (b) $6.3 \times 10^{-5} N$

Example T 5.30

(a)

(b) $1.8 \times 10^{-7} N$

(c) The force on both particles is always perpendicular to the motion of the particle, so the speed of each particle will remain constant. The magnetic force on each particle will make them travel in a circle with centripetal acceleration. The proton, having a much greater mass than the electron, will have a much smaller acceleration than the electron. This means that the proton will describe a circle with a much greater radius than the electron.

Example T 5.31 $3.2 \times 10^{-5} N \ per \ metre$. Force direction is directly out of the page.

Topic 6: Circular Motion and Gravitation

Example T 6.1

- (a) 12 seconds
- (b) 0.083 Hz (0.083 per second)
- (c) 5.2 radians (10/12 x 2π)
- (d) 0.52 radians per second (0.52rad/s) [2π/12 or 5 x 2π/60]

Example T 6.2

A string is used to twirl a 300g mass in a horizontal circle of radius 25 cm, in zero gravity conditions, so that the mass moves at a speed of 2 ms^{-1}

(a) 4.8N

(b)

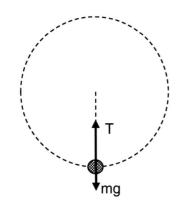

T = 7.7N (first find F$_c$)

Example T 6.3

- (a) 1.8s
- (b) 3.5rad/s
- (c) 1.83m/s^2
- (d) 0.015N
- (e) Weight (downwards) = 0.082N; normal force (upwards) = 0.082N; friction (towards centre, providing centripetal force) = 0.015N
- (f) Period and angular velocity would be the same; acceleration and centripetal force would be half as big (using $F = m\omega^2 r; a = \omega^2 r$).

Example T 6.4

- (a) 834N (W=mg with g=9.81N/kg gives the same answer)
- (b) 138N
- (c) $1.98 \times 10^{20} N$
- (d) $5.35 \times 10^{-6} N$

Note that this force of attraction is the force on both objects: equal in magnitude, in accordance with Newton's 3rd law.

Example T 6.5

(a)
(b) $T = 2.37 \times 10^6 s = 27.4 \; days$

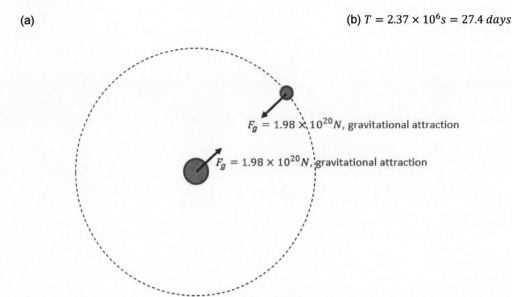

$F_g = 1.98 \times 10^{20} N$, gravitational attraction

$F_g = 1.98 \times 10^{20} N$, gravitational attraction

Example T 6.6

Bags of sand with various masses are used to test the surface gravitational field strength of various (made up) planets. A newton-metre is used to determine the gravitational force.

(a) For each, calculate the surface gravitational field strength:

Planet	Mass of sand-bag	Force on sand bag	Gravitational field strength
X	12kg	92N	7.7N/kg
Y	200g	18N	90N/kg
Z	460kg	230N	0.5N/kg

(b) $W_X = 498N$, $W_Y = 5850N$, $W_Z = 32.5N$

Example T 6.7

Planet Y is either very small and quite massive, or very massive and quite large (a very large surface gravity implies that the planet is either very small or very massive or both: essentially that the density of the planet must be very large. Planet Z is the opposite (low mass or very large or both). Planet X is between these two extremes.

Example T 6.8 *(a)* 9.81N/kg *(b)*1.62N/kg *(c)* 7.33N/kg

Example T 6.9

(a) $3.5 \times 10^{-5} N/kg$
(b) The net gravitational field strength will decrease by the above amount since the moon is pulling in the opposite direction as the Earth.
(c) $3.2 \times 10^{-5} N/$
(d) The net gravitational field strength will increase by the above amount since the moon is pulling in the same direction as the Earth.
(e) Low tides will occur when the gravitational field strength is stronger (furthest from the Moon) and high tides where the field strength is weaker (closest to the Moon) because a stronger field will pull the oceans closer to the Earth.

Topic 7: Atomic, nuclear and particle physics

Example T 7.1 (a) $4.3 \times 10^{-19} J$ (b) $3.8 \times 10^{-17} J$

Example T 7.2 (a) $2.7 eV$ (b) $240 eV$

Example T 7.3 $5.0 \times 10^{-7} m$

Example T 7.4 (a) $2.18 \times 10^{-18} J$ (b) $3.28 \times 10^{15} Hz$

Example T 7.5 (a) $0.70 eV$ (b) $n = 4 \; to \; n = 3$

Example T 7.6

Using the energy level diagram, I shall identify the wavelengths of light emitted when the electron jumps from $n = 3 \; to \; n = 2$ and from $n = 4 \; to \; n = 2$. Hopefully this will correspond to two of the lines in the spectrum shown (note that the spectrum only shows transitions to the $n = 2$ level, as stated).

$$E_{(4 \to 2)} = 3.4 - 0.8 = 2.6 eV$$

$$2.6 eV \approx 4.16 \times 10^{-19} J$$

$$E = \frac{hc}{\lambda} \Rightarrow \lambda = \frac{hc}{E} = \frac{hc}{4.16 \times 10^{-19}} m = 4.78 \times 10^{-7} m = 478 nm$$

This transition, from $n = 4 \; to \; n = 2$, corresponds to the pale blue line shown towards the centre of the spectrum.

$$E_{(3 \to 2)} = 3.4 - 1.5 = 1.9 eV$$

$$1.9 eV = 3.04 \times 10^{-19} J$$

$$E = \frac{hc}{\lambda} \Rightarrow \lambda = \frac{hc}{E} = \frac{hc}{3.04 \times 10^{-19}} m = 6.54 \times 10^{-7} m = 654 nm$$

This transition, from $n = 3 \; to \; n = 2$, corresponds to the red line shown on the diagram towards the right of the spectrum

---

Example T 7.7

Method 1: $^{63}_{29}Cu$; Method 2: $Cu - 63$

Any copper nuclide must have 29 protons, since the copper atom is defined by its proton number. So from the mass number 63 we know that the neutron number must be 63 − 29 = 34.

Example T 7.8

(a) a= 210, b=84, c=4, d=2, e=0, f=0

(b) It is an alpha decay reaction

Example T 7.9

a) $^{238}_{92}U \rightarrow \, ^{234}_{90}Th \, + \, ^{4}_{2}\alpha$

b) $^{14}_{6}C \rightarrow \, ^{14}_{7}N \, + \, ^{0}_{-1}\beta \, + \, \bar{v}$

c) $^{60}_{27}Co \rightarrow \, ^{60}_{28}Ni^* \, + \, ^{0}_{-1}\beta \, + \, \bar{v}$

$$\downarrow$$

$$^{60}_{28}Ni \, + \, \gamma$$

Half-life

Reaction (a) is an alpha decay reaction; (b) and (c) are beta minus decay reactions. The latter involves the production of a daughter nucleus in excited state, leading to the emission of a gamma-ray photon.

Example T 7.10 $\frac{1}{32}$

Example T 7.11   8 days

Example T 7.12

(a) Uranium – 237 and uranium – 238

(b) Atomic mass = 238, nucleon number = 238, 92 protons, 146 neutrons.

Example T 7.13   42 counts per minute

Example T 7.14   (i) 12u   (ii) 12.09894u

Example T 7.15 $9 \times 10^{13} J$

Example T 7.16

Mass defect: $5.2256 \times 10^{-29} kg$ (0.03146u); binding energy = $4.70 \times 10^{-12} J$ (29.4MeV)

Example T 7.17   492.3632MeV

Example T 7.18

Pb-206 is the most stable nuclide because according to the graph it has the highest binding energy per nucleon. If Po-210 undergoes a fission reaction to produce a lighter, more stable nuclide (Pb-206), energy will therefore be released.

Mass of reactants (left hand side) $= 209.983u$

Mass of products $= (205.974u + 4.003u) = 209.977u$

$\therefore$ Mass difference $= 0.006u$

$E = mc^2 = 0.006 \times 1.661 \times 10^{-27} \times (3.00 \times 10^8)^2 = 8.969 \times 10^{-13}$

Answer : $8.969 \times 10^{-13} J$

This may not seem like much energy, but it equates to over 2,500 megajoules of energy per gram of polonium!!

Example T 7.19

    (a)   *csd* feasible: baryon
    (b)   *b$\bar{s}$* feasible: meson
    (c)   *t$\bar{c}$b*: not feasible (non-integer charge)
    (d)   *c$\bar{c}$*: not feasible (we would have annihilation)
    (e)   *ud* not feasible (pairs must be particle/antiparticle)

Example T 7.20

Interaction	charge		lepton number		baryon number		interaction possible?
	left	right	left	right	left	right	
$n \rightarrow p + e^+$	0	1+1	0	0+(-1)	1	1+0	no
$p \rightarrow e^+ + n$	1	1+0	0	-1+0	1	0+1	no
$n \rightarrow p + e^- + \bar{v}$	0	1-1+0	0	0+1-1	1	1+0+0	yes
$p \rightarrow n + e^+ + v$	1	0+1+0	0	0-1+1	1	1+0+0	yes
$n + p \rightarrow e^+ + v$	0+1	1+0	0+0	-1+1	1+1	0+0	no
$e^- + p \rightarrow n + \bar{v}$	-1+1	0+0	1-1	0-1	0+1	1+0	no
$e^+ + e^- \rightarrow 2\gamma$	1-1	0	-1+1	0	0	0	yes

(red areas show where conservation laws are broken)

Example T 7.21

(a) a proton   0
(b) a neutron   0
(c) an electron   0
(d) a K^+ meson 1
(e) a K^0 meson 1
(f) a K^- meson -1

Example T 7.22   (a) W^-, W^+, Z bosons   (b) gluons   (c) photon

Example T 7.23

(a) Electromagnetic
(b) Gravitational, electromagnetic, weak, strong (all)
(c) Electromagnetic
(d) Gravitational
(e) Gravitational, strong, electromagnetic
(f) Weak.

Example T 7.24

24: 6 quarks + 6 antiquarks; 6 leptons + 6 antileptons (there are also exchange particles)

Example T 7.25

(a) A hadron- made up of quarks & is classed as a baryon (has 3 quarks): uud
(b) Same as proton, except udd
(c) A fundamental particle, classed as a lepton.

Example T 7.24

(a) $n \rightarrow p + e^- + \bar{\nu}$
(b) The W− boson is needed to neutralize the charge of the proton produced from the neutron (so charge is conserved)
(c) See example T7(20)

Example T 7.25

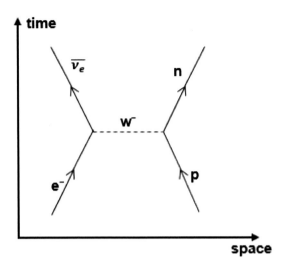

This process is called electron capture, by a proton. An electron splits into a W⁻ boson and an antineutrino. The W⁻ boson interacts with the proton to become a neutron.

The boson is a W– since the negative charge is required for conservation of charge during the intermediate (virtual) stage.

Example T 7.26

(a) The proton and the neutron are fundamental particles F – neither are fundamental
(b) The electron has no antiparticle F – all particles have antiparticles
(c) The antiparticle always has a different charge to a particle F – if particle has no charge, so does its antiparticle
(d) All particles (excluding antiparticles) are constituents of ordinary matter F – many are not, for example 2nd and 3rd generation (family) leptons
(e) Particles and antiparticles have the same mass and average lifetime T
(f) For annihilation to occur, the interaction must be between a particle and its antiparticle T
(g) In particle interactions, mass must be conserved, and so must energy F – mass can be converted to energy and vice versa – mass-energy jointly must be conserved
(h) The observable fundamental particles are leptons, quarks and gauge bosons F – these are all fundamental particles, but quarks are not observable – they do not even exist in isolation
(i) Exchange particles are mediators of the fundamental interactions T
(j) Gluons, photons and the intermediate vector bosons are all exchange particles T
(k) Exchange particles are all gauge bosons T
(l) Gauge bosons are fundamental particles T
(m) Exchange particles are all quarks F – they are gauge bosons!
(n) An electron is a lepton T
(o) An electron neutrino is the antiparticle of an electron F – the antiparticle of an electron is a positron
(p) Quarks come in 6 flavours T – up, down, top, bottom, strange and charmed
(q) Protons and neutrons are made up from quarks T – uud and udd
(r) Isolated quarks have never been observed but they do exist in isolation F – they have never been observed and it is believed to be impossible for them to exist in isolation
(s) The observable fundamental particles are leptons, hadrons and gauge bosons F- these are the groups of observable particles, but hadrons are not fundamental – they are made up from quarks
(t) The uud is the particle from which protons are made F – uud is not a particle, it is the three particles – quarks – from which a proton is made: up, up, down
(u) The udd is the antiparticle of the uud, from which neutrons are made F – the antiparticle of uud is $\overline{uud}$ - the antiproton (udd is a neutron)
(v) Hadrons are observable particles, made from quarks T
(w) Hadrons are fundamental particles F – they are made up from quarks
(x) Mesons and baryons are the two subgroups of quarks T
(y) Charge, lepton number and baryon number are always conserved T
(z) Protons and neutrons are mesons F – they are baryons

Topic 8: Energy Production

Example T 8.1   (a) 50kJ   (b) 45kJ   (c) 25kJ(d) 88,250,000,000kJ

Example T 8.2   (a) $5.3 \times 10^{-8}m^3$, $0.053cm^3$ (b) $4150m^3, 2200m^3, 2.4\ million\ m^3$

Example T 8.3

(a) Chemical or nuclear → internal energy → elastic energy → kinetic energy → electrical energy
     (note that this energy chain is an interpretation: others will also be valid)
     (elastic energy is the energy stored in the compressed, expanded steam)

(b) During the burning of the fuels (chemical or nuclear reactions) thermal energy can easily be released
     from the system: complete insulation is difficult to attain
     This transfer of thermal energy out of the system will occur at all stages
     There will always be some friction whenever we have moving parts (turbine, generator) causing un-
     wanted transfer of kinetic energy to internal energy
     During each cycle, the water used for driving the turbines will need to be cooled so energy is extracted
     from the system (there are now systems in place at many power stations to use this energy – for exam-
     ple, for direct heating outside of the power station).

Example T 8.4

Using efficiency = 0.42, power input = 950MW

So energy input in 1 week = $5.76 \times 10^{14}J$

Specific energy of coal = 25MJ/kg so mass of coal needed = 2304000kg

The following schematic flow diagram shows the basics of how thermal energy is extracted from a nuclear fuel in
a power station

Example T 8.5

(a) Once the reaction is initiated, further neutrons are produced by subsequent reactions. These neutrons
     initiated further reactions, and so on. So the reaction is self-sustaining, and hence a chain reaction (and
     if not controlled, explosive!).
(b) Control rods are used to absorb neutrons and control the rate of reaction/thermal energy production
     (more than 1 neutron is produced from each reaction so if neutrons are not absorbed the reaction be-
     comes exponential)
(c) The moderator slows down neutrons emitted, making them likely to initiate another fission reaction(if
     neutrons are too fast, this reduces this probability).

Example T 8.6   1.6m

Example T 8.7

Efficiency is approximately 30%

Power consumption is approximately 4MW

Example T 8.8

(a) False, it also occurs in liquids and gases although not usually very effectively since the particles are further apart
(b) True – convection requires the mobility of the medium
(c) False - radiation actually occurs most effectively without a medium, i.e. in a vacuum. If a medium is present it depends on transparency rather than solid, liquid or gas
(d) False – do not confuse radioactivity with electromagnetic radiation, which is what we are talking about as a method of thermal energy transfer.

Example T 8.9

9100K - it does follow the pattern shown on the spectra-graph

Example T 8.10
(a) $1.8 \times 10^{17} W$ (b) $700 W m^{-2}$ (c) $350 W m^{-2}$

Example T 8.11
$1.3 \times 10^{17} W$

Example T 8.12
Sun: $3.8 \times 10^{26} W$; *Earth:* $1.6 \times 10^{17} W$

Topic 9: Wave Phenomena

Example T 9.1

(a) Plot acceleration (y axis) versus displacement (x axis). A straight line through the origin (with negative slope) confirms that the motion is shm. The slope of the graph gives $-\omega^2$, so the angular frequency, ω, can be found by taking the square root of the slope magnitude.

(b) We could plot the graph (exam question will probably provide axes) or we could determine the ratio $\frac{a}{x}$ for each point (since, for shm, $\frac{a}{x} = a\ constant\ (-\omega^2)$)

Thus:

for 1st point: $\frac{a}{x} = \frac{5.5 ms^{-2}}{-5.0 \times 10^{-2} m} = -110 s^{-2}$

for 2nd point $\frac{a}{x} = \frac{2.7 ms^{-2}}{-2.5 \times 10^{-2} m} = -108 s^{-2}$

for 3rd point $\frac{a}{x} = \frac{-3.3 ms^{-2}}{3.0 \times 10^{-2} m} = -110 s^{-2}$

This ratios are very consistent (some variation would be expected, due to experimental uncertainty) so the motion is very likely to be shm.

(c) Taking an average of these 3 ratios, we get:

$$-\omega^2 = -109 \Rightarrow \omega = \sqrt{109} = 10.5 s^{-1}$$

(Note that the unit for angular frequency, ω, is s^{-1}, or $rads^{-1}$: ie "per second" or "radians per second")

Example T 9.2
(a) (i) D (ii) B   (b) (i) A (ii) C

Example T 9.3
(a) A   (b) C   (c) B   (d) D

Example T 9.4
(a) D   (b) B   (c) B   (d) A

Example T 9.5   (a) C   (b) B   (c) C

Example T9.6

(a) C

(b) The displacement/time graph would be B. Its slope gives velocity, so correct velocity graph would be a negative cosine graph, D. Answer: D

(c) The acceleration graph would be C (positive cosine graph) , so the displacement graph would be D (negative cosine graph), and so the velocity graph would be A. Answer: A

Example T 9.7   (a) (i) C (ii) B   (b) (i) C (ii) D   (c) (i) B (ii) D

Example T 9.8

(a) $T = 2\pi\sqrt{\frac{l}{g}} = 2.73s$ (b) $\omega = \frac{2\pi}{T} = 2.30 rads^{-1}$ (c) amplitude (x_0) = 18cm = 0.18m

(d) $E_k(max) = E_T = \frac{1}{2}m\omega^2 x_0^2 = 0.0125J$ (e) 0.0125J

(f) $v = \pm\omega\sqrt{(x_0^2 - x^2)} = \pm 0.309ms^{-1}$ (we do not know which way it is moving)

(g) $E_k = \frac{1}{2}m\omega^2(x_0^2 - x^2) = 0.00934J$ (the negative sign on displacement does not matter: it is squared and will be moving at the same speed whether negative or positive displacement)

(h) First, we must select appropriate equations. Displacement will be negative cosine, velocity will be positive sign and acceleration will be positive cosine.

$x = -x_0 cos\omega t = 0.157m$ (15.7cm forwards from equilibrium)

$v = \omega x_0 sin\omega t = -0.202ms^{-1}$ (i.e. moving backwards)

$a = \omega^2 x_0 cos\omega t$ (or $a = -\omega^2 x$) $= -0.833ms^{-2}$ (accelerating towards equilibrium)

Example T 9.9

(a) Energy transfers back and forth from GPE to KE to GPE etc. As height (and, therefore, GPE) is lost, speed (and, therefore, KE) is gained, and vice-versa.
(b) $E_p = E_T - E_k = 0.0125J - \frac{1}{2}(0.145)(0.202^2)J = 0.00949J$

Example T 9.10

(a) 0.0125 rad (angular displacement from central line)
(b) 6.25cm (minimum-minimum distance)

Example T 9.11

(a) 6.9° (0.12 rad)Calculate the angle (in degrees) from centre-line to the first minimum when light with wavelength $600nm$ passes through a single slit of width $5\mu m$.
(b) 1st order: 0.69° 2nd order: 1.4° 3rd order: 2.1°

Example T 9.12

    (a) The individual maxima within the single slit envelope (pattern) will narrow and move closer together so that more fit into the single slit envelope

    (b) The single slit envelope (pattern) becomes narrower

Example T 9.13

(a) Referring to diagram on right (it is clearer) Single slit envelope → 1 slit; primary maxima → 2 slits; 4 additional slits. We therefore have 6 slits.

(b) Arrangement A has a narrower single slit envelope than B => slits width is greater

Arrangement A has its primary maxima closer together => slits spacing is greater

(c) We would get more of the small, secondary maxima but they would be diminished in height and the primary maxima would get taller and narrower.

Example T 9.14

(a) $36.5°$ $(37°)$

(b) The maximum number of maxima corresponds to $n = 3$, since $n = 4$ yields $sin\theta = 1.2528$

This gives 7 maxima: 1 central (zeroth order)+ 2 for each of $n = 1, 2$ and 3

Example T 9.15
Light is shone from air into a thin film, with refractive index X and thickness D. The material immediately below the film has refractive index Y. Complete the table below to determine the nature of the interference for each situation:

Refractive indices	Number of phase changes	Film thickness	$\therefore$ value of 2dn	Type of interference
X>Y	1	$\dfrac{1}{4}\dfrac{\lambda}{X}$	0.5λ	constructive
X>Y	1	$\dfrac{1}{2}\dfrac{\lambda}{X}$	λ	destructive
X>Y	1	$\dfrac{3}{4}\dfrac{\lambda}{X}$	1.5λ	constructive
X>Y	1	$\dfrac{\lambda}{X}$	2λ	destructive
X>Y	1	$\dfrac{5}{4}\dfrac{\lambda}{X}$	2.5λ	constructive
X<Y	2	$\dfrac{1}{4}\dfrac{\lambda}{X}$	0.5λ	destructive
X<Y	2	$\dfrac{1}{2}\dfrac{\lambda}{X}$	λ	constructive
X<Y	2	$\dfrac{3}{4}\dfrac{\lambda}{X}$	1.5λ	destructive
X<Y	2	$\dfrac{\lambda}{X}$	2λ	constructive
X<Y	2	$\dfrac{5}{4}\dfrac{\lambda}{X}$	2.5λ	destructive

Example T 9.16

There will be a phase change on initial reflection from surface of coating (since $1.8 > 1.0$) and there will be a phase change on reflection form lower boundary of coating (since $2.6 > 1.8$) so there will be a total of 2 phase changes. This is equivalent to no phase changes. So for destructive interference we need the coating thickness to be right so as to produce a half wavelength path difference. Hence:

$$2dn = \left(m + \frac{1}{2}\right)\lambda \Rightarrow d = \frac{\left(m + \frac{1}{2}\right)\lambda}{2n}, \qquad \lambda = \frac{v}{f} = \frac{3.0 \times 10^8}{6.25 \times 10^{14}} = 4.8 \times 10^{-7}m$$

Taking $m = 0$, to give minimum thickness, we get thickness, $d = 1.33 \times 10^{-7}m$

Example T 9.17

(a) Since the bubble has air at either side we get one phase change. Thus:

(i) For elimination, we need $2dn = m\lambda \Rightarrow \lambda = \frac{2dn}{m} = 6.48 \times 10^{-7}m$ ($m = 1$ is the only value which gives a wavelength in the visible range)

(ii) For enhancement, we need $2dn = \left(m + \frac{1}{2}\right)\lambda$, gives $\lambda = 4.32 \times 10^{-7}m$ (with $m = 1$ being the only value which gives a visible wavelength).

We would probably observe the bubble, under these conditions, as a green-blue (cyan) colour since we would be removing red (648nm) and adding violet (432nm)

(b) We see a multitude of colours since a bubble will vary considerably in thickness at various parts of the bubble, especially top versus bottom, due to gravitational effects.

Example T 9.18

$$\theta = 1.22\frac{\lambda}{b} = 2.68 \times 10^{-4}rad, \quad s = r\theta \Rightarrow r = \frac{s}{\theta} = \frac{2 \times 10^{-3}}{2.68 \times 10^{-4}} = 7.45m \ (7.5m)$$

Example T 9.19

(a) $R = mN, N = 540 \times 8.2 = 4428. So, (i)(m = 1) R = 4428 \ (ii) \ (m = 2) R = 8856$

(b) $R = \frac{\lambda}{\Delta\lambda} = \frac{(502.132 + 502.214)/2}{(502.214 - 502.132)} = 6124$

(i) We can see that the resolvance required to resolve the two wavelengths (6124) is more than that of possible the grating (4428) when resolving for the first order. Hence the grating will not resolve these two wavelengths in the first order part of the spectrum.

(ii) However, the resolving power (resolvance) of the grating (8856) is sufficient to resolve the two wavelengths in the second order part, since only 6124 is required.

(c) The zeroth order maximum is the central part of the spectrum for all light, regardless of the wavelength so at this part of the spectrum none of the wavelengths will be resolved.

(d) The spreading of the maxima increases as we move further out from the centre, so the separation of wavelengths will also increase. This makes it more likely, for any given two wavelength, that they will be resolvable as we increase the order number (i.e. distance from centre).

Example T 9.20

As the car travels away from Asaf and towards Buha, Asaf will hear the sound at a constant frequency of 470Hz and Buha will hear the sound at a constant frequency as 559Hz.

Example T 9.21

$1.6 \times 10^7 ms^{-1}$ away from the Earth

Topic 10: Fields

Example T 10.1

(a) It will move upwards with a uniform acceleration

(b) It will follow a parabolic path, curved upwards – identical in shape to a gravitational projectile but upside down

Example T 10.2

(a) False: it measures a place, not an object

(b) True: $E_g = mV_g$ ("high" in gravitational terms means close to zero)

(c) False: A high PE implies it is being repelled – this would require a negative potential

(It could also be "high" in an attractive field, like gravitational, but high would mean negative and close to zero – in which case the statement could be taken as true)

(d) True: for attractive fields object would be high and drop, for (electrostatic) repulsive field object would be low and pushed away – in both cases the field is doing work on the object causing an increase in KE

Example T 10.3

(a) False – they are concentric 3D spheres (although they appear as circles when drawn on paper)

(b) True – equal potential means equal potential energy for a given object

(c) False – they are parallel to the surface ($90°$ to field lines)

(d) False – increased spacing implies reduced potential gradient and reduced field strength magnitude

(e) True – since magnitude depends on distance

(f) False – equipotentials do not have direction (only shape)

(g) False – in general (although, due to symmetry true for spherical or point objects) – for asymmetric shapes this is not true

(h) False – field lines show direction of force (on small object in field) they are not "equi-field-strengths"!

Example T 10.4

(a) False – from infinity to where it is

(b) True – since g-fields are attractive and GPEs always negative

(c) False – EPE is negative if charge attracted, positive if repelled: depends on charge sign and field

Example T 10.5

(a)   (i) $-3.5 \times 10^9 J$ (ii) $-1.7 \times 10^8 J$

(b) If we take the negative of each of these values, they tell us the energy required to completely remove a 56kg person from the Earth (then the moon) , to zero field strength

Example T 10.6

(a) $-1.4 \times 10^{-18} J$

(b) It tells that we need $-1.4 \times 10^{-18} J$ of energy to move the electron from infinity (outside the field to this position, near to the carbon nucleus. The negative sign tells us that energy is actually released, not needed. So we can also deduce that we would need $1.4 \times 10^{-18} J$ to remove the electron completely from this position, near the carbon nucleus.

(c) The answer to (a) would be the same number, but positive and energy would now be required to move the proton (from infinity) to this position.

Example T 10.7   (a) negative   (b) positive   (c) negative

Example T 10.8

(a) $8 MJkg^{-1}$ (b) $4.4 Jkg^{-1}m^{-1}$ (c) $520 MJ$ (energy needed to get from 1st to 2nd point)

Example T 10.9

(a) (i) $0.8 eV$ $(1.3 \times 10^{-19} J)$

(ii) $-3.8 eV$ $(-6.1 \times 10^{-19} J)$, here the negative sign shows work is actually done by the electron, not on it.

(iii) $-3.0 eV$ $(-4.8 \times 10^{-19} J)$

(b) Assuming that no other forces are available, except that provided by the field:

from A → B: the electron has lost kinetic energy and gained electric potential energy

from B →C: the electron has lost electric potential and gained kinetic

from A → C: the electron has lost EPE and gained KE

Example T 10.10   (a) $6 eV$ $(9.6 \times 10^{-19} J)$ (b) $6 J$

Example T 10.11

(a) $98.1 J$ (b) $49 Jkg^{-1}$ (c) $9.81 Jkg^{-1}m^{-1}$ (d) $17000 J$

(e) 870m (assuming g remains constant)

Example T 10.12

(a) (i) $-3.51 \times 10^7 Jkg^{-1}$ (ii) $-3.51 \times 10^7 Jkg^{-1}$ (very slightly higher) (iii) $3.08 Jkg^{-1}m^{-1}$

(b) By taking an even smaller height difference   (c) $-3.08 Nkg^{-1}$

(d) It can be shown that potential gradient has the same magnitude as field strength, but they have opposite signs since gravitational potential increases as field strength decreases. The equation for field strength will give the exact value of potential gradient (assuming r and M values are exact). However, to find the exact value of potential gradient using $\frac{\Delta V_g}{\Delta r}$ either Δr must be very close to zero or V_g should be graphed against r and the gradient found. The value of Δr used in (a) (iii) was very small compared with distances involved, so gave a quite accurate value of potential gradient. It can be shown that the units: Nkg^{-1} and $Jkg^{-1}m^{-1}$ are the same (can be interchanged).

Example T 10.13

(a) $460V$ (b) $102kVm^{-1}$

(c) $F = Eq = 102 \times 10^3 \times 1.6 \times 10^{-19} = 1.6 \times 10^{-14}N$

(d) (i) $1.8 \times 10^{16}ms^{-2}$ (ii) $9.0 \times 10^6 ms^{-1}$ (iii) $3.7 \times 10^{-17}J$ (iv) $3.7 \times 10^{-17}J$

(v) As the electron moves from midway between the plates it falls in electric potential energy and gains kinetic energy. The fall in potential energy is the same as the work done by the electric field. So, we can find the increase in kinetic energy by calculating the work done by the field.

Example T 10.14

$\Delta KE = \Delta E_g = m\Delta V_g = 240(-25 \times 10^6 - -50 \times 10^6) = 60 \times 10^9 J$

Example T 10.15

Energy required to escape = change in GPE

Final necessary potential = zero

Initial potential = $V = -\frac{GM}{r}$ where M is the mass of the planet and r, the distance from the planet = planet radius.

Change in potential = $\Delta V = final - initial = 0 - -\frac{GM}{r} = +\frac{GM}{r}$

Change in potential energy, $\Delta E_P = m\Delta V$ where m is the mass of the object escaping

$\therefore \Delta E_P = m\frac{GM}{r}$

If we provide the object with this amount of energy as kinetic energy, its kinetic energy will therefore equate to the above energy. Hence:

kinetic energy = $m\frac{GM}{r}$

$\therefore \frac{1}{2}mv^2 = m\frac{GM}{r} \Rightarrow v^2 = 2\frac{GM}{r} \Rightarrow v = \sqrt{\frac{2GM}{r}}$

$v_{esc} = \sqrt{\frac{2GM}{r}}$ where v_{esc} is the velocity required for a mass to escape from a planet of mass M and radius r

Example T 10.16

(i) $2400ms^{-1}$ (ii) $11200ms^{-1}$

Example T 10.17

Its time period will be 2.8 ($\sqrt{8}$) times greater

Example T 10.18

$2.86 \times 10^{12}m$ about 19 times further from the sun (exact ratio = $\sqrt[3]{84^2}$)

Example T 10.19

$4.2 \times 10^7 m$ from centre of Earth. This equates to $3.6 \times 10^7 m$ from surface of Earth. (take T = 1 day, convert to seconds, find r)

Example T 10.20

$E_K = 3.1 \times 10^9 J$ $E_p = -6.2 \times 10^9 J$ $E_T = -3.1 \times 10^9 J$

Example T 10.21

(a)

$F_1 = F_2 = G\dfrac{m_1 m_2}{r^2} = 0.013N$

(b)

$F_1 = F_2 = k\dfrac{q_1 q_2}{r^2} = 3.2\times10^{-4}N$

Topic 11: Electromagnetic Induction

Example T 11.1 $5.1 \times 10^{-4} Wb$

Example T 11.2 $61 mWb$

Example T 11.3   Aircraft is moving faster so rate of flux cutting is greater; angle at which flux is cut may be closer to 90°

Example T 11.4   (a) $10.6mV$ (b) $52.9mV$

Example T 11.5

(a) (i) as the coil begins to enter the magnetic field electrons on the right hand side will experience a force and there will be an induced current, upwards in the wire (using FRHR). Electrons actually experience a downwards force, and move downwards, opposite to conventional current direction. There will be an anti-clockwise current in the coil.

(ii) when the coil is moving through the field, electrons on the right hand side of the coil experience a downwards force, but electrons on the left of the coil also experience a downwards force these forces oppose each other so there is no overall current in the coil while it is completely in the field. It is important to note though, that there is an emf across the coil – there will be an excess of electrons on the bottom of the coil (as viewed from the page) and a deficit on the top.

(iii) as the coil begins to leave the magnetic field electrons on the right hand side are no longer affected by the field. Electrons on the left hand side continue to experience a downwards force, and therefore move downwards. Hence there will be a clockwise (conventional) current in the coil (opposite to direction of electron flow).

Note that there is no induced emf across the top or bottom part of the coil – electrons only experience a downwards force, not a horizontal force, in accordance with FLHR.

(b) Maximum current is attained when the coil is entering or leaving the field.

$\varepsilon = nBLv = 35\times35\times10^{-3}T\times8.5\times10^{-2}m\times0.1ms^{-1} = 1.04\times10^{-2}V$

Using $V = IR, I = V/R \Rightarrow I = 1.04\times10^{-2}V/0.01\Omega = 1.04A$

Answer : 1.0A

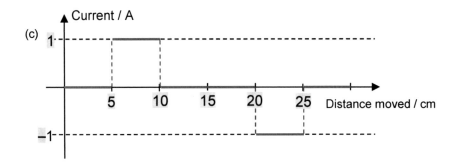

Example T 11.6

There are two alternative ways of looking at this. One is to use FRHR, and consider the side of the loop nearest the wire as it moves towards the wire at this part of the loop. Using FRHR, there will be a current induced in the wire of the top part of the coil, going from right to left. So there is an anti-clockwise current induced in the loop.

The other method is to use Lenz's Law. There will be a current induced in the loop so as to oppose the change causing it. The change is the movement of the straight wire, so the current will be induced so as to repel the straight wire. The top part of the loop will therefore have current induced in it in the opposite direction of the straight wire so that the two wires repel. There is therefore an anti-clockwise current induced in the loop.

Example T 11.7   8.5V

Example T 11.8   340V

Example T 11.9   (a) 8.3A (b) 12A (c) 29Ω

(d) The heater will run on a lower power and put out less heat (per second) because a peak voltage of 240V is equivalent to $\frac{240}{\sqrt{2}}V = 170V$ d.c. Note also that halving voltage causes current to also halve (for the same resistance) and so power quarters. In this case power would reduce by a factor of $\left(\frac{170}{240}\right)^2 \approx 0.5$. So using a.c with peak voltage of 240V would result in only about half the power compared to running it with rms voltage of 240V.

Example T 11.10   2500 turns

Example T 11.11   (a) $192kW$ (b) $19.2MW$

Example T11.12   They must all flow "across the diamond" in one direction, so A would work (all flow to left) and C would work (all flow upwards)

For A: connect supply to 2 & 4, connect output to 1 & 3

For C: connect supply to 1 & 3, connect output to 2 & 4

Example T 11.13   (a) 1.2mC   (b) 7.5×10^{15} (c) 4x as much, i.e. $24\mu F$

Example T 11.14

(a) permittivity = relative permittivity (dielectric constant) x permittivity of free space
$$= 3.18 \times 8.85 \times 10^{-12} = 2.81 \times 10^{-11} C^2 N^{-1} m^{-2}$$

(b) $C = \frac{\varepsilon A}{d} = \frac{2.81 \times 10^{-11} \times 0.3 \times 0.3}{0.2 \times 10^{-3}} = 1.3 \times 10^{-8} F$

$q = CV = 1.3 \times 10^{-8} \times 40 = 5.1 \times 10^{-7} C$

(c) (i) If the two sheets touch each other they will cause a short circuit (since they are made from a conductor) – this could cause damage to the sheets, the wiring or the supply.

(ii) For the capacitor to work (store charge) the two conducting plates must be separated from a dielectric, non-conducting material – otherwise, no charge can be stored, since charge will just flow through the conductor.

Example T 11.15   (i) 2.16nC (ii) 4.32nC

Example T 11.16

(a) 80pF (b) 1.44nC   (c) $q_1 = +1.44nC,\ q_2 = -1.44nC, q_3 = +1.44nC, q_4 = -1.44nC$

(d) $V_1 = 12V,\ V_2 = 6V$ (use $V = \frac{q}{C}$)

Example T 11.17

(a) 360pF   (b) 6.48nC   (c) $V_1 = V_2 = 18V$

(d) $q_1 = +2.16nC, q_2 = -2.16nC, q_3 = +4.32nC, q_4 = -4.32nC$

Example T 11.18

(a) The capacitor can be charged by closing switch S1 (whilst keeping switch S2 open)

When S1 is closed there is an anticlockwise current (electrons flow clockwise) in the upper circuit, and it is initially maximum magnitude. As the capacitor charges up the current decreases exponentially, reducing down to zero when the capacitor reaches full charge.

Switch S1 can now be opened and the capacitor will remain fully charged.

The capacitor can now be discharged by closing switch S2.

When S2 is closed there will be an anticlockwise current (electrons flow clockwise) in the lower circuit, and it is initially maximum magnitude. As the capacitor discharges the current decreases exponentially, reducing down to zero when the capacitor charge drops to zero.

(b) $5.64 \times 10^{-5} C$ (c) $3.4 \times 10^{-4} J$ (d) $1.5 \times 10^{-4} A$

(e) (i) $t = 0.5$: $I = 3.9 \times 10^{-5} A,\ V = 3.2V, q = 1.5 \times 10^{-5} C$

(ii) $t = 1.0$: $I = 1.0 \times 10^{-5} A,\ V = 0.85V, q = 4.0 \times 10^{-6} C$

Example T 11.19

(a) $\tau = RC, q = CV$ Capacitor fully charged, $V = 12V$ (supply), $q \approx 0.0058C$ (from graph)

So, $C = \frac{q}{V} = \frac{0.0058}{12} = 4.8 \times 10^{-4}F$

To estimate τ:

Either use τ = time for q to reach 63% full charge when charging,

Thus: $q(t = \tau) \approx 0.63 \times 0.0058C = 0.0037C$, From graph, $t \approx 1s$ ($\pm 0.15s$ would be acceptable)

Answer: Time constant is approximately 1s

or use $q = q_0 e^{-\frac{t}{\tau}}$ and rearrange to give $\tau = \frac{t}{\ln\left(q_0/q\right)}$ and choose any pair of values for t, q

But – this must be for the capacitor discharge process – so we have to work from around t=5.7s as our t=0 time

Thus: $q_0 \approx 0.0058C$, When t=2 (1 "block forwards from start of discharge curve (orange)), $q \approx 0.001C$

This gives $\tau = \frac{2}{\ln\left(0.0058/0.001\right)} = 1.1s$

Answer: Time constant is approximately 1.1s

The correct answer, impossible to find using only the information given here, is $\tau = 1.128s$

To find resistance we use $\tau = RC \Rightarrow R \approx 2400\Omega$ ($\pm 400\Omega$ would be acceptable)

(b) $V = V_0 e^{-\frac{t}{\tau}} = 12e^{-1} = 4.4V$

(c) Use $I = \frac{V}{R}$, taking R as resistance of resistor and V as the supply voltage (emf), since the initial p.d. across capacitor is zero → all p.d. is across resistor. We get $I = 0.005A$ ($\pm 0.001A$)

We can also estimate the approximate initial current by calculating the approximate slope of the charge / time graph given – it will give us the same result.

Topic 12: Quantum and Nuclear Physics

Example T 12.1	(a) 2.23eV	(b) $2.88 \times 10^5 ms^{-1}$

Example T 12.2	(a) 0.236V	(b) 1.09V

Example T 12.3	2.91nm	

Example T 12.4	$8.25 \times 10^6 ms^{-1}$	

Example T 12.5

$$E_k = \frac{p^2}{2m}, \Rightarrow p = \sqrt{2mE_k}, \quad \lambda = \frac{h}{p} = \frac{h}{\sqrt{2mE_k}}$$

$$n\lambda = d\sin\theta \Rightarrow d = \frac{n\lambda}{\sin\theta} = \frac{nh}{\sin\theta\sqrt{2mE_k}} = 2.19 \times 10^{-10}m$$

$$\begin{cases} n = 1, \\ E_k = 52 \times 1.6 \times 10^{-19} \end{cases}$$

Answer: approx. 220nm

Example T 12.6

$2.5 \times 10^{20}Hz$, It must be at least this size since (i) this assumes that the pair produced have zero kinetic energy, which may not be the case (ii) there will also be a nucleus involved in the interaction, which will also gain a small amount of kinetic energy, coming from the gamma-ray photon. This is neglected.

Example T 12.7

$1.3 \times 10^{-15}m$, If either of the particles have non-zero kinetic energy this will result in a (slightly) higher photon energy and, therefore, lower wavelength (deviations may be due to the particles having non-zero KE)

Example T 12.8

$1.4 \times 10^{20}Hz$ first calculate KE(electron) + $2mc^2$ (for the electron& positron), then divide by 2 (to find energy of each photon), then use E=hf (to find f)

Example T 12.9

Using $r = \frac{n^2h^2}{4\pi^2ke^2m}$ (i) with n=1, we get $r = 5.3 \times 10^{-11}m$ (ii) n=2, $r = 2.1 \times 10^{-10}m$

Example T 12.10

$$\Delta E = E_{n=2} - E_{n=1} = 10.2eV = 1.6 \times 10^{-18}J, \quad E = \Delta E = hf = \frac{hc}{\lambda} \Rightarrow \lambda = \frac{hc}{\Delta E} = 1.2 \times 10^{-7}m$$

Answer: 120nm

Example T 12.11

(a) The probability of an electron being at a given position
(b) the dimensions of the maximum possible space occupied by an electron
(c) the square of the amplitude of the standing wave gives us the probability

Example T 12.12

Taking $\Delta x \approx 10^{-11}m$ *(approx diameter)*, $\Delta P \geq \frac{h}{4\pi\Delta x} = 5.3 \times 10^{-24}$

Answer: $10^{-23}kgms^{-1}$

Example T 12.13

$$\Delta E = 0.05 \times 34 \times 1.6 \times 10^{-19}J = 2.7 \times 10^{-19}J, \quad \Delta t \geq \frac{h}{4\pi\Delta E} = 1.9 \times 10^{-16}s$$

Answer: $1.9 \times 10^{-16}s$

Example T 12.14

(a) the electron, since it has the smaller mass
(b) electron B, since it has the greatest energy, therefore the smallest energy deficit
(c) they have equal probability of tunnelling, since the energy deficit is the same for both
(d) proton A, since it has a smaller energy deficit (energy difference between proton and barrier is less)

Example T 12.15

$$r = \frac{kq_1q_2}{E_K}, q_1 = 2e, q_2 = 79e, E_k = 4 \times 10^6 \times 1.6 \times 10^{-19}$$

Answer: $5.7 \times 10^{-14}m$

Example T 12.16   (a) $4.5 \times 10^{-15}m$ (b) $3.5 \times 10^{-15}m$

(c) the closest distance of the alpha particles may have been due to repulsion from the nuclear strong force rather than electrostatic repulsion, as the method assumes. This will yield an inaccurate answer (in a).

Example T 12.17

Using $sin\theta \approx \frac{\lambda}{D}, \lambda = \frac{h}{P} = \frac{h}{\sqrt{2mE_K}}$, $gives \ \theta = 13°$ (note, here: m is mass of a neutron)

Example T 12.18

Carbon-14 has 14 nucleons, of which 6 are protons and 8 are neutrons. It is an unstable nucleus because it has a high neutron:proton ratio. It therefore decays by conversion of one of its neutrons into a proton and an electron. The neutron:proton ratio therefore changes from 8:6 = 4:3 (in C–14) to 7:7 = 1:1 (in N–14).

Reaction:

$^{14}_{6}C \rightarrow \ ^{14}_{7}N + \ ^{0}_{-1}\beta$. The radiation emitted is a negative beta-particle (electron)

(Note: the reaction products should also include an antineutrino – see neutrinos section)

Example T 12.19

$^{22}_{11}Na \rightarrow \ ^{22}_{10}Ne + \ ^{0}_{1}\beta$ (products should also include a neutrino – see neutrinos section)

The sodium nucleus decays because its proton:neutron is too high for stability. It therefore decays by positron emission, whereby a proton changes into a neutron + a positron. The proton:neutron ratio changes from 11:11 (1:1) to 10:12 (5:6)

Example T 12.20

$^{14}_{6}C \rightarrow \ ^{14}_{7}N + \ ^{0}_{-1}\beta + \bar{v}$

$^{22}_{11}Na \rightarrow \ ^{22}_{10}Ne + \ ^{0}_{1}\beta + v$

Example T 12.21

$(a) \ N = N_0 e^{-\lambda t} = 2.2 \times 10^{19} e^{-(1.21 \times 10^{-4} \times 2000)} = 1.7 \times 10^{19}$

$(b) \ N = N_0 e^{-\lambda t} = 2.2 \times 10^{19} e^{-(1.21 \times 10^{-4} \times 5730)} = 1.1 \times 10^{19}$

Example T 12.22

(a) To sketch the graph, one only needs to plot approximate coordinates after every 10 hours – and N drops by 50% every 10 hours

Note though, that the graph can be accurately plotted using the decay law equation, after first calculating the decay constant.

(b) 10 hours = 1 half-life, so amount remaining after 10 hours = $\frac{(10^{18})}{2} = 5 \times 10^{17}$

(c) $\lambda = \dfrac{\ln 2}{T_{\frac{1}{2}}} = \dfrac{\ln 2}{10} = 0.069 \ hours^{-1}$

$N = N^0 e^{-\lambda t} = 10^{18} e^{-0.069 \times 24} = 1.9 \times 10^{17}$